A HISTORY OF
ANCIENT GEOGRAPHY

BY

H. F. TOZER

Second edition
with additional notes by

M. CARY, D.Litt.

BIBLO AND TANNEN
New York
1964

Reprinted by permission of Cambridge University Press

Biblo & Tannen Booksellers & Publishers, Inc.
New York, N.Y., 10003

Library of Congress Catalog Card No. 64-13396

Printed in U.S.A. by
NOBLE OFFSET PRINTERS, INC.
NEW YORK 3, N. Y.

PREFACE.

THE subject which is treated of in the present volume has been already dealt with on a scale adapted to the needs of advanced scholars by the late Sir E. H. Bunbury in his *History of Ancient Geography*—a book equally conspicuous for learning and for judgement, and one which, it may safely be affirmed, will not readily be superseded. But the size of that comprehensive work unfits it for the use of ordinary students, and its elaborate detail and numerous digressions, though none of these are superfluous, tend to withdraw the mind of the reader from the process of development of the story which it tells. For these reasons it has been thought that a shorter and simpler book on the same topic may be of service by bringing out to view the more salient points which it involves, and by rendering clearer the continuous progress of the science from its early dawn in the Homeric period to its fullest extension in the Augustan age. It is hoped that in this way the interest of other than classical readers may be enlisted in the subject—an interest which it deserves on account of the variety of the questions with which it deals, and its direct connexion with the study of modern geography. The narratives of expeditions—such as that of Alexander in Asia, and, on a smaller scale, those of Hanno on the west coast of Africa and of Pytheas in the northern sea—and the history of early enquiries into the causes which regulate the movement of the tides, and of the progressive attempts that were made to construct a scheme of latitudes and longitudes, possess an interest which is not limited to the period at which these were made. With a view to the convenience of this class of readers technical phraseology has been as far as possible avoided, and quotations from classical writers have been relegated to the notes. On the other hand, to suit the requirements of students these quotations have been given in full, whenever the subject which they illustrate is affected by the expressions used in the original, or the works in which they occur are not easily accessible.

The author desires to express his obligations in the first place to Sir E. H. Bunbury's work, already mentioned, which he has consulted throughout; and also, though in a lesser degree, to Dr C. Müller's *Geographi Graeci Minores*, and Dr Hugo Berger's *Geschichte der Wissenschaftlichen Erdkunde der Griechen*. On the subject of the spread of the Greek colonies he has consulted the chapter in Curtius' *History of Greece* on "The Hellenes beyond the Archipelago," and for Alexander's Eastern expedition the twelfth volume of Grote's History. His other obligations have been acknowledged in the notes.

Five of the maps which accompany the book—viz. No. 2, "The World according to Hecataeus"; No. 3, "The

World according to Herodotus"; No. 5, "Alexander's Eastern Expedition"; No. 7, "The Periplus of the Ery- thraean Sea"; and No. 9, "The World according to Ptolemy"—have been based partly on the corresponding maps in Bunbury's *Ancient Geography*, and partly on those in Smith and Grove's *Ancient Atlas*.

H. F. T.

OXFORD,
February 17, 1897.

CONTENTS.

CHAPTER I.

INTRODUCTORY.

Importance of the History of Geography—Subdivisions of Geography: (1) Mathematical, (2) Physical, (3) Descriptive and Political, (4) Historical—The Mediterranean Sea the Starting point in the Enquiry—Its Advantages—Commerce and Settlements of the Phoenicians in the Aegean Sea, in Africa and Sicily, and at Gades—Their selfish Policy detrimental to Knowledge—The Greeks; their Qualifications for the Study of Geography—Greece a suggestive Country for this Subject, in its General Features, and its Peculiar Phenomena—Disappearance of Rivers—Currents of the Euripus—Volcanic Phenomena and Earthquakes—The Study of Geography almost confined to the Greeks—Greek Explorers—Greek Scientific Geographers—Hardly any Roman Geographers—Geographical Eras and Centres—Greek Colonies—Miletus and the Ionian School—Herodotus—Early Expeditions—Alexander's Campaigns—Foundation of Alexandria—Roman Conquests—Augustan Age—Ptolemy—Stimulating Influence of Geographical Discoveries—Curious Information thus obtained—Means of testing the Reports of Early Travellers—Marvellous Narratives not necessarily Incredible   .   .   .   .   1—18

CHAPTER II.

GEOGRAPHY OF THE HOMERIC PERIOD.

The Argonautic Legend—Its Historical Significance—Homeric Conception of the Earth—The River Oceanus—The Giant Atlas—Geography of the Homeric poems—The North and East of the Aegean—Interior of Asia Minor—Greece—Accuracy of Local Epithets—Description of the Styx—Inaccurate Account of Ithaca—Outer Geography of the Iliad; of the

Odyssey—Ignorance of the Western Countries—Wanderings of Ulysses—
Their Mythical Character—Exceptions to this—Rumours about far distant
Countries—The Pygmies—Long Days and Nights of Northern Europe—
Primitive Trade-routes—The Amber Trade—Route through Pannonia—
Route through Gaul—Entrepôt at the Mouths of the Po—Story of the
Sisters of Phaëthon—The River Eridanus—The Tin Trade—Tin not
imported from India, but from Spain, and Britain—The Cassiterides
Islands—Opinions as to their Situation—Trees imported into Greece ; the
Palm, the Pomegranate, the Cypress, the Plane—The Cardinal Points
determined by the Winds—The Four Winds in Homer—Character of the
Greek Winds .   .   .   .   19—42

CHAPTER III.

SPREAD OF THE GREEK COLONIES.

Geography advanced by the Greek Colonies—Causes of their Establishment—
Qualifications for a Site—Early development of the Colonies—Communi-
cation with the Natives—Information transmitted to Greece—Colonies on
the Euxine—Dangers and Attractions of that Sea—Sinope, *circ.* 770 B.C.—
Cyzicus on the Propontis—Colonies on the North Coast of the Euxine—
Olbia, 645 B.C.—Panticapaeum (Kertch)—Dioscurias—Chalcidic Colonies
in Thrace—Megarian Colonies in the Propontis : Byzantium, 658 B.C.—
Greek Colonies in Italy, Cumae, Neapolis, Rhegium and Messana—
Sybaris, 721 B.C.—Croton, 710 B.C.—Paestum—Metapontum—Locri—
Tarentum, 708 B.C.—Colonies in Sicily : Naxos, 735 B.C.—Syracuse,
734 B.C.—Gela, 690 B.C.—Agrigentum, 580 B.C.—Himera, 648 B.C.—The
Phocaeans at Massilia, 600 B.C.—Colonies of Massilia—Its Influence in
Gaul—Cyrene, 631 B.C.—Its Site and Commerce—The Greeks in Egypt—
Their Settlement at Naucratis, *circ.* 650 B.C.—Summary .   .   43—58

CHAPTER IV.

EARLY GEOGRAPHICAL SPECULATIONS : HECATAEUS.

Speculations on Mathematical Geography—Anaximander, *circ.* 580 B.C.—
Spherical Form of the Earth—Theory of Zones—Speculations on Physical
Geography—Volcanic Phenomena—The Delta of Egypt—Inundation of
the Nile—Explanations of it, by Thales, Hecataeus, Anaxagoras, Herodotus, Aristotle, and Eratosthenes—Invention of the Gnomon—Map-making—Its Early Difficulties—Aristagoras and his Map at Sparta, 499 B.C.—
Delphi the Centre of the Earth's Surface—Origin of the Belief—Division

of the World into Continents—Twofold or Threefold Partition—Principles
of Demarcation—Boundary of Europe and Asia—Names of the Continents
—Their Origin—Hecataeus of Miletus (*circ.* 520 B.C.) the Father of
Geography—His Political Wisdom—His Sources of Information—His
Geographical Work — Its Arrangement — Its General Geography — Its
Contents—Europe—Asia—Africa .   .   .   .   .   .   59—74

CHAPTER V.

HERODOTUS.

Importance of Herodotus to Geography—His Life, and Travels—His General
Views of Geography—His Primitive Cosmical Beliefs—Symmetrical Correspondences—Courses of the Nile and the Ister—Attempts at Drawing a
Meridian—His Conception of the Map of the World—No Northern Sea—
Continuity of the Southern Ocean—Inlets from the Ocean—The Caspian
an Inland Sea—Size of the Palus Maeotis—The Three Continents—Bound-
aries between them—His Confusion about the Araxes—His Actae, or Pro-
jecting Tracts—Central and Western Europe—His Imperfect Knowledge
of them—Scythia—His Acquaintance with it—Its Shape, and Inhabitants
—Peoples to the North of Scythia—The Agathyrsi, Neuri, Budini, and
Geloni—Lands to the North-east—Gold of the Ural Mountains—The
Argippaei—The Issedones—Asia—Sources of his Information—Scanty
Notices of the Geography—Error about Asia Minor—Ignorance of the
Mountain Chains—Knowledge of the Rivers—The Royal Road—Its
Course through Asia Minor, Cilicia, Armenia, Matiene and Cissia—India
—Its Races, and Products—The Nile Valley—Meroë—The Two Branches
Unnoticed—The Automoli—The Macrobian Aethiopians—Northern Coast
of Africa—Eastern Portion—Western Portion—Dumb Commerce—In-
terior of Africa—The Three Tracts—The Oases—The Garamantes—The
Troglodyte Aethiopians—Expedition of the Nasamones—Narrative of
Herodotus   .   .   .   .   75—97

CHAPTER VI.

EXPEDITIONS BEFORE THE TIME OF ALEXANDER.

Real and Fictitious Expeditions—Circumnavigation of Africa under Necho—
The Story derived from the Egyptians or Phoenicians—Argument from the
Sun being seen on the Right Hand—Criticism of it—Improbability of the
Voyage—Expedition of Scylax of Caryanda—Objections to its Authen-
ticity—Voyage of Sataspes—Reasons for believing in it—Expedition of

Hanno—His Narrative of it—Island of Cerne (Herne)—Promontory of Soloeis (C. Cantin)—River Lixus (Wady Draa)—River Bambotum (Senegal River)—(Cape Verde and Gambia River)—The Western Horn (Bay of Bissagos)—Flaming Mountain-sides—Explanation of the Phenomenon— Mt. Theon Ochema (Mt. Sagres)—The Southern Horn (Sherboro Sound)— Capture of Gorillas—Expedition of Himilco—The 'Ora Maritima' of Avienus—Account of the Oestrymnides—Of the Mid-Atlantic—Of the Sargasso Sea—The Retreat of the Ten Thousand—Character of Xenophon's 'Anabasis'—Geographical Features of Armenia—Its Mountains and Rivers—Sources of the Euphrates and Tigris—Lake of Van—The March from Cunaxa to Armenia—The Zabatus (Greater Zab)—Land of the Carduchi (Kurdistan)—The Centrites (River of Sert)—Source of the Tigris—The Teleboas (Kara-su)—Eastern Euphrates (Murad-su)—Highlands of Armenia—Underground Dwellings—The Phasis (Aras)—The Harpasus (Tchoruk)—Gymnias—Trapezus (Trebizond)—The first view of the Sea—The Poisonous Honey—The 'Periplus' of Scylax—Its probable Date—Its Contents—Doubts as to its Genuineness—Interesting Notices in it . . . . 98—121

CHAPTER VII.

ALEXANDER'S EASTERN EXPEDITION.

Effects of Alexander's Conquests—His Political and Social Aims—Development of Geography—Novel Aspects of Nature—Narratives of the Expedition—The Expedition originated by Philip—His Death, 336 B.C.—The Project renewed by Alexander—Battle of the Granicus, 334 B.C.—Battle of Issus, 333 B.C.—Siege of Tyre, 332 B.C.—Occupation of Egypt—Visit to the Temple of Zeus Ammon—March to the Tigris, 331 B.C.—Battle of Arbela—March to Persepolis—Depôt at Ecbatana (Hamadan) 330 B.C.— Description of Iran or Ariana—Flight of Darius into Parthia—The Caspian Gates (Sirdar Pass)—Death of Darius—Hecatompylus in Parthia—The Hyrcani and Mardi—The Caspian Sea—Artacoana (Herat)—Drangiana (Seistan)—Arachosia (Candahar)—Paropamisus Range (Hindu Kush)— Alexandria ad Caucasum—Invasion of Bactria, 329 B.C.—The Oxus (Jihoun)—Its Ancient Course—Maracanda (Samarcand)—The Polytimetus (Zerafshan)—Alexandria Eschate—Mistakes concerning the Jaxartes and the Caspian—March to the Indus, 327 B.C.—Campaign in the Punjab, 326 B.C.—The Hydaspes (Jhelum)—The Hyphasis (Bias)—Descent of the Indus—Pattala (Hyderabad) 325 B.C.—Bore of the Indus—Indian Trees —Return March of Craterus through Drangiana, of Alexander through Gedrosia—Arrival at Persepolis—Embassies from the West—Death of

Alexander, 323 B.C.—The Voyage of Nearchus—Alexandri Portus (Karachi)—Harmozia (Ormuz)—Pearl Fishery—Encounter with whales—Arrival at Susa . . . . 122—143

CHAPTER VIII.

GEOGRAPHY UNDER THE SUCCESSORS OF ALEXANDER.
THE VOYAGE OF PYTHEAS.

Intellectual Influence of this Period—Egypt under the Ptolemies—Position of Alexandria—Canal from the Red Sea to the Nile—Stations on the Red Sea—The Cinnamon Country (Somaliland)—The Upper Nile—Megasthenes in India, *circ.* 290 B.C.—Envoy to Chandragupta at Pataliputra—His Work—Verified from Native Sources—His Knowledge of India—Its Boundaries—The Indus and Ganges—The Royal Road—The Rainy Season—Administration of the Country—The Caste-system—Life of the Indians—The Brahmans—The Voyage of Pytheas, *circ.* 330 B.C.—Varying Estimates of him—His Work—Twofold Object of his Voyage—His Scientific Attainments—His Route to Britain—The Armorican Promontory (Brittany)—The British Tin Mines—Island of Ictis (St Michael's Mount)—His Account of Britain—Customs of the Inhabitants—Evidence in Favour of his Northern Voyage—Did Pytheas enter the Baltic?—The Northern Sea—Thule (probably Mainland in the Shetlands)—The Arctic Circle—"Sleeping place of the Sun"—Pytheas' Parallels of Latitude—Wonders of the Arctic Regions—Comparison to the Pulmo Marinus—The Amber Coast—Testimony of Pliny and Diodorus—The Word 'glaesum' . . . . 144—164

CHAPTER IX.

MATHEMATICAL GEOGRAPHY.

Slow Development of Mathematical Geography—Impulse given to it by Aristotle, by Subsequent Expeditions, and by the Museum of Alexandria—Spherical Form of the Earth—Aristotle's Arguments for it—Argument from Objects seen on the Sea Horizon—Strabo's Statement of it—Measurement of the Earth—Method employed before Eratosthenes—Method of Eratosthenes—Criticism of it—Eratosthenes' Measurement of the Habitable World—Its Breadth—Its Length—Parallels of Latitude—First Parallel of Eratosthenes—Other Parallels—The Climata of Hipparchus *circ.* 140 B.C.—Meridians of Longitude—Theory of Zones—Aristotle's View—Virgil's Description—Eratosthenes' Map of the World—Shape of the Inhabited World—His Sphragides or 'Seals'—His Geographical Treatise—Its Contents—Its Chief Errors . . . . 165—183

CHAPTER X.

PHYSICAL AND HISTORICAL GEOGRAPHY.

Physical Features of Greece—Impression produced by them on Aristotle—
Physical Geographers—Agatharchides—His Account of the Aethiopian
Gold-mines—Similar Description in the Book of Job—Eudoxus of Cyzicus
—Artemidorus—Posidonius—His Travels—His Varied Interests—Error
about the Circumference of the Earth—Tides—Observations of Aristotle,
of Pytheas, and of Posidonius—Winds—Aristotle's Scheme—Timosthenes'
Scheme—Popular Scheme—'Temple of the Winds' at Athens—Period-
ical Winds—Rivers—Their Sources, Underground Courses, Power of
Erosion, Deposit of Alluvium, Tidal Waves—Earthquakes and Volcanic
Action—Views of Anaximenes, Anaxagoras, and Aristotle—Earthquakes
relieved by Volcanoes—Observations of Posidonius—Flora—Theophras-
tus' *History of Plants*—The *Descriptio Montis Pelii*—Fauna—Anthropo-
logical Notices—Agatharchides on the Ichthyophagi and Aethiopians—
Posidonius on the Iberians and Gauls—Historical Geography as found in
Aristotle—His Restricted Views—Ephorus the Forerunner of Polybius—
Geographical Section of his History—His Advanced Criticisms—Polybius
circ. 210-128 B.C.—How affected by the Circumstances of his Age—His
Travels in Western Europe—His Opinion of the Importance of Travel—
Interest in Physical Geography—His Application of Geography to History
—Descriptions of Countries—Cisalpine Gaul—Media—Descriptions of
Cities—Sinope—Agrigentum—New Carthage—General Remarks

184—215

CHAPTER XI.

GEOGRAPHY AS PROMOTED BY THE ROMAN CONQUESTS.

Exploration of Unknown Lands by the Greeks and by the Romans—Opportunity afforded by the Mithridatic War—Campaigns of Lucullus in
Armenia and Mesopotamia—Pompey in Iberia and Albania—Narrative
of Theophanes—His Description of the Caucasus, of the Cyrus and
Araxes, and of the Tribes—The Iberi—The Albani—The Tribes
bordering on the Euxine—Expedition of Balbus against the Garamantes,
of Petronius in Aethiopia—The 'Atlantic Islands' (Madeira)—Fortunatae
Insulae (The Canaries)—Progressive Conquest of Spain by the Romans—
Southern and Eastern Provinces—Lusitania—Central Districts—Tribes
of the North-West—Formation of the Roman Province in Gaul—

Caesar's Conquest of Gaul—His Ethnographical and Geographical Notices—Transference to Towns of Names of Tribes—Caesar's Description of the Country of the Veneti—His Expeditions into Britain—His Information about it—Acquaintance of the Romans with Germany—Campaigns of Drusus and of Tiberius—Conquest of Rhaetia, Vindelicia, and Noricum—Of Pannonia—Importance to Geography of the Roman Roads—Careful Measurement of Distances—The Wall-map of Agrippa—Itineraries derived from it .   .   .   .   216—237

CHAPTER XII.

STRABO.

Strabo and the Augustan Age—His Geography a Summary of the Knowledge then existing—Strabo's Life, Teachers, and Places of Residence—Extent of his Travels—Almost Limited to Asia Minor, Egypt, and Central Italy—Advantages which he Derived from them—His Philosophical Opinions—Stoic Tenets—His Political Opinions—Imperial Sympathies—Strabo's Historical Work—Date of Composition of his *Geography*—Place where it was written—Readers for whom it was intended—Its Comprehensiveness—Subjects Incidentally introduced—Predominance of Historical Geography—Influence of a Land on its Inhabitants—Artistic Treatment of the Subject—Methods of lightening the Narrative—Neglect of Strabo's Work in Antiquity—Admiration of it in the Middle Ages—Modern Estimates—Limits of Strabo's Survey, in Europe, Asia, and Africa—Contents of the *Geography*—The Introduction—Remarks on Mathematical, Physical, and Historical Geography—Spain, Gaul, and Britain—Italy and Sicily—Northern and Eastern Europe—Greece—Veneration for Homer as a Geographical Authority—Northern and Central Asia—Asia Minor—Southern Asia—Egypt and the Rest of Africa

238—260

CHAPTER XIII.

GEOGRAPHY FROM THE DEATH OF AUGUSTUS TO THAT OF TRAJAN (14—117 A.D.).

Roman Writers on Geography—Pomponius Mela—Pliny—His *Historia Naturalis*—Its Deficiencies—Its Statistical Geography—Notices of Places in Asia—The Jordan—The Dead Sea—The Essenes—Palmyra—The Tigris—Its Upper Course—Strabo's Account—The Lake of Van—Criticisms of the Ancient Accounts—Strabo's and Pliny's Stories—Disappearance of the Tigris—Common Source of the Tigris and Euphrates

—Possible Explanation of the Fable—Pliny's Information about Tapro-
bane—Ambassadors sent thence to Rome—Their Account of the In-
habitants—The *Periplus Maris Erythraei*—African Coast—Aromata
Prom. (Cape Guardafui)—Menuthias (Zanzibar)—Arabian Coast—Arabia
Eudaemon (Aden)—Syagrus Prom. (Cape Fartak)—Island of Dioscorides
(Socotra)—Indian Coast—Baraces and Eirinon Inlets (Gulf and Runn of
Cutch)—Barygaza (Baroche)—Bore of the Nerbudda—Nelcynda—The
Direct Route to India—Voyage of Hippalus—Notices of Eastern Asia—
This (China)—Dionysius Periegetes—His Date—His Geographical Poem
—Its General Geography—Description of Africa—Of Europe—Of the
Islands—Of Asia—General Remarks upon it—Progressive Knowledge of
Britain—Conquests of Claudius, Suetonius Paullinus, Agricola, and
Antoninus Pius—Germany and Scandinavia—Dacia conquered by Trajan
—Suetonius Paullinus crosses the Atlas—Nero's Expedition to the Nile—
The Marshy Region .   .   .   .   261—292

CHAPTER XIV.

ROMAN FRONTIER DEFENCES AND ROADS.

Natural Limits of the Roman Empire—Frontier Defences—Chiefly organised
by Hadrian—The *Periplus* of Arrian — Dio's Account of Hadrian's
System—The German Limes—Chains of Military Posts—Defences of
the Upper Euphrates—The Roman Roads—The Via Aurelia—Via
Aemilia Scauri—Via Julia—Road through Southern Gaul and Spain—
The Via Flaminia—Via Aemilia—Passes of the Alpes Cottiae, Graiae,
and Penninae—Roman Roads in Gaul, and in Britain—Watling Street—
Fosse Way — Ermine Street — Icknield Street — Passes of the Alpes
Rhaeticae and Juliae—Road through Pannonia to Byzantium—The Via
Appia—The Via Egnatia—Main Roads through Asia and Africa—Roman
Itineraries—The Antonine Itinerary--Its Probable Date—Not a com-
pletely Homogeneous Document—Its Contents—The *Itinerarium Mari-
timum*—The Jerusalem Itinerary—The Peutinger Table—Its Transcription, and probable Date of Composition .   .   .   .   293—312

CHAPTER XV.

ESTIMATES OF MOUNTAINS IN ANTIQUITY.

Hadrian's Mountain Ascents—Indistinct Conception of Mountain Summits—
Strabo on Alpine Features—Use of Crampons and Tobogganing—Mountains differently viewed by the Ancients and the Moderns—Religious

Feeling in Antiquity—Ascents of Etna prompted by Research—Strabo on the Summit of Etna—The Poem of *Aetna*—Ascents of Mount Argaeus— Of Tmolus—Ascents for the Sake of the Panorama—Sunrise seen from Mt. Ida—Lucian on a Mountain View—Description of a Mountain Climb—Mountains regarded as Look-out Places—Story of Lynceus— Mountains as Signalling Stations—The Beacon-fires in Aeschylus, probably corresponding to a Real Line of Stations—The Shield at Marathon— Mountain Telegraphy in Thucydides, Xenophon, and Polybius—Development of the Art of Signalling—Estimates of the Heights of Mountains— Scientific Measurement by Dicaearchus, and Xenagoras . 313—337

CHAPTER XVI.

PTOLEMY AND LATER GEOGRAPHERS.

Marinus Tyrius—His Attempt to reform the Map of the World—Its Deficiencies—Ptolemy—His Great Reputation—His Error about the Circumference of the Earth, and the Length of the Habitable World— The Fortunate Isles his Prime Meridian—His System of Projection—His Geographical Treatise—His Maps—His Corrections of Previous Maps— His Chief Errors—His Account of Britain—Accurate Delineation of the Coast—Erroneous Position of Scotland—Possible Explanation of this— Ptolemy's Tables of the Coast of Britain—The Southern Coast—The Western Coast—The Eastern Coast—Ireland—Other Additions to Geographical Knowledge—The Volga (Rha)—The Altai Chain (Imaus)— Direct Trade Route to China—Sources of the Nile—Mountains of the Moon—The Soudan—Rivers Gir and Nigir—Pausanias—His Resemblance to Herodotus—His Illustrations of Physical Geography—Fountains—Their Different Colours—Warm Springs—Fountain of Deine—Caverns—The Corycian Cave—Trees—Cotton—Pausanias' Researches in Greece—His Descriptions of Olympia and Delphi—Routes which he followed—Contents of his Book—The Question of his Veracity—The View Adverse to Pausanias—Explanations of his Statements—Difficulties involved in the Supposition—Recent Testimonies in his Favour—Stephanus Byzantinus— His *Ethnica*—Character of its Contents—Solinus—His *Memorabilia*— Mediaeval Estimate of him—Modern Estimate—Orosius—His *Historiae*— Its Geographical Section—Transient Character of Ptolemy's Influence— Earlier Errors revived—Retrospect and Summary—Continuous Advance of Knowledge of General Geography, and of Scientific Geography

338—370

ADDITIONAL NOTES.

Pages 3, 4. The Mediterranean Sea i

4. Exclusiveness of the ancient Egyptians . . . i

4–6. Phoenicians and Minoans i

7. Tarshish or Tartessus iv

8. High peaks attract storms iv

10. Dangerous currents near headlands . . . v

11. The Mediterranean a tideless sea v

11. Heracles a fire-god v

13. Geographical works in Latin v

19, 20. The Argonauts v

20, 21. The River Oceanus vi

24. Ithaca vi

24, 25. The Homeric Catalogue vi

26, 27. The Aethiopians vii

29, 30. The Pygmies vii

31–33. Amber vii

32. The Hyperboreans vii

34. The amber river Eridanus viii

35, 36. The early tin trade viii

37–39. The Cassiterides viii

38. P. Crassus ix

43. Greek colonisation ix

46. Phoenicians at Lampsacus ix

46. Black Sea fisheries ix

47. Sinope ix

50. Cumae x

54, 55. Massilia x

55. Greek colonies in Spain x

55, 56. Cyrene x

57. Note 1 xi

58. Colaeus xi

60, 61. Xanthus of Lydia xi

63. The supposed rise of the Nile out of the Ocean . xi

63. The Nile inundations xi

Pages			
	64.	Map-making	xii
	66.	The influence of Delphi on colonisation . .	xii
	69.	Europe and Asia	xii
	70.	Hecataeus	xiii
	73.	Hecataeus on Spain	xiii
	73.	The Araxes	xiii
	75.	Herodotus	xiii
	84.	Herodotus and the Alps	xiii
	84.	Alpis and Carpis	xiii
	85.	Rivers of South Russia	xiv
87, 88.		The Argippaei and others	xiv
	90.	The Royal Road	xiv
	95.	Dumb commerce	xv
	96.	The Troglodyte Aethiopians	xv
96, 97.		The expedition of the Nasamones. . . .	xv
99–101.		The circumnavigation of Africa	xv
	101.	Scylax of Caryanda	xvi
	103.	The voyage of Sataspes.	xvi
104–109.		The expedition of Hanno	xvi
109, 110.		The expedition of Himilco	xvii
	109.	Avienus.	xvii
	110.	Albion and Hierne	xvii
112–118.		The retreat of the Ten Thousand	xviii
118–120.		The 'Periplus' of Scylax	xviii
120, 121.		The bifurcation of the Ister	xviii
135, 136.		Mistakes concerning the Jaxartes. . . .	xviii
	136.	Patrocles on the Caspian Sea	xviii
	137.	The fortress of Aornus	xix
	138.	Alexander's turning point	xix
141–143.		The voyage of Nearchus	xx
	146.	The Red Sea canal	xx
	147.	Ptolemaic colonies in Somaliland . . .	xx
147, 148.		Megasthenes	xx
152–164.		The voyage of Pytheas	xx
	155.	Travel by the N. coast of Spain	xxi
	156.	Ictis	xxi
	157.	Pytheas' measurement of Britain	xxi
	158.	Pytheas' visit to the German coast . . .	xxi
	159.	Tides in Pentland Firth	xxi

Pages 159. Thule xxii
163. The Pulmo marinus xxii
164. The 'Guttones' xxii
164. Scythia xxii
168 ff. The measurement of the earth xxii
172. Eratosthenes' great circle xxiii
190. The return of Eudoxus xxiii
191. Soundings in the Mediterranean xxiii
192, 193. Observations on the tides xxiii
194. Aristotle's wind-points xxiv
196, 197. Erosion by rivers xxiv
197. Posidonius' visit to Britain xxiv
209. Polybius' journeys in Libya xxiv
209. Polybius' passage over the Alps xxiv
219. The site of Tigranocerta xxv
225. Madeira xxv
226. The Canaries xxv
229. Caesar's conquest of Gaul xxv
231. Portus Itius xxvi
231. Caesar's report on Britain xxvi
233. The Roman naval campaign of A.D. 5 . . xxvi
234. The Roman campaigns in the Danube lands . xxvi
238. The *Geography* of Strabo xxvii
239. Cicero's sons xxvii
243. Date of Strabo's *Geography* xxvii
252. Strabo on the British Isles xxvii
258. Strabo on Asia Minor xxvii
260. The expedition of Aelius Gallus xxviii
262. Pomponius Mela xxviii
274. The *Periplus Maris Erythraei* xxviii
275. Zanzibar xxviii
279. Hippalus and the direct route to India . . xxviii
280, 281. Eastern Asia xxix
287, 288. Agricola xxx
289. Germany and Scandinavia xxx
294. The Roman frontier system xxx
294. Hadrian's 'allocutio' xxxi
299. The Roman roads xxxi
306. Roman Itineraries xxxi

Pages 313. Ancient lore of mountains xxxi

323. Erroneous beliefs about views from high points . xxxi

325. A military mountain-climb xxxii

328–335. Ancient signals xxxii

335, 336 Measurement of mountains xxxii

338. Ptolemy xxxii

341, 342. Ptolemy's error about the length of the habitable
world xxxii

346. The Indian Ocean a lake xxxiii

352. The land route to China xxxiii

352. The Nile and the Mountains of the Moon . . xxxiv

SELECT BIBLIOGRAPHY xxxv

INDEX . . . . 371—387

LIST OF MAPS.

1. The Greek Colonies . . . . . . *To face page* 43

2. The World according to Hecataeus . . . ., ,, 71

3. The World according to Herodotus . . . ,, ,, 75

4. Xenophon's Route across Armenia . . . . ,, ., 113

5. Alexander's Eastern Expedition . . . ,, ,, 123

6. The World according to Strabo . . . . ,, ,, 239

7. The Periplus of the Erythraean Sea . . . ,, ,, 275

8. The Chief Lines of Road in the Roman Empire . ,, ,, 299

9. The World according to Ptolemy . . . . ,, ., 341

10. The Coasts of the British Islands according to Ptolemy , ,, 347

CHAPTER I.

INTRODUCTORY.

Importance of the History of Geography—Subdivisions of Geography: (1) Mathematical, (2) Physical, (3) Descriptive and Political, (4) Historical—The Mediterranean Sea the Starting-point in the Enquiry—Its Advantages—Commerce and Settlements of the Phoenicians in the Aegean Sea, in Africa and Sicily, and at Gades—Their selfish Policy detrimental to Knowledge—The Greeks; their Qualifications for the Study of Geography—Greece a suggestive Country for this Subject, in its General Features, and its Peculiar Phenomena—Disappearance of Rivers—Currents of the Euripus—Volcanic Phenomena and Earthquakes—The Study of Geography almost confined to the Greeks—Greek Explorers—Greek Scientific Geographers—Hardly any Roman Geographers—Geographical Eras and Centres—Greek Colonies—Miletus and the Ionian School—Herodotus—Early Expeditions—Alexander's Campaigns—Foundation of Alexandria—Roman Conquests—Augustan Age—Ptolemy—Stimulating Influence of Geographical Discoveries—Curious Information thus obtained—Means of testing the Reports of Early Travellers—Marvellous Narratives not necessarily Incredible.

THE History of Geography forms an integral part of the history of the development of the human race. It chronicles the gradual advances which men made in their intercourse with their fellow men, and the results of those advances in enlarged views of life and increased civilisation. It notes their progress in speculation on such subjects as the shape and magnitude of the earth, the position of the continents on its surface, the tides and other recurring phenomena, and on the changes which they either saw taking place before their eyes, or inferred as having happened in the past from the appearance of existing objects. Finally, as its most rightful function, it traces the increase of the knowledge which they possessed of various countries—of their outline and surface, their mountains and rivers, their products and commodities. And as geography is the most central in its position of all the sciences,

Importance of the History of Geography.

standing as it does half-way between history, sociology and the other studies which relate to man on the one side, and those which deal with the composition of the earth which is his dwelling-place, such as geology, on the other; so the history of geography, especially that of its earlier stages, when these cognate subjects were still in their infancy, is fruitful in information relating to them.

It will be seen from this that geography is a comprehensive subject, and requires to be studied from several different points of view; and for this reason it may be well at starting that we should consider the subdivisions under which it may be most advantageously treated. These are Mathematical, Physical, Descriptive or Political, and Historical Geography. Mathematical Geography deals with those questions which depend on the sciences of astronomy and geometry—the relation of the earth to the other heavenly bodies, the measurement of its circumference, the division of its surface into zones, the alternations of the seasons, and the like; and also all such points as are connected with map-making—the relative position of places and countries on the face of the globe, the altitude of mountains, the determination of parallels and meridians, and eventually the construction of a scheme of latitude and longitude, and the delineation of these on a round or plane surface. Physical Geography treats of the surface of the earth, together with its component elements and the influences that affect it. Under this head fall the distribution of land and water, the composition of the rocks and the metals which they contain, the changes in the ground together with the causes which have produced them, and varieties of soil, climate and vegetation. Descriptive and Political Geography sets forth in detail the characteristics of the several portions of this area, regarding it especially as the habitation of man, and subdividing it according to the political aggregation of its occupants. To this head also belongs all information respecting the works which have been produced upon its surface by the hand of man—the dwelling-places which he has constructed, the changes which he has effected by means of

Subdivisions of Geography:

(1) Mathematical,

(2) Physical,

(3) Descriptive and Political,

harbours, embankments and drainage, and the development of
the products of the soil.   Historical Geography
regards the earth from the point of view of its effect   (4) Historical.
on human society and the progressive development of the race.
With this object it considers the modifying influence on national
character which has been produced by the aspect of a country, by
the facilities or impediments which it presents in respect of
communication with other peoples, and by the occupations which
it naturally fosters.   And it also points out the effect which
geographical features have produced, both in determining campaigns and battles, which have been the turning-points of the
world's history, and in fixing beforehand the routes which must
be followed by trade and commerce; and, on a larger scale,
in affecting the power which particular countries have exercised at
certain periods.   It is easy to perceive from this review how many
points of contact with other studies geography presents; and none
of these can be ignored in a history of geography, if it is to afford
an adequate survey of the subject.

The natural starting-point for such a history must be the
shores of the Mediterranean, because the peoples
that dwelt in the neighbourhood of that sea first   The Mediterranean Sea
cultivated the science of geography on an extended   the Starting-
point in the
scale, and it was from that quarter that the in-   Enquiry.
formation was originally derived which furnished
the material for such a study.   The reason of this is to be found
fully as much in the geographical features of that portion of the
globe, as in the character of the nations that inhabited it.   Thus
Strabo in the Introduction to his Geography[1] draws attention to
the superiority of the coasts of the inland seas—such as the
Persian Gulf, the Red Sea, and the Mediterranean—over those of
the ocean, from which they are inlets, in respect of the variety of
their outline; and he adds that from that point of view the
Mediterranean has the advantage over all the
others.   By means of this multiplicity of form,   Its Advantages.
communication was promoted between distant races
through the islands which served as stepping-stones from one
country to another, and the numerous creeks and harbours which

[1] 2. 5. 26.

provided a place of refuge in bad weather. The conformation of its northern shore is especially noticeable in this respect; and, in addition to this, the relative position of the peninsulas of Greece, Italy and Spain, which project into it on this side from the continent of Europe, tended still more to facilitate the intercourse between them. Thus the same causes which promoted the civilisation of the inhabitants of this region of the globe by enlarging their minds and enabling them to communicate to one another the arts of life, laid at the same time the foundations of a progressive and comprehensive study of geography. The case was widely different with countries like India and China, which from their remote situation and strongly marked boundaries were cut off from any but the most limited contact with others; and the same thing is almost equally true of Egypt, which land, though it communicated with the Mediterranean, was developed on lines of its own owing to its dependence on the Nile, and was traditionally exclusive in its ideas and policy. Whatever knowledge of geography was possessed by the nations which occupied these countries, was too much restricted in its horizon to be of service for general study.

The people who were the first depositaries of geographical knowledge in the Mediterranean were the Phoe-

Commerce and Settlements of the Phoenicians

nicians. Long before the dawn of Greek history that wonderful race had established their trading stations at various points on the shore of that sea, and even on the confines of the ocean. The names of their two principal cities—Tyre, originally Sur, "the rock," with reference to its site on a barren island, and Sidon, "the fishers' town"— sufficiently indicate their early aptitude for maritime pursuits; and the narrow strip of coast which formed their country, cut off as it was from the rest of Syria by the rocky wall of Libanus, denied them any other outlet for their boundless vigour than that offered by the sea. We can trace their advance along the three basins into which the Mediterranean is naturally divided— from the Syrian coast to the Cyrenaica, which here advances towards the southernmost parts of Greece; from thence to the still more strongly marked limit which is formed by Sicily and the Carthaginian territory; and at last to the Pillars of Hercules at

its western end.   In the first of these seas we note their progress
by way of Cyprus and Rhodes to Crete, which island, from its
position at the southern limit of the Aegean, and between the
extremities of the continents of Greece and Asia Minor, was
suited to be a starting-point for future advances.
In the Aegean itself we find numerous evidences   in the Aegean
                                                   Sea,
of their presence.   Thus the name Samos, which,
whether it occurs in the island of that name or in Samothrace,
was recognised by the Greeks as meaning 'a height[1],' is derived
from the Semitic *shamah* 'to be high.'   Lampsacus, as the city at
the entrance of the Hellespont from the Propontis was called,
signified in that language the town "at the ford."   Atabyrium,
the highest summit in Rhodes, is the same as Tabor; in fact the
Greeks thus designated the well-known mountain in Palestine.
Iardanos also, the stream in Crete, has the same name as the
Jordan, *yarden* being the Phoenician word for 'river'; and
Adramyttium in Mysia corresponds to Hadrumetum in Africa.
Elsewhere we find traces of the Phoenician religion.   In Thasos
there was a temple of the Tyrian Heracles[2], *i.e.* Melcarth; and
in several places where the local name Macaria is found associated
with traditions of Heracles, it would seem to be a corruption of
the title of the same god.   The cult of Aphrodite Urania which
existed in Cythera, a Phoenician station, was in reality that of
Astarte, and in several places called Astyra we find the traces of
her name.   Again, the 'Great Gods' that were worshipped in
Samothrace, though in all probability they were not originally
Semitic divinities, yet seem at one time to have passed under the
influence of the Phoenicians from their name Cabeiri, which is
derived from *kabir* 'great,' a title applied by that people to their
leading deities.   In connexion with the purple fisheries, by which
they obtained the Tyrian dye, we find the Phoenicians in the
Laconian gulf and at Hermione in the Argolic Acte, both of
which places were famed for their purple; and in the same
connexion we discover their traces at Corinth, on the coins of
which city the purple-mussel appears, and where Sisyphus is said
to have been father of Porphyrion, that is the purple-trade, and

---

[1] Strabo, 8. 3. 19, σάμους ἐκάλουν τὰ ὕψη.
[2] Herod. 2. 44.

to have founded the worship of Melicertes or Melcarth. Nor were they behindhand in the pursuit of the precious metals in these parts, for Herodotus[1] tells us that they worked the gold mines in Thasos; and in other places there are evidences of their mining operations.

At an early period also we meet with the Phoenicians at the western extremity of the central basin of the Mediterranean. Here on the African coast they founded their colony of Utica, the date of which, if we may trust the authorities, was about eleven hundred years before Christ; and the same neighbourhood three centuries later saw the establishment of the more famous city of Carthage. The causes of the prosperity of that place, which was destined to be the rival of its parent state, were its central position in the Mediterranean, owing to which it commanded the spaces of sea both to the east and west of it, its nearness to Sicily and Italy, which brought it into communication with Europe, and the access which it enjoyed to the interior of Africa; these advantages rendered it an almost ideal trading station. On the opposite coast of Sicily, also, the most favourable points were occupied either by Phoenician or Carthaginian settlements. At the westernmost point stood Lilybaeum—the town 'opposite Libya,' as its Semitic name signifies; to the northward of this rose the conspicuous mountain on which Eryx stands, with its famous temple of Venus Erycina, in which the worship of Astarte was perpetuated; and not far off they had a station at Panormus, where they commanded one of the finest harbours in the island. Again, in the third bay of the Mediterranean, that which reaches from Sicily to the Straits, they established themselves in Sardinia and Corsica, along the Spanish coast, and in the neighbouring Balearic islands; and even Massilia was probably one of their stations before the arrival of the Greek settlers. Yet, wonderful to relate, all these advances had been anticipated by more adventurous voyages, for long before this time, and several centuries before the Greeks were even aware that the Mediterranean was an enclosed sea, these energetic traders had passed the Pillars of Hercules, and reached the ocean. There—a few years earlier,

in Africa and Sicily,

---

[1] Herod. 6. 47.

as it would seem, than the foundation of Utica—they fortified
themselves in an impregnable position at Gades or
Gadeira—Agaddir, "the enclosure"—which became
and at Gades.
thenceforth their starting-point for expeditions to Britain, and
for the establishment of trading stations on the western coast of
Africa.   The neighbouring region of southern Spain was known
through them as Tarshish or Tartessus—a name which was
derived from the tribe that inhabited it, the Turti or Turdetani.
Of this we hear even in the genealogy in the tenth chapter of
the book of Genesis[1], and in Solomon's time (1000 B.C.) it is
mentioned in connexion with the navy of Hiram, King of Tyre[2].

The geographical information about various countries which
was thus obtained by the Phoenicians must have
been very great, and this, together with the astronomical and other scientific knowledge which enabled them to undertake such extensive expeditions,
Their selfish
Policy detri-
mental to
Knowledge.
would have been extremely valuable for the study of geography, if
they had come down to us.   Unfortunately the whole of it is lost
beyond recovery.   This is the result of the narrow and jealous
commercial policy of that people, which caused them to keep
secret their maritime discoveries, so as to prevent other nations
from entering on the same field.   In Herodotus we meet with
various stories relating to the difficulties incurred in obtaining the
products of distant lands, which were circulated by the Phoenicians
with the object of discouraging competition and concealing the
origin of those articles.   The trees from which they obtained the
frankincense in Arabia were reported to be guarded by winged
serpents[3]; the lake where cassia was gathered was infested with
large bats, as a defence against which those who collected it had
to wrap themselves in the hides of oxen[4]; and cinnamon was
acquired by artifice from the nests of birds, which were built on
inaccessible rocks.   The historian's report of the last of these
fables, which recalls some of the stories in the Arabian Nights,
runs as follows :—"Great birds, they [the Arabians] say, carry the
sticks which we Greeks, taking the word from the Phoenicians,
call cinnamon to their nests, which are formed of clay and attached

---

[1] Gen. 10. 4.   [2] 1 Kings 10. 22.
[3] Herod. 3. 107.   [4] *Ibid.* 3. 110.

to precipitous mountains, which no foot of man can approach. So the Arabians, to get the cinnamon, use the following artifice. They cut up the limbs of the oxen and asses and other beasts of burden which die in their land into large pieces, and carry them into those regions, and when they have placed them near the nests withdraw to a distance. Thereupon the birds swoop down, and carry with them the pieces of meat up to their nests, which, being unable to sustain the weight, break and fall to the ground; after which the Arabians come and collect the cinnamon, which is then transported into other countries[1]." Under these circumstances it is not surprising that, while the Phoenicians themselves were familiar with the western parts of the Mediterranean, all that the Greeks learnt from them at an early time was vague rumours of a great mountain called Atlas, which supported the heavens, or of lofty rocks, called the Pillars of Hercules, which marked the limit of the world in that direction. The tradition of this system of exclusiveness was maintained until a late period. Strabo tells us, when speaking of the Cassiterides[2], that a Phoenician shipmaster from Gades, when on his way to those islands, being followed by a Roman vessel which desired to discover the region from which tin was obtained, purposely ran his ship on a shoal in order to involve the other in the same destruction; and that, when he returned home, he was indemnified by the state for the loss of his cargo. We cannot wonder if posterity also has suffered from the effects of this selfish policy.

The loss to geography, however, which has arisen from this

The Greeks; their Qualifications for the Study of Geography.

cause, has been amply compensated by that study having passed into the hands of the Greeks. That people, more than any other nation in antiquity, were fitted to deal with the subject, and to give the due proportion to its various branches. They too were a maritime race, and had learnt to regard the sea as the highway of nations, or, as Homer expresses it, the "watery ways[3]." The uncertain navigation of the Aegean, studded as it is by high peaks which attract the storms, taught the Greek mariner a lesson of caution and hardihood; and this, combined with the adventurous

---

[1] Herod. 3. 111.   [2] Strabo, 3. 5. 11.

[3] ὑγρὰ κέλευθα.

spirit which characterised the people, fitted them to undertake
expeditions into distant lands. But it was the national intellect
of the Greeks that especially qualified them for geographical
investigation. Their comprehensiveness of mind was suited to a
subject which, as we have seen, embraces a wide area of knowledge, and imparted to it a philosophical as well as a scientific
character. Hence at an early period we find that the information
gathered by their traders was recorded, and made the basis for
enquiries into the origin and constitution of the world. Their
acuteness of observation caused them to notice the peculiarities
of the countries which they visited, and of the objects which they
met with in them; and these they learnt to compare with one
another, and to speculate on their resemblances. This was the
commencement of physical geography, which formed a link
between the study of the earth at large and the detailed investigation of physical phenomena. The versatility of their intellect
prevented them from confining themselves to one side of the
study, and led them to regard it from several points of view.
Thus mathematical, and physical, and historical geography, each
in its turn, obtained recognition, and at last systematic treatises
were written, in which all these aspects of the subject were
combined. To this we may add a certain expansiveness of
temperament—the very reverse of the exclusiveness of the
Phoenicians—which impelled them to communicate to others
the knowledge which they themselves obtained.

The country also which was inhabited by the Greeks on both
sides of the Aegean was peculiarly suggestive for
geographical study, both in its general characteristics
and in the peculiar phenomena which it exhibits.
For a science like astronomy, requiring as it does
above all things a clear atmosphere and an unimpeded range
of view, the plains of Babylonia were a more fitting home.
Geometry, which, we are told, originated in the necessity of
measuring the ground in Egypt after the landmarks had been
obliterated by the inundation of the Nile, would naturally look
to that country as its birthplace. But for geography Greece had
lessons to teach which nowhere else could be learnt to equal
advantage on account of the extraordinary variety of its natural

features.   It was a land of mountains, many of which were of sufficient altitude to be snow-clad in winter; and these,
while they were ranged in definite chains, at the same
time displayed conspicuous summits.   The levels
that were interposed between them were either upland plains, like
that of Mantineia, which lies more than 2000 feet above the sea,
or maritime plains, such as those of Athens and Argos, which,
though enclosed on three sides by lofty barriers, terminated on
the fourth in an open line of coast.   The rivers were for the most
part torrents, which flowed with a rushing current in winter and
were dry in summer; but there were not wanting streams of
greater volume, like the Achelous and the Alpheius, which had a
perennial supply of water.   The promontories of Greece, which
project conspicuously into the sea, while they inspired the sailor
with dread on account of the dangerous currents in their neighbourhood, were recognised as landmarks for which to steer, and as
geographical limits, which bounded the intervening spaces of sea.
Everywhere, too, the islands met the eye in endless succession,
with an infinite variety of form.   Yet none of these features were
as characteristic as the sea itself, which penetrated the land in
innumerable bays, which it subdivided again into smaller creeks
and harbours, thus producing a great irregularity of outline, and
a seaboard of extraordinary length in proportion to the area of the
country.   By means of these the Greeks were familiarised with
every phase of that element, and learnt to watch its changes, and
to notice the influence which it exercised on human life and
history.

But besides these general features, there were many peculiar
phenomena in the lands which bordered on the
Aegean which could not fail to interest an imaginative people.   This was the case with the sudden
disappearance of rivers—a feature which is not uncommon in
limestone districts, but is unusually frequent in
Greece—and their reappearance after a subterranean course.   The Alpheius was a well-known
instance, for it sinks into the ground in the earlier part of its
course in the district of Asea, between the territory of Megalopolis
and that of Tegea; and this is thought to have been the origin

in its General Features,

and its Peculiar Phenomena.

*Disappear-
ance of Rivers.*

of its earlier name, Nyctimus, i.e. the river of night or darkness. The currents of the Euripus at Chalcis, which sway to and fro at irregular intervals in the twenty-four hours, were noticed at an early time by the Greeks,

Currents of the Euripus.

many of whom must have traversed it owing to the safe passage afforded by the land-locked Euboic sea; and thus their minds were prepared for the strange recurrence of the tides of the Ocean, with which those who lived about the tideless Mediterranean sea could have no acquaintance. Still more impressive were the earthquake movements, to which throughout its history Greece has been greatly exposed, and the volcanic phenomena with which these are connected.

Volcanic Phenomena and Earth-quakes.

The volcanic island of Thera in the middle of the Aegean, with its calcined and strangely coloured rocks and precipices, though it was not in activity during the early part of the historic period, presented a weird aspect to the eyes of the Greek mariner. The jets of mephitic vapour which were of frequent occurrence in Western Phrygia suggested the idea of a connexion with the infernal regions, aïd were called Charonia or Plutonia, among which the Plutonium at Hierapolis was the most famous. The numerous hot springs in Greece, especially those of Thermopylae, and of Aedepsus in the north of Euboea, were associated with Heracles in his character of the fire-god; and the Peloponnese, on account of the frequent occurrence of earth-quakes in that district, as well as for other reasons, became the focus of the worship of Poseidon, the 'earth-shaker.' In these and similar ways the peculiar features of the country in Greece attracted the attention of its inhabitants, and their observations upon them took the form of superstitions and religious fancies; but these in their turn formed the basis for further investigation, and furnished the facts which were afterwards turned to account by philosophers and men of science. Aristotle in particular, when discussing physical theories, constantly draws his illustrations from objects and places in his native land. So too, the connexion between the conformation of a country and the politics of the states which occupy it—an idea which is of primary importance for historical geography—was impressed on the minds of the Greeks by the feeling that the limits of their own states were assigned by nature, and that both their occupations and their sphere of action were determined by their local position.

It is not unreasonable to dwell at some length on the character of the Greeks and the influence exercised upon them by the land which they inhabited, because the study of geography in ancient times was from first to last almost entirely in their hands. We might have expected that a people like the Romans, whose conquests were widely extended, and whose interests in distant countries were numerous on account of their commerce and the needs of their administration, would have borne their part in cultivating a subject of so great practical importance. But this was not the case. Not only were the foundations of the science laid by the Greeks, but it was mainly through them that the observations made in the course of military campaigns, and the knowledge gained through the spread of trade, were recorded. The first explorer who brought back information with regard to the north-western portions of Europe was Pytheas, a Greek of Massilia; and his discoveries in the ocean to the northward of Britain, though they were made at a period nearly coeval with Alexander the Great, were hardly superseded even when the greater part of that island was in the power of the Romans. Almost everything that was known in antiquity concerning the interior of India was derived, either from the companions of Alexander, or from Megasthenes, who was sent by Seleucus Nicator as ambassador to Chandragupta at Pataliputra on the Ganges. The shores of the western part of the Mediterranean, both on the side of Europe and of Africa, were investigated, and their noticeable features recorded, by Artemidorus and Polybius; while the interior of Spain, of Gaul, and of the southern part of Britain was visited by Posidonius, who devoted especial attention to the races that inhabited those countries, and to their occupations, customs, and religious rites. When Pompey in the course of his campaigns against Mithridates opened out the countries that lay between the Euxine and the Caspian, it was his Greek companion and friend, Theophanes of Mytilene, who collected and published the results of his discoveries. Meanwhile the study of mathe-

The Study of Geography almost confined to the Greeks.

Greek Explorers.

matical geography was monopolised by Greek *savants*, from Eratosthenes to Ptolemy; and in the Augustan age, when the Roman empire embraced the whole of the civilised world, it was Strabo, a Greek of Amasia in Pontus, who described it in a systematic treatise. In fact, the only two geographical works in Latin which we possess are those of Pomponius Mela and Pliny, both of them writers of the post-Augustan period; and the former of these books is a mere *résumé*, which adds but little to our knowledge, while that part of Pliny's *Natural History* which deals with geography is both unskilful in its arrangement of facts, and uncritical in its treatment of them. Strabo, though he was ultra-Roman in his views of politics, and desired to approve his work to Roman readers, cannot conceal his contempt for that people as geographers. "Roman writers," he says, when speaking of Spain, "imitate the Greeks, but not with much success; for they borrow their statements from them, and do not themselves bring to the subject much love of enquiry; so that, where the Greeks fail us, these do not greatly help to supplement them[1]." And Pliny is even severer in his judgment of his countrymen; for he remarks with regard to the contradictory reports that were current in his day concerning the interior of Mauretania, that "the Roman authorities, while they take no trouble to investigate the truth, are not ashamed to invent falsehoods; and nowhere is there greater liability to error than where misstatements are supported by persons in high position[2]."

> *Greek Scientific Geographers.*

> *Hardly any Roman Geographers.*

The study of geography among the Greeks when once it had been started was continuously progressive, but, as might be expected, a more rapid advance was made during certain periods and at certain centres. It was natural also that different aspects of the subject should attract attention at different times, since in one age greater facilities were offered for the accumulation of materials, while in another there was a tendency to speculate on the facts thus obtained, and to start new theories on the larger scientific questions involved. As soon as the Greek colonies began to be thickly sown along the coasts of the Mediter-

> *Geographical Eras and Centres.*

> *Greek Colonies.*

---

[1] 3. 4. 19.   [2] *Hist. Nat.* 5. 12.

ranean and the Euxine, information flowed in abundantly to the parent states concerning the countries in their neighbourhood, and was rapidly disseminated among the Greeks at large. At this early period Miletus, owing to its important colonies on the Euxine, became the chief centre of geographical enquiry; and the philosophers of the Ionian school, of which that city was the headquarters, availed themselves of the knowledge thus obtained to aid their speculations on the origin and nature of the earth. The theories which they put forward on these points may have been crude and tentative, but they mark an important advance in the treatment of the subject, because the spirit of mere wonder which had hitherto prevailed, and had associated unfamiliar sights with the working of supernatural agencies, was now giving way before the investigation of natural causes. Miletus also gave birth to the first treatise on geography in the work of Hecataeus. The westward advance of Persia to the neighbourhood of the Aegean, and the subsequent conflict between that empire and Greece, together with the increasing familiarity of the Greeks with Egypt, further widened the field of view; and the progress thus obtained is embodied in the History of Herodotus. Then follow a succession of expeditions in lands hitherto unknown—the voyage of Hanno along the western coast of Africa, the retreat of the Ten Thousand under Xenophon through Armenia, and above all the eastern campaigns of Alexander, in the course of which a vast area of country was for the first time revealed. The cities which were founded by that great conqueror, and the interest in the pursuit of knowledge that was displayed by his successors in Egypt and in Asia, aided still further the advance of discovery. But the event which more than any other served to foster the science of geography was the foundation of Alexandria. That city, from its central position in respect of the three continents, and from the attractions which it offered to traders, at once became a focus of information; and its famous Museum was the resort of men of science, like Eratosthenes and Hipparchus, by whose researches mathematical geography was established on a

Miletus and the Ionian School.

Herodotus.

Early Expeditions.

Alexander's Campaigns.

Foundation of Alexandria.

firm basis. The influence which it thus exercised continued to be felt until the latest period, for Ptolemy is spoken of by Suidas and other writers as an Alexandrian. Meanwhile the rise of the power of Rome was bringing into prominence the countries of Western Europe, and that city, from the patronage which its leading men extended to geographical research, attracted persons who were interested in that study. Under such circumstances we cannot be surprised that the political and practical side of the subject made itself felt; and so we find that historical geography assumed a conspicuous position, with Polybius for its most prominent exponent. In the epoch that followed, the conquests of the Romans were the principal agency in advancing the frontiers of knowledge; and the war against Mithridates in Asia, and Caesar's campaigns in Gaul, made extensive additions to this field. The Augustan age, owing to the good order that everywhere prevailed, and the facility of communication caused by the encouragement given by the Romans to the construction of roads, marked the culminating point of the study; and whatever additions were made to the subject during the remainder of the first century of our era, related to outlying regions, such as Britain, the inland parts of Mauretania, and the coasts of the Indian sea. After this, the scientific side of geography came once more to the front, for it was discovered that map-making was serviceable for purposes of administration, and on this account it was encouraged by the Romans. Hence in the second century, when other branches of the study were becoming decadent, mathematical geography reached its highest development in the works of Ptolemy.

Roman Conquests.

Augustan Age.

Ptolemy.

It is no easy matter for us at the present day to realise to ourselves the feelings of the ancients with regard to geographical enquiry. We are sated with discoveries; and since the sources of the Nile have been reached by travellers, and the leading features of the interior of Africa have been made known to us, only small portions of the habitable globe remain still to be explored, so that we are forced to turn to the Polar regions as the last re-

Stimulating Influence of Geographical Discoveries.

maining stimulus to investigation. But in antiquity the case was different, because of the numerous questions that then remained unsolved, and the ignorance which prevailed concerning wide tracts of country. The belief that the earth was surrounded by water, which we find to have existed as early as the Homeric age, continued to be a subject for speculation down to the latest period. Even when the Roman empire had reached its furthest limits, it was acknowledged that there were peoples, such as the Chinese at the extremity of Asia, the tribes in the interior of Africa, and others by the northern sea, of whom nothing was known beyond uncertain rumours; and, in addition to this, a large portion of the surface of the globe still remained to be accounted for, which might in part be covered by continents, and these perhaps inhabited. But at an earlier period these influences made themselves much more strongly felt. The excitement awakened in the minds of the Greeks by narratives of voyages to Tartessus, when once their pioneers had made their way in the wake of the Phoenicians to that remote land, can only be compared to the feelings of the European nations during the age of American discovery, when the strange objects and stranger tales which were brought back by adventurers suggested the hope of extensive conquests and of subsequent profit. The reports which reached them about the increasing cold and heat of the climate as the traveller advanced toward the north or the south, suggested questions respecting the limits of the habitable world. Differences in the colour, the dress, and the modes of life of various tribes in remote regions, the mention of which we frequently meet with in the pages of Herodotus, aroused their curiosity with regard to the lands which these inhabited. From the time that they became acquainted with Egypt, the rise of the Nile in summer and its inundations presented to them an endless subject of speculation; and still greater was the impression made upon them by the evidences of the ancient civilisation of that country—the Pyramids and other extraordinary buildings, the highly developed arts of life, and the results of scientific enquiry, as shown in the calendar and the principles of geometry. These are specimens of the stimulating influence on the Greeks of an extended knowledge of

Curious Information thus obtained.

foreign lands; and by these they were impelled towards the further prosecution of such researches, and the attempt to determine their bearing on other studies.

Since the sources of information about distant lands in antiquity were so various, and in some respects so uncertain, it required, and still requires, the exercise of considerable judgement to determine the amount of credibility that attaches to the evidence which was thus obtained. **Means of testing the Reports of Early Travellers.** No doubt, the suspicion with which "travellers' tales" have been received in all ages is in many ways unreasonable, for truth is stranger than fiction, and those who have seen unwonted sights in far countries, however much they may be tempted to exaggerate by the impossibility of putting their statements to the proof, have less need than others to draw on their imagination. At the same time there is a marked difference between the observations of professed explorers and those of traders, or of soldiers who have returned from foreign campaigns; and it was almost entirely from these and similar classes of men that intelligence was obtained in ancient times. To determine the value of such statements a certain exercise of criticism is required, so as to distinguish what has been gathered by hearsay from that which is the result of personal enquiry; and the character of the narrator himself, and the circumstances under which his information was procured, have also to be taken into account. It is the privilege of a later age, when additional facts bearing on these points have been brought to light, to be able to pronounce with greater confidence on the trustworthiness of such testimony. By this means fully as much has been done in the way of confirming, as in that of disallowing, the traditions of a past age. Thus it is easy to understand that the statements of Pytheas with regard to the wonders of the northern sea, and even his voyage to that region, would appear incredible, when they were subjected to the criticism of an unimaginative thinker, like Polybius, who declined to believe anything that he could not verify or explain; **Marvellous Narratives not necessarily Incredible.** and yet we may acknowledge that, since that time, confidence in that traveller has been restored by a comparison of his narrative with the results of modern enquiry. We shall have to return to this subject at a later time, when we come to speak of Pytheas' travels: for the present we may remark, as a proof of his having been in Britain, that he mentions mead, the favourite British beverage, as being made and drunk there, when he says, "those of the inhabitants who have corn and honey make a drink of those ingredients[1]"; and further, he is shewn to have reached the northern extremity of that island by his noticing the extraordinary rise of the tide in the adjoining sea, which is at all times a remarkable phenomenon[2]. In such cases we may feel confident that these peculiar statements, corresponding as they do to what are now well ascertained facts, were not mere inventions, but the result of observation on the spot. In other instances, too, where information of this kind has been more indirectly transmitted—even in the mythical accounts of distant portions of the earth which Homer gives us—when we meet with facts which were marvels to the men of that time, but now are capable of easy explanation, we need find no difficulty in accepting them as true. In this way we are to a certain extent provided with landmarks to guide us in exploring a region of knowledge, the outlines of which are vague and shadowy. It is not unreasonable to assume a sceptical attitude towards narratives of extraordinary voyages, which profess to have been undertaken at a time when it is highly improbable that they would have been carried out, unless such narratives are corroborated by further evidence. Strange statements, also, about unknown countries and peoples may fairly be relegated to the region of fable, if their tone is extravagant, and nothing has subsequently been brought to light that may confirm them. But, on the other hand, the verification of such statements goes far to establish the truthfulness of the reporter, the more so because of their original unlikelihood; and when these occur in accounts of extended voyages and travels, a further presumption is created in favour of the authentic character of those expeditions themselves.

[1] Strabo, 4. 5. 5; see Elton, *Origins of English History*, p. 30.
[2] Pliny, 2. 217; see Elton, p. 71.

CHAPTER II.

GEOGRAPHY OF THE HOMERIC PERIOD.

The Argonautic Legend—Its Historical Significance—Homeric Conception of the Earth—The River Oceanus—The Giant Atlas—Geography of the Homeric poems—The North and East of the Aegean—Interior of Asia Minor—Greece—Accuracy of Local Epithets—Description of the Styx—Inaccurate Account of Ithaca—Outer Geography of the Iliad; of the Odyssey—Ignorance of the Western Countries—Wanderings of Ulysses—Their Mythical Character—Exceptions to this—Rumours about far distant Countries—The Pygmies—Long Days and Nights of Northern Europe—Primitive Trade-routes—The Amber Trade—Route through Pannonia—Route through Gaul—Entrepôt at the Mouths of the Po—Story of the Sisters of Phaëthon—The River Eridanus—The Tin Trade—Tin not imported from India, but from Spain, and Britain—The Cassiterides Islands — Opinions as to their Situation—Trees imported into Greece; the Palm, the Pomegranate, the Cypress, the Plane—The Cardinal Points determined by the Winds—The Four Winds in Homer—Character of the Greek Winds.

IN endeavouring to discover the ideas on the subject of geography that existed among the Greeks at a primitive period, we naturally turn to the Homeric poems, as being the earliest literary creations of that people, *The Argonautic Legend.* and as furnishing a singularly comprehensive view of the range of knowledge of that time. Yet even before the Iliad and Odyssey were composed we meet with intimations of attempts on the part of the Greeks to extend their field of observation, in the stories of maritime enterprise which were already in circulation. Foremost among these is the fabled voyage of the Argo, a tale of adventure which is spoken of in the Odyssey as being even then 'world-famous[1].' The elaborate development which this story underwent at a later time, and the numerous details which gathered round it, render it difficult to reduce it to its original form, for the tale of Medea's love became attached to it, and the return of the Argonauts from Colchis to Greece became the basis of fanciful narratives of the circumnavigation of the

[1] Ἀργὼ πᾶσι μέλουσα, *Od.* 12. 70.

eastern or the western continent: but the name of Jason, and the story of the passage of the vessel between moving rocks, by which the Symplegades appear to be meant, form part of it from the first, so that we seem to be justified in associating it with the Euxine.   Aeetes is mentioned as the ruler of the land which Jason visited, but the country itself is not named; and it is more reasonable to suppose that it was identified with Colchis after the commerce of the Greeks had been extended to the Phasis by the advance of their colonies, than that a band of adventurers should have penetrated at that early age to the east of the Black Sea.   Still, after making all deductions,
Its Historical Significance.   we can hardly avoid the conclusion that some expedition of this kind took place, and that the fame of it was widely spread in the neighbourhood of the Aegean.   In other cases where notices of distant countries are found imbedded in the early legends of the Greeks, they can usually be traced to a Phoenician source; and when they refer to the far west, the same thing is true even with regard to a much later period. The mythological personage who is most frequently found in this connexion is Heracles; and this divinity, where he appears in the character of a traveller—for instance, when he drives off the herds of Geryon, the scene of which incident is laid near Gades, or when he slays the giant Antaeus in Libya—is to be regarded as representing the Phoenician Melcarth.

The form of the earth, as it was conceived by Homer, is a
Homeric Conception of the Earth.   circular plane—an idea which would be naturally suggested by the appearance of the horizon, as it is seen in any extensive view, especially from a mountain height.   This plane was encircled by the Ocean, a
The River Oceanus.   broad and deep river, which was the parent of all waters—not only of the various seas, but of the rivers and fountains[1]—and this stream flowed continually onward, so that in its revolving course it is spoken of

---

[1] *Il.* 21. 195—7;

> ......βαθυρρείταο μέγα σθένος Ὠκεανοῖο,
> ἐξ οὗπερ πάντες ποταμοὶ καὶ πᾶσα θάλασσα
> καὶ πᾶσαι κρῆναι καὶ φρείατα μακρὰ νάουσιν.

as returning upon itself[1]. It is difficult to determine what was the origin of this notion, which appears to us all the more strange, because the question whether the habitable world was surrounded by water was never solved in ancient times. It may have been simply mythological, though this view is not supported by our finding it associated with any similar myths, which might illustrate it. Perhaps it is more probable that it emanated from a Phoenician source, since traders of that nation were acquainted with the outer sea, both in the direction of Spain and in that of Arabia; and the belief in the continuity of its waters may have been suggested to them in the same way as it was to the scientific men of a later age, by their observing the recurrence of the movement of the tides wherever they met with it. The name Oceanus, also, seems to be more easily explained by a Semitic than by a Greek etymology[2]. Over the earth was *The Giant Atlas.* reared a vaulted firmament of bronze, in which the stars were set, and the pillars by which this was supported were upheld by Atlas. This giant, also, and the story associated with him, were probably creations of the Phoenicians, and were connected in their minds with the chain of mountains of that name, with which they were familiar in the north-west of Africa. Of the area which was comprehended within this framework only a very small portion was known, or even made the subject of conjecture, in the Homeric age. The geographical knowledge of the Greeks at that time was confined almost entirely to the lands in the neighbourhood of the Aegean.

With these countries the author of the Iliad shews a more or less familiar acquaintance. The features of the *Geography of the Homeric poems.* Trojan plain, the stream-like current of the Hellespont, the opposite coast of Thrace, and the island of Tenedos, are all well known to him. The same thing is true of the district immediately to the southward of *The North and East of the Aegean.* this, where the territory of Troy is bounded by the wooded range of Ida, which reaches the sea at its western extremity in the promontory of Lectum; and the islands in the north of the Aegean, and the conspicuous heights on the

---

[1] ἀψόρροος, *Il.* 18. 399.
[2] Kiepert, *Lehrbuch d. a. Geographie*, p. 30.

neighbouring mainland, are introduced into the narrative with
due observance of their relative position. All these are mentioned
in the description of the course pursued by Hera, when she passed
from Olympus to Ida to meet Zeus on the summit of that
mountain. There we are told that she first visited the Thracian
mountains and Athos, and thence took her flight by way of
Lemnos and Imbros to Lectum, where she left the sea and
ascended over the ridges to Gargarus, the highest point of Ida,
leaving the God of Sleep, who had accompanied her, to keep
watch on one of the lofty pines[1]. Samothrace, which reaches the
greatest elevation of all the islands in these parts, and commands
a view of the plain of Troy, is selected for the station from which
Poseidon viewed the combats of the Greeks and Trojans[2], as
Zeus did from Gargarus. Olympus itself is rightly designated
as a long and snowy and many-crested mountain[3]. Along the
coast of Asia Minor to the south of Mt. Ida, and in the neighbouring inland districts, various features of the ground are mentioned, either incidentally, or in connexion with the tribes who
furnished contingents to the army of the Trojans. Thus we hear
of Mt. Tmolus and the Gygaean lake as being in the territory
of the Maeonians, the river Maeander and the heights of Mycale
in that of the Carians, and the Xanthus in Lycia[4]; while the
Cayster is introduced in a simile as being the haunt of innumerable
waterbirds[5], and Mt. Sipylus figures in the story of Niobe[6].
But there is no intimation of Greek colonies existing on the
mainland of this country, though Rhodes and the islands in its
vicinity, as well as parts of Crete, were occupied by them[7]. Of the
districts of Asia Minor that lay further to the east
Interior of
Asia Minor. very little knowledge is shown; the Halys is not
mentioned, and the Paphlagonians, and beyond
them the Halizones, are only noticed as being allies of the
Trojans[8]. It is worthy of remark that in the Odyssey also, though
the scene of that poem is laid in western Greece, quite the most

---

[1] *Il.* 14. 225—230, 280—291.

[2] *Il.* 13. 10—14.

[3] μακρὸς ἀγάννιφος πολυδειράς, *Il.* 1. 402, 420, 499.

[4] *Il.* 2. 865, 866, 869, 877.   [5] *Il.* 2. 461.   [6] *Il.* 24. 615.

[7] *Il.* 2. 645—680.   [8] *Il.* 2. 851, 856.

reliable piece of geography relates to the Aegean. This is the description of the course pursued by the Greek chieftains after leaving Troy. We find them sailing first from Tenedos to Lesbos, and there debating whether of two routes they shall take across the sea to reach Greece; the one being straight to Euboea, leaving Psyra on their left—a voyage which according to the ideas of navigation of that time could only be undertaken in fair weather—the other between Chios and cape Mimas on the peninsula of Erythrae, from whence they would pass to Geraestus, the southern Euboean promontory[1].

In these poems also a generally accurate knowledge of Greece is shown, though that land is not described by any collective name. Hellas, in particular, the sub- Greece. sequent appellation of the entire area, is here confined to a district of Thessaly. The Achelous, which is spoken of as the mightiest of rivers, and only second to the ocean stream[2], forms the western limit, for while Aetolia is known to the poet, Acarnania and Epirus are not mentioned. The clearest evidence of familiarity with the country is furnished by the epithets by which places are designated; for instance, Accuracy of Local Epithets. the 'well-walled' Tiryns[3], to describe the still famous fortifications of that city; and especially the 'hollow' Lacedaemon 'full of fissures[4],' by which the valley of Sparta is graphically delineated, deeply sunk as it is between the heights of Parnon and Taygetus, and seamed with rifts on its surface. The accuracy of the local epithets in Homer was noticed in ancient times by Eratosthenes[5], and his judgement is corroborated by the observation of modern travellers. The most remarkable description of a geographical feature in Greece which we meet with in the poems, is that of the cascade of the Description of the Styx. Styx in Arcadia, which falls over a perpendicular cliff of great height at the side of one of the deepest and wildest

---

[1] *Od.* 3. 159—178.   [2] *Il.* 21. 194.   [3] *Il.* 2. 559.

[4] κοίλην Λακεδαίμονα κητώεσσαν, *Il.* 2. 581; *Od.* 4. 1.

[5] Strabo, 1. 2. 3; τὰ δὲ δὴ κατὰ τὴν Ἑλλάδα καὶ τοὺς σύνεγγυς τόπους καὶ λίαν περιέργως ἐξενηνοχέναι, πολυτρήρωνα μὲν τὴν Θίσβην λέγοντα, Ἁλίαρτον δὲ ποιήεντα, ἐσχατόωσαν δὲ Ἀνθηδόνα, Λίλαιαν δὲ πηγῆς ἔπι Κηφισσοῖο, καὶ οὐδεμίαν προσθήκην κενῶς ἀπορρίπτειν.

chasms in that country. This was associated in the minds of the
people with their primitive traditions about a river of Hades,
which they conceived of as a mighty stream falling down in a
cataract to the underworld, and then running with a great volume
of water to infinite distance. Homer speaks of this as the 'down-
dropping' water of Styx[1], and the 'precipitous streams of the water
of Styx[2]'; and the same thing is expressed by Hesiod in a somewhat amplified form when he calls it the 'cold water which is
poured down from a lofty inaccessible cliff[3],' and the 'primaeval
imperishable water of Styx, which it pours down through a precipitous spot[4].' The account, however, which is given of the
islands to the west of Greece, though it contains sufficient elements
of truth to prevent it from being characterised as fictitious, is
irreconcilable with the idea of personal observation. Not only
is the poet's conception of the grouping of those objects different

Inaccurate
Account of
Ithaca.

from the reality, but in the description of Ithaca,
which forms the central point among them, there
are features which no ingenuity can harmonise with
the actual appearance of that island. No person who had seen it
could have spoken of it as in any sense 'low-lying[5],' and there
is nothing in its vicinity that at all corresponds to the islet of
Asteris, which figures conspicuously in one portion of the story[6].
All the information which the poet possessed about this neighbourhood would appear to have been obtained at second-hand. In
concluding the review which has thus been given of the Homeric
geography of Greece and of the neighbourhood of the Aegean,
it should be added that the so-called 'Catalogue of Ships' has
been admitted as an authority alongside of the poems themselves.

[1] *Il.* 15. 37; τὸ κατειβόμενον Στυγὸς ὕδωρ.
[2] *Il.* 8. 369; Στυγὸς ὕδατος αἰπὰ ῥέεθρα.
[3] *Theog.* 785—7;

> ......πολυώνυμον ὕδωρ,
> ψυχρὸν, ὅ τ' ἐκ πέτρης καταλείβεται ἠλιβάτοιο
> ὑψηλῆς.

[4] *Ibid.* 805, 6;

> ......Στυγὸς ἄφθιτον ὕδωρ
> ὠγύγιον, τό θ' ἵησι καταστυφέλου διὰ χώρου.

[5] χθαμαλή, *Od.* 9. 25.
[6] *Od.* 4. 846.

That document, no doubt, is of a later date than they are, and it is necessary, also, to allow for some interpolations that were subsequently introduced into it; but, notwithstanding this, it is of great value as an evidence of the condition of Greece at the early time when it was compiled, and since we are now considering as a whole the period which is spoken of as the Homeric age, there is no reason for excluding the testimony which it affords.

When we turn to what has been called the 'outer' geography of the Homeric poems, that is, to the knowledge possessed by the Greeks at that early date of the countries which were not in their immediate vicinity, Outer Geography of the Iliad; we find that the extent of their acquaintance with them was very limited. At the time when the Iliad was composed, rumours seem to have reached them from the northern regions of wandering tribes, like the Scythians, though that people itself is not mentioned. Zeus is described as turning away his eyes from the combats on the plain of Troy, and looking "upon the land of the Thracian horse-breeders, and the Mysians, fierce fighters hand to hand, and the proud Hippemolgi that drink mare's milk, and the Abii, the most righteous of men[1]." The Mysians who are here introduced are the tribe in Thrace, from whom the people of the same name in Asia Minor originally sprang, while the Abii, or 'men without property,' whose poverty and simplicity of life obtained for them the reputation of justice, are, like the Hippemolgi, nomad races inhabiting the lands beyond the Haemus. At the same time, the name of the great river of those parts, the Ister, does not occur. In the east of the Mediterranean, Sidon is known as the chief city of the Phoenicians, and it was regarded as coming within the range of Greek experience, for we hear of Hecuba as possessing "embroidered robes, the work of Sidonian women, whom godlike Alexandros himself brought from Sidon, when he sailed over the wide sea, that journey wherein he brought home high-born Helen[2]." Yet the existence of the great empires of Assyria and Babylonia is not suspected. Egypt, again, is only mentioned in connexion

---

[1] *Il.* 13. 4—6. The quotations from Homer that are given in this chapter are taken from Lang, Leaf and Myers' translation of the *Iliad*, and Butcher and Lang's translation of the *Odyssey*.

[2] *Il.* 6. 289—292.

with the fame of the wealth of Thebes—"Egyptian Thebes, where the treasure-houses are stored fullest—Thebes of the hundred gates, whence sally forth two hundred warriors through each with horses and chariots[1]." Beyond this, on the borders of the Ocean stream, dwell the Aethiopians, a 'blameless' people, whom the Gods themselves visit, and partake of their feasts[2]. This description would lead us to regard them as a semi-mythical race; but their name, the 'burnt-faced' or 'swarthy' men[3], proves that the Greeks were already aware of a dark-skinned nation inhabiting the far South.

In the Odyssey the geographical horizon is somewhat more widely extended, as might be expected in a poem which is rather later in date, and has for its subject a story of travel. Communication with the East has now become more frequent, and Egypt is several times mentioned. Menelaus, when, on his return journey from Troy, he was driven by a storm from the shores of Crete to that country, spent eight years in wandering to and fro along the coasts of Phoenicia, Cyprus, and Libya; and the presents which he brought home with him thence to Greece imply that he was hospitably received[4]. The Nile, however, is known as yet by no distinctive name, but only as the 'river Aegyptus[5]'; and the island of Pharos, which was destined in the future from its opportune position near the coast to shelter the harbours of Alexandria, is described as being a day's sail from land. "There is an island," Menelaus says, "in the wash of the waves over against Egypt, and men call it Pharos, within one day's voyage of a hollow ship, when shrill winds blow fair in her wake[6]." The region called Libya, which the same hero visits, and of which the poet says, "there the ewes yean thrice within the full circle of a year; there neither lord nor shepherd lacketh aught of cheese or flesh or of sweet milk, but ever the flocks yield store of milk continual[7]," is the Cyrenaica, which was especially renowned for its fertility.

of the Odyssey.

---

[1] *Il.* 9. 381—4.   [2] *Il.* 1. 423; 23. 206.
[3] Αἰθίοπες from αἴθω ὤψ.
[4] *Od.* 3. 300; 4. 81—5, 128, 617.
[5] Αἰγύπτοιο, διιπετέος ποταμοῖο, *Od.* 4. 477.
[6] *Od.* 4. 354—7.   [7] *Od.* 4. 86—9.

The Aethiopians are now sufficiently well known to be divided
into two families, eastern and western—"the Aethiopians that
are sundered in twain, the uttermost of men, abiding some where
Hyperion sinks and some where he rises[1]"—a distinction which
corresponds to that drawn at a later time by Herodotus, who
speaks of "the Aethiopians above Egypt" and "the Aethiopians
towards the rising of the sun[2]." Of the countries to the west of
Greece great ignorance still prevails; Sicania, the
old name of Sicily[3], and the race of Sicels that
inhabited that island[4], are introduced; but beyond
these, and an incidental mention of the Thesprotians in Epirus[5],
scarcely any advance appears to have been made. This need
hardly surprise us, when we consider that the outlets of Greece,
and consequently the opportunities for communication which it
provides, are all towards the east. The coast on that side is
deeply indented with bays, which provide a shelter for the mariner,
and the principal maritime plains, like those of Attica and
Argolis, open out in that direction; whereas the western coast of
the Peloponnese has hardly a harbour to offer except those of
Pylos and Methone in Messenia, and the inlets which lie further
to the north are backed on the land side by inhospitable
mountains.

Ignorance of the Western Countries.

In the wonderland of Ulysses' adventurous wanderings we
look almost in vain for any real information about
distant countries. Not that these strange scenes are
to be regarded as the mere creation of the poet's
brain; they were rather the product of the popular fancy, which
had combined a variety of old mythological fables
with reports derived from Phoenician traders. But
the attempt to associate the incidents of the journey
with definite places—to identify the land of the Cyclopes with
Sicily, or the island of Aeolus with one of the Lipari islands, or
Circe's isle with the Circeian promontory—cannot bear the test
of examination. Even Phaeacia, notwithstanding the venerable
tradition which both in ancient and modern times has placed it
at Corfu, and the fitness of that delectable island to represent

Wanderings of Ulysses.

Their Mythical Character.

[1] *Od.* 1. 23, 24.　　[2] Herod. 7. 69, 70.　　[3] *Od.* 24. 307.
[4] *Od.* 20. 383.　　[5] *Od.* 14. 315.

what is described in the Odyssey, must be relegated to the region
of myth. In two instances only can we trace with
tolerable certainty a basis of truth underlying the
story—in the account of the land of the Lotophagi,
and in that of the dangers of Scylla and Charybdis. As regards
the former of these we are told that Ulysses was driven out to sea
by a violent wind from Malea—a cape which in all ages has
been dreaded on account of its storms—and that on the tenth
day he reached the country of the Lotophagi. There the natives
gave to his companions the lotus to taste; "and whosoever of
them did eat the honey-sweet fruit of the lotus, had no more wish
to bring back tidings nor to come back, but chose rather to abide
there with the lotus-eating men, ever feeding on the lotus, and
forgetful of returning[1]." A storm such as is here described would
naturally carry a ship towards the coast of Africa; and as a
district is found there, in the neighbourhood of the Lesser Syrtis,
where the lotus-shrub grows, and bears a sweet fruit—a fact which
might easily reach the ears of the Greeks through the Phoenicians
—it is reasonable to suppose that we are dealing with reality.
Polybius himself visited this region of Libya, and has left a
description both of the tree and of its fruit[2], and his account is
confirmed by those who have recently followed in his footsteps.
Scylla and Charybdis also, notwithstanding the weird imagery with
which they are decked out in the Homeric story, may well have
been an embodiment of the dangers presented by the rocks and

Exceptions to this.

---

[1] *Od.* 9. 94—7.

[2] Polyb. 12. 2. The description is so graphic that it deserves to be quoted
in full. "The lotus is not a large tree; but it is rough and thorny, and has a
green leaf, like the rhamnus, a little longer and broader. The fruit is like
white myrtle-berries when they are come to perfection; but, as it grows, it
becomes purple in colour, and in size about equal to round olives, and has a
very small stone. When it is ripe they gather it; and some of it they pound
up with groats of spelt, and store in vessels for their slaves; and the rest they
also preserve for the free inhabitants, after taking out the stones, and use it for
food. It tastes like a fig or a date, but is superior to them in aroma. A wine
is made of it also by steeping it in water and crushing it, sweet and pleasant to
the taste, like good mead; and they drink it without mixing it with water. It
will not keep, however, more than ten days, and they therefore only make it
in small quantities as they want it. Vinegar also is made out of it." (Shuckburgh's translation.)

eddies of the Straits of Messina, as reported to the Greeks by those who had passed through them[1].

But, although the knowledge of the world which the Greeks of this age possessed was so narrowly limited, there are not wanting intimations that reports had penetrated to them of strange races and strange sights in the remotest parts of the habitable world, both towards the south and the north. There was a proverbial saying current among the Greeks, which Aristotle has preserved for us, that Africa has always some novelty to offer[2]; and it is to that land that we may look to furnish our first instance. At its furthest extremity, by the Ocean stream, where we have already found the Aethiopians located, we hear of a diminutive people, the Pygmies, or 'men no bigger than your fist[3].' Their deadly enemies are the cranes; and when those birds migrate southwards at the approach of the cold season, they are supposed to be preparing to attack these puny foes. Thus in the Iliad the war-shouts of the Trojan army are compared to the cries of the embattled cranes, "which flee from the coming of winter and sudden rain, and fly with clamour towards the streams of ocean, bearing slaughter and fate to the Pygmy men[4]." Now, if this mention of a race of dwarfs in Africa stood alone, we might consign them to the same class of imaginary beings as the Idaean Dactyls and similar mythological figures. Tom Thumbs, like giants, have ever been familiar personages in folk-tales. But the case is different when we find good evidence, both in ancient and modern times, of the existence of such a diminutive people in the heart of the Dark Continent. In the story of the Nasamones in Herodotus, to which we shall have occasion hereafter to recur, we are told that far in the interior of Libya those explorers were seized and carried off by dwarfish men, under the middle height, and black-complexioned[5]. Aristotle also speaks of similar tribes as dwelling beyond the marshy tracts about the upper Nile[6].

Rumours about far Distant Countries.

The Pygmies.

---

[1] For a thorough discussion of the questions connected with the wanderings of Ulysses, see Bunbury's *Hist. of Anc. Geography*, vol. I. pp. 49—67.

[2] *Hist. Animal.*, 8. 28. 7; ἀεὶ φέρει τι Λιβύη καινόν.

[3] Πυγμαῖοι from πυγμή.   [4] *Il.* 3. 3—6.   [5] Herod. 2. 32.

[6] Ar. *op. cit.* 8. 12. 2; μεταβάλλουσι γὰρ [αἱ γέρανοι] ἐκ τῶν Σκυθικῶν πεδίων

And in our own days the experiences of Du Chaillu, Schweinfurth and Stanley in the course of their travels in Central Africa leave no doubt of their existence. We may conclude therefore that the Pygmies of Homer were a real people, and that their smallness of stature caused them to be regarded as fit antagonists for the cranes. The Egyptians might easily have heard of these, and through them the story may have found its way into Greece.

Still more interesting are the evidences which we discover of a faint acquaintance with the wonders of a northern clime in certain passages in Homer, which can hardly be otherwise explained than as referring to the long summer days and winter nights of the lands in the neighbourhood of the Arctic Circle. Ulysses, when narrating his visit to Telepylus, the city of the Laestrygones, which he reached in the course of his wanderings, describes it as a place, "where herdsman hails herdsman as he drives in his flock, and the other who drives forth answers the call. There might a sleepless man have earned a double wage, the one as neatherd, the other shepherding white flocks: so near are the outgoings of the night and of the day[1]." The meaning of the last clause, which at first sight is somewhat enigmatical, becomes clear if for· 'night and day' we substitute 'darkness and dawn,' or 'sunset and sunrise': in fact, we could hardly wish for a better paraphrase of it than is given in Tacitus' description of the shortness of the summer nights in the north of Britain—'finem atque initium lucis exiguo discrimine internoscas[2].' No sooner does Night appear, than Day reappears; and consequently there need be no intermission of work, such as the darkness causes. Again, the long unrelieved nights of an arctic winter seem to be described in the account which the poet gives of the Cimmerians, a people who dwell by the Ocean stream, which here we meet once more at the opposite extremity of the earth. The hero's ship, we are told, "came to the limits of the world, to the deep-flowing Oceanus. There is the land and the city of the

(Marginal note:) Long Days and Nights of Northern Europe.

εἰς τὰ ἕλη τὰ ἄνω τῆς Αἰγύπτου, ὅθεν ὁ Νεῖλος ῥεῖ, οὗ καὶ λέγονται τοῖς Πυγμαίοις ἐπιχειρεῖν· οὐ γάρ ἐστι τοῦτο μῦθος, ἀλλ' ἔστι κατὰ τὴν ἀλήθειαν γένος μικρὸν μὲν, ὥσπερ λέγεται, καὶ αὐτοὶ καὶ οἱ ἵπποι, τρωγλοδύται δ' εἰσὶ τὸν βίον.

[1] Od. 10. 82—6.   [2] Agr. c. 12.

Cimmerians, shrouded in mist and cloud; and never does the shining sun look down on them with his rays, neither when he climbs up the starry heavens, nor when he again turns earthward from the firmament, but deadly night is outspread over miserable mortals[1]." The same conception is expressed in a modified form, though still only approximating to the reality, in the story mentioned by Herodotus, that in the furthest countries to the northward of Scythia there existed a people who slept for six months in the year[2].

From these evidences of a knowledge, however vague, of the remote regions of the earth, which the Greeks of a primitive age possessed, we may now pass to the consideration of certain objects of commerce with Primitive Trade-routes. distant lands that are mentioned in Homer––a subject which is full of geographical interest, because of its bearing on the early trade-routes. The two principal articles which we hear of in this connexion are amber and tin, both of them substances of small bulk relatively to their value, and therefore easy of transport. The former of these, which served no useful purpose, and was only employed as an ornament, was esteemed on account of its beauty and curiosity, The Amber Trade. as well as its rarity. We hear of it more than once in the Odyssey as being used for necklaces––in the story of Eumaeus, whose nurse was tempted by Phoenician traders with a present of this nature to betray him[3]; and in the description of the gifts made to Penelope by the suitors[4]. Amber beads were also discovered by Schliemann in the tombs at Mycenae[5]. Now this material, which is a resinous substance formed by exudation from pine-trees, was found in antiquity almost entirely on the northern coasts of Europe. A certain amount of it, though somewhat different in character, was also brought from Liguria; but chemical analysis has shewn that that which reached Greece belonged to the northern species[6]. On the shores of Friesland and the neighbouring islands, between the mouths of the Rhine and the Elbe, it is washed up by the tide; and the coasts of the Baltic in

[1] Od. 11. 14—19.   [2] Herod. 4. 25.   [3] Od. 15. 460.
[4] Od. 18. 296.   [5] Schliemann, Mycenae, pp. 203, 245.
[6] Schliemann, Tiryns, p. 372.

North Germany furnish large quantities : in Courland also, towards
the Gulf of Riga, it is dug up as a fossil.   The question therefore
arises, by what line of traffic it reached the Mediterranean.   In
Roman times we have clear evidence that it was
brought across Germany by way of Pannonia to the
head of the Adriatic, for Pliny tells us that in
Nero's reign a Roman knight, who was despatched for that
purpose, brought a large supply by that route to Rome[1].   It is
highly probable that the northern traffic had followed the same
direction from a very early time.   The testimony which is borne
to this by archæological discoveries is very strong[2]; and it is only
thus that we can explain the legends that existed among the
Greeks concerning offerings that were sent at a primitive period
on several occasions by the Hyperboreans in the far north to
Delos by the way of the Adriatic and Dodona, sometimes under
the escort of maiden envoys of that race[3].   This supposition also
furnishes the easiest explanation of the numerous intimations which
connect the amber trade with the mouth of the Po ; for, though it
has been attempted to explain these by supposing the existence
of another route from the German Ocean to the head of the
Adriatic by the way of North Italy, yet this view has little more
than conjecture to support it.   At the same time it may well have
happened that amber found its way to the Mediterranean in
another direction ; and this was undoubtedly the case subsequently
to the expedition of Pytheas to Northern Europe in
the fourth century B.C., when both the tin and
amber trades were opened out to the merchants of
Massilia by means of the overland route across Gaul and down
the valley of the Rhone.   Indeed, there is evidence to show that
even before that date these articles followed that line of traffic, as

Route through Pannonia.

Route through Gaul.

  ¹ Pliny, *H. N.*, 37. 45; Sexcentis millibus passuum fere a. Carnunto
Pannoniae abesse litus id Germaniae ex quo invehitur percognitum nuper;
vivitque eques Romanus ad id comparandum missus ab Juliano curante gladia-
torum munus Neronis principis, qui et conmercia ea et litora peragravit, tanta
copia invecta ut retia coercendis feris podium protegentia sucinis nodarentur,
arma vero et libitina totusque unius diei apparatus esset e sucino.

  ² See Mr A. J. Evans's remarks in Freeman's *History of Sicily*, vol. 4,
p. 220.

  ³ Herod. 4. 33—5.

Müllenhoff has proved by an ingenious comparison of passages relating to this subject in Diodorus and Pliny. For, while the former of these writers tells us, though without giving his authority, that tin and amber were brought to the Mediterranean by this route, it is clear from the corresponding notices in Pliny that the source from which his information was drawn was Pytheas; and thus Pytheas is made to testify that the overland trade existed before his day[1]. How far back it may have dated we have no means of knowing, but possibly it may have been earlier than the foundation of Massilia. In any case, however, and by whatever route amber may have reached the shores of the Mediterranean, it is certain that in the Homeric age, if it was transported by sea to Greece, it must have passed through the hands of the Phoenicians, inasmuch as they were the only seafaring people of that time. We have already seen that in one passage of the *Odyssey* persons of that race are mentioned as having it in their possession.

The idea that there was an *entrepôt* for amber at the mouths of the Po, which has been hinted at above, is con- nected with two interesting and much debated points—viz. first, the origin of the legend of the sisters of Phaëthon, which was localised in this spot; and secondly, the etymology of the name Eridanus, which was ap- plied to the river Po by the Greeks, and after them by the Roman poets. According to the well-known story, Phaëthon, the son of Helios, persuaded his father to allow him for one day to drive the chariot of the sun through the heavens: but, being unable to check the horses in their career, he first set the heavens on fire, and then approached too near the earth; whereupon Zeus struck him with a flash of lightning, and he fell to the ground near the mouth of the Eridanus. His sisters, who there lamented his untimely fate, were changed into poplars, and their tears became amber. The last trait here mentioned is a clear proof that amber circulated in that neighbourhood, and also that it was believed to exude from the trunks of trees. How the myth of Phaëthon's death came to be naturalised there, we have no means of ascer-

Entrepôt at the Mouths of the Po.

Story of the Sisters of Phaëthon.

---

[1] Diodor. 5. 22. 4 and 5. 23. 1, 5 compared with Pliny 4. 94 and 37. 35, 36; see also Müllenhoff, *Deutsche Altertumskunde*, I. p. 476.

taining; but Pliny's explanation of that part of it which relates
to the sisters is reasonable enough; for he refers it to the
custom of wearing amber necklaces, which still continued in his
time to be practised by the women in that region, partly for the
sake of ornament, and partly as a supposed remedy for the *goître*,
and other evil results of drinking the water of Alpine streams[1].
The belief that amber exuded from trees may perhaps have been
derived, along with the material, from its original home in
Northern Europe; but it is more probable that it was inferred
by observation from the analogy of the gum which was seen to
drop from pine trees, and which the amber resembled, both in its
appearance, and in its inflammable nature and its aromatic scent
when burnt.   By the Greeks it was associated with the familiar
tree of North Italy, the poplar, though it was in reality totally
unconnected with it.

The origin of the name Eridanus is a still more perplexing
question.   Kiepert would explain it by a Phoenician etymology, as if it were a perversion or adaptation of the word *yarden* (Jordan) 'river,' which
we have noticed as being found in Crete in the form Iardanos[2].
Others have thought, with greater probability, that it is connected
with the river-name Rhodanus, and perhaps also Rhenus, and
that the early Greeks associated it at first with a great river in
north-western Europe, from which amber came; whence, after the
head of the Adriatic became a great centre of the amber trade, the
title was transferred to the principal stream of those parts, the
Padus[3].   The name of the little river Rhodaune, which flows into
the Baltic near Dantzig, has also been introduced in this connexion.   Still, as Herodotus observed[4], Eridanus is a purely
Greek word; and as the myth with which it is associated is also
genuinely Greek, there is no need to go further afield to discover

The River
Eridanus.

---

[1] Pliny, 37. 44.   Pado vero adnexa fabula est evidente causa, hodieque
Transpadanorum agrestibus feminis monilium vice sucina gestantibus, maxume
decoris gratia, sed et medicinae, creditur quippe tonsillis resistere et faucium
vitiis, vario genere aquarum juxta Alpis infestante guttura hominum.

[2] *v. supra*, p. 5.

[3] Bunbury in *Dict. Geogr.*, art. 'Eridanus,' and other authorities: cp. Herod.
3. 115.

[4] Herod. *loc. cit.*

its etymology. The root from which it is derived signifies 'early morn,' so that the word would originally be an epithet of the Sun[1], which is the case also with the name Phaëthon, or the 'shining' deity.

If amber was a valuable article of commerce on account of its quaint beauty, tin was much more so because of its usefulness. In the Homeric age it was employed, both for decorative purposes—thus, for instance, in the *Iliad* we find it introduced in the description of the inlaying of the figures on the shield of Achilles[2]—and still more as an alloy, for, by the mixture of this with copper, bronze was produced, a metal which on account of its superior hardness was especially serviceable for armour. Of this the weapons of that time were regularly made, and consequently the supply of tin that was required to produce it must have been very large. Yet tin is one of the scarcest of metals, and is found in but few countries of the world. In ancient times the only places where it was known to exist in any quantity were Spain and Britain. At the present day it is also imported into Europe from the Malay peninsula and islands, but it is an error to suppose that this was the case in antiquity The mistake arose from the idea that the Greek name for tin, *kassiteros*, was derived from the corresponding word in Sanscrit, *kastira*: but it is now known that *kastira* does not occur in that language until late in the middle ages, and from this we may conclude that the Greek word was the original. The same remark applies to the Arabic word for tin, *kasdir*. In Spain it was principally found in Galicia, in the north-west corner of the peninsula, where, though the supply is now exhausted or nearly so, tin mines are known to have existed from the testimony of Strabo and Pliny[3], and traces

The Tin Trade.

Tin not imported from India,

but from Spain,

---

[1] Ἠριδανός, like ἠριγενής, from ἦρι, 'early': see Müllenhoff, *op. cit.* r. p. 221.

[2] *Il.* 18. 564;

ἀμφὶ δὲ κυανέην κάπετον, περὶ δ' ἕρκος ἔλασσε
κασσιτέρου·

ibid. 574; αἱ δὲ βόες χρυσοῖο τετεύχατο κασσιτέρου τε.

[3] Strabo, 3. 2. 9, where Posidonius is quoted as saying γεννᾶσθαι [τὸν κατ-

of the workings have been found in modern times.   But by far

and Britain. the largest amount was brought from Britain, where
the Cornish mines furnished that metal in an abundance elsewhere unknown.   The Phoenicians were the importers,
and their *entrepôt* for what was obtained from both those countries
was Gades; though, as we have seen in the case of amber, an
overland route for this traffic through Gaul to the mouth of the
Rhone probably existed at an early period.   It is a reasonable
conjecture that in Northern Gaul this line of trade passed by way
of Brittany, for the Veneti, who occupied part of that district, are
spoken of by Caesar as being bold navigators, and accustomed to
make the voyage to Britain[1].   And if, as seems probable, Ushant
and the other islands in the neighbourhood of the Armorican
peninsula are the Oestrymnides which are mentioned by Avienus,
we have direct testimony to the presence of tin in connexion with
them even before the time of Pytheas.   For Avienus, whose
account of the inhabitants of the Oestrymnides tallies in many
points with what Caesar says of that region, speaks of those
islands as being rich in tin; and his description is professedly
based on that of Himilco, the Carthaginian explorer, whose
voyage took place not later than the fifth century before our era[2].

τίτερον] ἐν τοῖς ὑπὲρ τοὺς Λυσιτανοὺς βαρβάροις: Pliny, 34. 156; nunc certum
est [plumbum album] in Lusitania gigni et in Callaetia.

[1] Caesar, *B. G.*, 3. 8. 1; Naves habent Veneti plurimas, quibus in Britanniam navigare consuerunt, et scientia atque usu nauticarum rerum reliquos
antecedunt, et in magno impetu maris atque aperto paucis portibus inter-
jectis, quos tenent ipsi, omnes fere qui eo mari uti consuerunt, habent vecti-
gales.

[2] Avien., *Ora Maritima*, 90—102;

> Et prominentis hic jugi surgit caput,
> Oestrymnin istud dixit aevum antiquius,
> Molesque celsa saxei fastigii
> Tota in tepentem maxime vergit notum.
> Sub hujus autem prominentis vertice
> Sinus dehiscit incolis Oestrymnicus,
> In quo insulae sese exserunt Oestrymnides
> Laxe jacentes et metallo divites
> Stanni atque plumbi.   Multa vis hic gentis est,
> Superbus animus, efficax sollertia,
> Negotiandi cura jugis omnibus,

The city of Corbilo at the mouth of the Loire, which is spoken of by Strabo[1] as having been a great emporium, seems to have been the place from which the tin was carried overland to Massilia and Narbo.

A question which is inseparably connected with the subject of the tin trade with Britain is that of the position of the Cassiterides, or Tin Islands. In modern times these have usually been identified with the Scilly Islands, on the ground of their being the nearest group of islands to the Cornish coast; but this view can hardly be maintained. It is not, perhaps, a fatal objection to it that tin is not found in Scilly, because, if these islands were made a depot for trade, it might have been conveyed thither from the mainland; but they do not in other respects correspond to the required conditions. The ideas which prevailed among the ancients respecting the situation of the Cassiterides were no doubt singularly vague, but the principal authorities whose testimony has come down to us, especially Strabo, Diodorus, and Ptolemy, connect them with Spain rather than with Britain[2]. Strabo and Diodorus also clearly distinguish between the tin which was brought from the Cassiterides and that from Britain[3]. The former of these writers, indeed, speaks of them as lying to the northward of the country of the Artabri (Galicia) in the latitude of Britain[4]; but according to his idea of the relative position of these countries this would place them a great distance to the west of the Scilly Islands. Some recent writers, again, are of opinion that by this name were meant either the Oestrymnides, or the islands in the neighbourhood of Vigo Bay and Corunna towards the north-west angle of Spain;

The Cassite-rides Islands.

Opinions as to their Situa-tion.

> Notisque cymbis turbidum late fretum
> Et belluosi gurgitem oceani secant.

(See Müllenhoff, *op. cit.* 1. pp. 90, 91; Berger, *Geschichte der wissenschaft-lichen Erdkunde der Griechen*, 2. p. 61.)

[1] 4. 2. 1.

[2] Strabo, 3. 5. 11; Diodor., 5. 38. 4; Ptolemy, 2. 6. 76.

[3] Strabo, 3. 2. 9; Diodor. 5. 38. 4, 5.

[4] 2. 5. 15; τοῖς Ἀρτάβροις ἀντικεῖνται πρὸς ἄρκτον αἱ Καττιτερίδες καλούμεναι νῆσοι πελάγιαι, κατὰ τὸ Βρεττανικόν πως κλίμα ἱδρυμέναι.

which latter view would connect them with the Galician tin mines : but neither of these suppositions, if it stood alone, would account for the idea which commonly prevailed, that they lay in the open ocean far away from land[1]. On the whole, the most probable explanation, and that which agrees best with what we know of the concealment practised by the Phoenicians in respect of commerce, is this—that while the trade in tin continued to be their monopoly, all that the Greeks learnt concerning its origin was, that it was found in islands in the northern sea—by which Britain, together with the islets off its coast, or perhaps Ireland, were vaguely meant. This indistinct conception of the Cassiterides may have prevailed for many centuries; and Herodotus, it should be observed, who is the first writer that mentions them, discredits their existence altogether[2]. At a later period, when the nations about the Mediterranean obtained more accurate information concerning the north-western coasts of Europe, it was natural that they should affix the name to one or other of the groups of islands with which they found the trade to be associated[3]. Thus by some writers it may have been attached to the Oestrymnides, by others to the islands of the Galician coast, and even the Scillies may in some cases have been intended; while at the same time the old fabulous notion of their remoteness from the continent maintained its ground. It may seem at first sight to militate against this view, that Strabo expressly tells us that the Romans after numerous attempts discovered the way to these islands; and that after Publius Crassus, who voyaged thither, learnt that the mines were worked at no great depth below the surface of the ground, and that the inhabitants were peacefully disposed, the communication with them was facilitated[4]. This would imply that they were a definite group of islands, the position of which was clearly ascertained. There is no reason to doubt that Crassus made such an expedition; but whatever the place was to which he went, his account is quite untrust-

---

[1] πελάγιαι, Strabo, *loc. cit.*; ἐν τῷ ὠκεανῷ, Diodor. 5. 38. 4; ἐν τῷ δυτικῷ ὠκεανῷ, Ptol., *loc. cit.*

[2] Herod. 3. 115.

[3] See Kiepert, *Lehrbuch d. a. Geographie*, p. 528.

[4] Strabo, 3. 5. 11.

worthy, because he represents the Cassiterides as producing tin, whereas that metal is not found in any of the groups of islands which lie off the coasts of Gaul, or Britain, or Spain. The explicit character of his statements, however, seems to have deceived his contemporaries, and Strabo among them. The geographer's ideas on the subject are simply fabulous, for, as we have seen, he believed that the islands, which he says were ten in number, lay in the open sea to the northward of Cape Finisterre, in which position no islands ever have been; and from this we may learn how little reliable information on the subject had been obtained by the Romans.

A further link of connexion between Greece and distant lands may be traced in the trees which were introduced from abroad into that country. These, like the *Trees imported into Greece;* objects of which we have just been speaking, were in most instances imported by the Phoenicians, but they came from a different direction, namely from the side of Asia. Foremost among them is the palm, the name of which in Greek, *phoenix*, at once reveals the region from *the Palm,* which it came. This tree is not mentioned in the *Iliad*, but in the *Odyssey* we hear of the famous palm-tree of Delos, of which Ulysses, who compares Nausicaa's beauty to it, says that it caused him, though a much travelled man, to stand still in amazement[1]. It continued to be held in reputation as the earliest specimen that was known in Greece, so that Euripides calls it "the first-born palm[2]." The exotic character of the tree, however, is proved by its fruit refusing to ripen in the climate of Greece; this Pausanias remarked in antiquity[3], and the same thing is true at the present day. The pomegranate, also, was a genuinely Phoenician tree; it was *the Pomegranate,* sacred to Adonis, and Aphrodite (*i.e.* Astarte) was said herself to have planted it in Cyprus[4]. In Homer it is

---

[1] *Od.* 6. 162—7.

[2] πρωτόγονος φοῖνιξ: Eur. *Hec.* 458.

[3] Speaking of the temple of Artemis in Aulis he says (9. 19. 8) φοίνικες πρὸ τοῦ ἱεροῦ πεφύκασιν, οὐκ ἐς ἅπαν ἐδώδιμον παρεχόμενοι καρπόν, ὥσπερ ἐν τῇ Παλαιστίνῃ.

[4] See Hehn, *Kulturpflanzen und Hausthiere*, (3ᵈ edit.) p. 206.

mentioned among the trees that grew in the garden of Alcinous, and also as one of the fruits, the sight of which contributed to the punishment of Tantalus[1]. The cypress, too, which the Cypress, we find growing in Calypso's garden[2], and which gave its name to two places that occur in the Homeric catalogue, Cyparissus and Cyparisseis[3], is to be referred to the same origin. Its primitive home was in the highlands of Afghanistan, and from that country it migrated first to Persia—where its spiry shape won for it a sacred character as a symbol of fire-worship—and afterwards to Syria and the coasts of the Mediterranean[4]. The last tree which shall be mentioned as having come the Plane. to Greece from foreign parts, and which is at the same time the most beautiful, is the plane-tree: but this, though its original habitat seems to have been in the interior of Asia, was unconnected with the Phoenicians, for it is not a Semitic tree[5]. It passed to Greece by way of Asia Minor, in which country it attained a remarkable growth[6]. The only passage in Homer in which it is noticed, is the description in the *Iliad* of the omen which appeared to the assembled Greeks at Aulis before they started for Troy, when a snake appeared from under the altar, "beneath a fair plane-tree, whence flowed a glittering stream[7]."

It remains to notice the winds as they are represented in Homer, for it is through them that the first attempts The Cardinal Points deter- mined by the Winds. were made to determine the cardinal points. It is true that two of these points, the east and the west, were already distinguished by the direction of sunrise and sunset,—or, as it is otherwise expressed, of dawn and darkness—which must, in fact, be the most natural starting-points for the observation of relative position among primitive races, except those who dwell towards the distant north or south. Hence in the *Iliad*, Hector, when professing his contempt for omens, says to Polydamas, "Thou bidst us be obedient to birds long of wing, whereto I give no heed, nor take any care

[1] *Od.* 7. 115; 11. 589.
[2] *Od.* 5. 64.
[3] *Il.* 2. 519, 593.
[4] Hehn, pp. 244 foll., 530.
[5] *Ibid.* p. 255.
[6] *Ibid.* p. 254
[7] *Il.* 2. 307.

thereof, whether they fare to the right, to the dawn and to the sun, or to the left, to mist and darkness[1]." And in the *Odyssey* Athena says of Ithaca, "it is not so nameless but that many men know it, both all those who dwell towards the dawning and the sun, and they that abide over against the light towards the shadowy west[2]." But the Greeks, who were familiar with a maritime life, soon found that the winds were their best guides in determining the quarters of the heavens. Homer is acquainted only with four winds—Boreas, Eurus, Notus and Zephyrus—which represent the four chief points of the compass. In the *Iliad* we meet with them in pairs; thus two of them are introduced in the description of the excitement of the meeting in the second book, when "the assembly swayed like sea-waves of the Icarian main, that east wind and south wind raise, rushing upon them from the clouds of father Zeus[3]"; and the two others in the ninth book—"like as two winds stir up the main, the home of fishes, even the north wind and the west wind that blow from Thrace[4]." In the *Odyssey* all four are mentioned together, where Poseidon raises a storm for the destruction of Ulysses—"the east wind and the south wind clashed, and the stormy west, and the north, that is is born in the bright air, rolling onward a great wave[5]." Each of these winds has its distinctive character. Boreas, coming from his home in the Thracian mountains, is a clear and strong blast, as has been described in the passage last quoted, while Notus is wet and stormy. These features correspond to the ideas which we associate with them in our climate, but the case is not the same with the other two winds. Eurus, instead of being cold and dry, as the east wind is with us, is spoken of as soft and warm, so that the snow which lies on the ground is melted by it[6]; here the *scirocco*, or south-east wind, is meant. Zephyrus appears in two

The Four Winds in Homer.

Character of the Greek Winds.

---

[1] *Il.* 12. 237—240.   [2] *Od.* 13. 238—241.
[3] *Il.* 2. 144—6.   [4] *Il.* 9. 4, 5.
[5] *Od.* 5. 295, 6.
[6] *Od.* 19. 205, 6;

ὡς δὲ χιὼν κατατήκετ' ἐν ἀκροπόλοισιν ὄρεσσιν,
ἥν τ' Εὖρος κατέτηξεν, ἐπὴν Ζέφυρος καταχεύῃ.

characters—both as a balmy gale, which refreshes the Elysian fields, and renders fruitful the gardens of Alcinous[1], and as a violent wind, which falls heavily on the crops[2]. In the latter case the north-west wind is intended—that Zephyrus, whose dwelling, we are told, was a cavern in the land of Thrace[3]. The simple conception of the cardinal points, which has been thus indicated, sufficed for a primitive age. At a later period, when observation had become more accurate, it was replaced by a more minute subdivision of the winds, and of the quarters from which they blew; and this was accompanied at the same time by a more elaborate nomenclature.

[1] *Od.* 4. 567; 7. 119.   [2] *Il.* 2. 148.
[3] *Il.* 23. 200 and 230.

Map I.

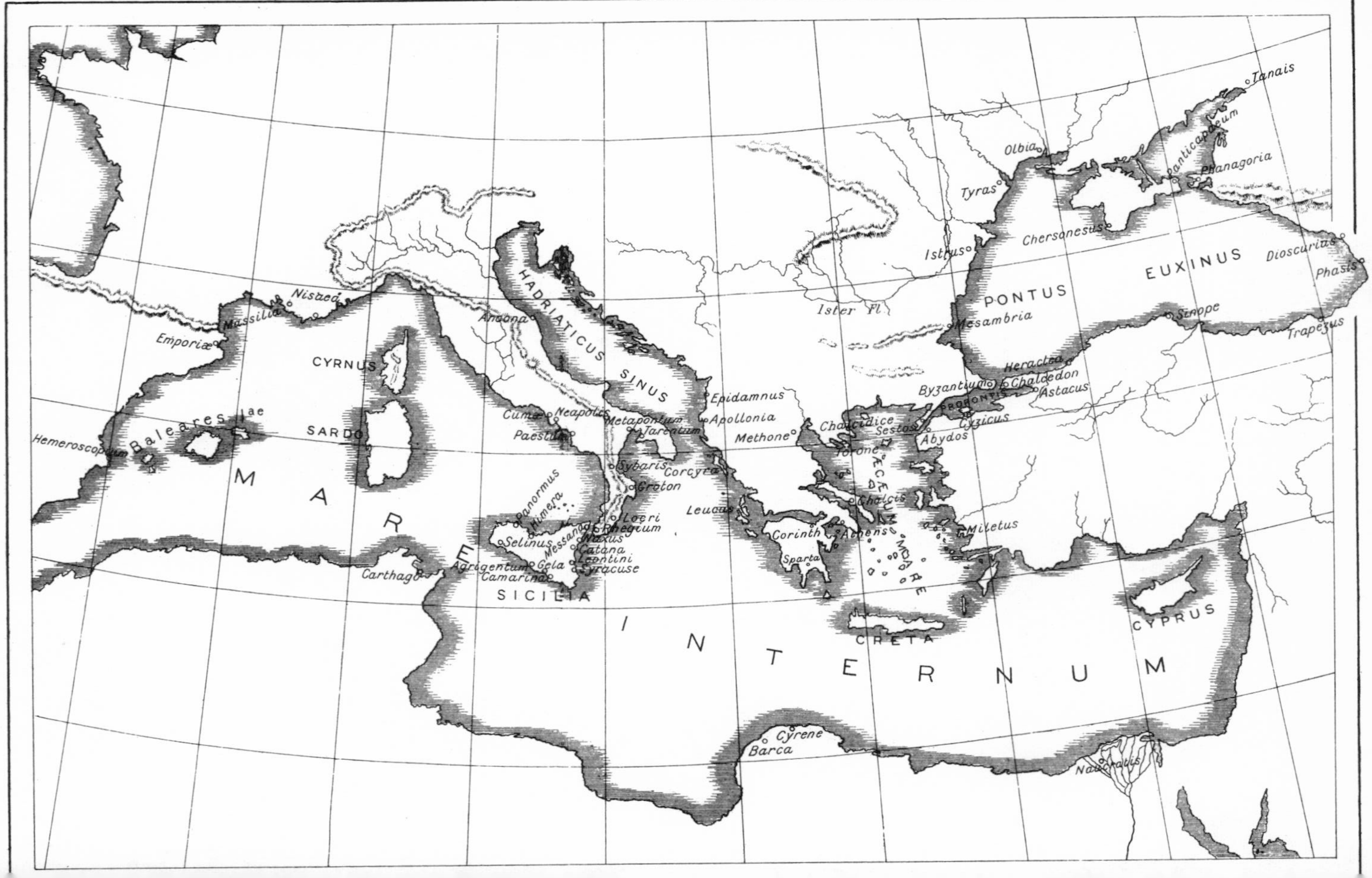

Tanais
Olbia
Tyras
Phanagoria
Chersonesus
Istrus
PONTUS
EUXINUS
Phasis
Sinope
Trapezus
Mesambria
Ister Fl.
Heraclea
Byzantium
Chalcedon
Astacus
Cyzicus
Abydos
Sestos
Chalcidice
Torone
Chalcis
Athens
Corinth
Sparta
Miletus
CRETA
CYPRUS
Cyrene
Barca
Methone
Epidamnus
Apollonia
Corcyra
Leucas
HADRIATICUS
SINUS
Ancona
Metapontum
Tarentum
Sybaris
Croton
Locri
Rhegium
Naxus
Messana
Catana
Leontini
Syracuse
Gela
Camarina
Agrigentum
Selinus
Panormus
Himera
SICILIA
Neapolis
Paestum
Carthago
CYRNUS
SARDO
Nisaea
Massilia
Emporiae
Hemeroscopium
M A R E
I N T E R N U M

CHAPTER III.

SPREAD OF THE GREEK COLONIES.

Geography advanced by the Greek Colonies—Causes of their Establishment—
Qualifications for a Site—Early Development of the Colonies—Communi-
cation with the Natives—Information transmitted to Greece—Colonies on
the Euxine—Dangers and Attractions of that Sea—Sinope, *circ.* 770 B.C.—
Cyzicus on the Propontis—Colonies on the North Coast of the Euxine—
Olbia, 645 B.C.—Panticapaeum (Kertch)—Dioscurias—Chalcidic Colonies
in Thrace—Megarian Colonies in the Propontis : Byzantium, 658 B.C.—
Greek Colonies in Italy, Cumae, Neapolis, Rhegium and Messana—
Sybaris, 721 B.C.—Croton, 710 B.C.—Paestum—Metapontum—Locri—
Tarentum, 708 B.C.—Colonies in Sicily : Naxos, 735 B.C.—Syracuse,
734 B.C.—Gela, 690 B.C.—Agrigentum, 580 B.C.—Himera, 648 B.C.—The
Phocaeans at Massilia, 600 B.C.—Colonies of Massilia—Its Influence in
Gaul—Cyrene, 631 B.C.—Its Site and Commerce—The Greeks in Egypt—
Their Settlement at Naucratis, *circ.* 650 B.C.—Summary.

THE first great advance that was made in the study of
Geography was due to the spread of the Greek
colonies along the shores of the Euxine and the
Mediterranean, commencing with the eighth century
before the Christian era.   By their means the
horizon of knowledge was rapidly and continuously extended,
enquiry was promoted into the natural features of the interior of
the neighbouring continents and the condition of their inhabitants, and an impulse was given to speculation on larger questions
connected with the formation and constituent elements of the
Earth.   This remarkable movement, a phenomenon
in early Greek history second only to that of the
creation of the Homeric poems, was due to more
than one cause.   In the first place, it provided an outlet for the
superfluous population of the Greek cities, which about that time
was increasing with extraordinary rapidity, and threatened to
involve them in serious domestic perplexities.   In other cases
colonisation served as a remedy for political feuds and party

spirit; as was notably the case in the foundation of Tarentum, when the Partheniae, or youths illegitimately born of Spartan mothers during the First Messenian war, after making an abortive attempt at revolution in their native city, were drafted off to a foreign country. At the same time, a vent was thus found for the ardent love of enterprise which accompanied the first vigorous growth of the Hellenic communities; and the trading spirit, which, combined with a fondness for nautical pursuits, was early developed among the Greeks, gave a practical turn to the pre-vailing feeling of restlessness. The last-named motive soon became all-absorbing, and the sites which were chosen for the new settlements were chiefly determined by their suitableness for commercial purposes. The conditions which were considered most favourable for these were a position on the sea-shore with a safe harbour in the recesses of a bay, and a steep height close at hand which admitted of being easily fortified: in the neighbourhood a moderate extent of fertile land, suitable for cultivation, and—most important of all—a ready access to a district of con-siderable area in the interior, the inhabitants of which by means of barter might furnish articles for export. Here and there an additional attraction was provided by the presence of some special source of wealth, such as fisheries, or mines, or forests for the supply of timber. The freedom which was thus exercised by the new settlers in the choice of an abode, enabling them, as it did, to select the position most suited to their wants, was the main cause of the early development of the colonies as compared with that of the parent states. Where the conditions were so advantageous, the natural result was the speedy accumulation of wealth, and, as a conse-quence of this, a more rapid development of culture than would have been possible elsewhere. In the fine arts this result is especially conspicuous. The noblest specimens of early Greek architecture are the temples of Paestum, Selinus, and Agrigentum, and no coins from Greece Proper will bear comparison with those of Magna Graecia.

The intercourse which thus sprang up between the foreign settlers and the natives soon became an abundant source of

Qualifications for a Site.

Early De-velopment of the Colonies.

information about remote countries. The Greeks established themselves in these in the character of traders, and therefore it was to their interest to maintain friendly communication with the inhabitants. Not unfrequently they intermarried with them, and thus a mixed race was formed, who were able to act as an intermediate agency between the two. The influence of Hellenic civilisation, also, gradually pervaded in some degree the neighbouring tribes, and broke down the barriers which fear and jealousy had at first interposed between them and the strangers. By this means the spirit of enquiry, which was never wanting to the Greeks, found constant opportunities of satisfying itself by collecting information concerning the tribes beyond, with whom they were only acquainted by hearsay. And the knowledge thus obtained was again transmitted to Greece. For, however much at a later period the colonies might be disposed to rebel against any dictation on the part of the mother city, at first, and for a long time, the bond of union between the two was very strong: the custom of taking the sacred fire from the hearth of the parent state, which was observed on the sending out of a colony, was emblematical of the close connexion which was afterwards maintained, and consequently there was frequent communication between the emigrants and those whom they left behind. We can picture to ourselves what happened, when a vessel returned home from one of these newly founded cities, bringing news of those who had gone forth to seek their fortunes;—on the one side, anxious enquiries by relations about their kindred, and eager questions about the prospects of trade or the need of despatching additional bands of settlers; and, on the other, narratives of dangers experienced on the voyage, and descriptions of the coasts and cities visited on the way; above all, elaborate accounts of the strange peoples and curious objects, which were peculiar to those regions. Reports such as these could not fail to awaken a keen interest on the part of the auditors, and to obtain a wide circulation. Moreover, all the Greek tribes had their share in collecting them, for all took part in the work of colonisation. Though the Ionians led the van, and sent forth the earliest expeditions both towards the east

Communication with the Natives.

Information transmitted to Greece.

and the west, yet the other races were not behindhand. The important colonies of Syracuse and Byzantium were established by the Dorians of Corinth and Megara; Sybaris and Croton by the Achaeans, and Locri Epizephyrii by the Locrians.

In reviewing the progress of the colonising activity of the Greeks we may commence from the Black Sea, on the shores of which some of the earliest settlements were planted. Here the Ionian city of Miletus—a place which was destined to promote the cause of geography at once by its discoveries and by its philosophical speculations—was the pioneer. Commerce, indeed, had already found its way to the Pontus, for the Phoenicians had established trading stations on the way thither, among which Lampsacus was especially important, as commanding the passage of the Hellespont, and Greek traders had followed in their wake; but the Milesians were the first to establish any regular colonies in those regions. The enterprise was a daring one, for the navigation of the Euxine, with its wide expanse—in this respect a strong contrast to the island-studded waters of the Aegean—and its stormy character, which has always rendered it the terror of sailors, was a new departure in the maritime experience of the Greeks. But when once the venture had been made, the fears which it inspired were soon neutralised by the advantages which it presented in respect of trade. Foremost among these were its fisheries, for the sea of Azov, which runs off from it at its north-eastern angle, is one of the most famous breeding-places of the tunny; and the shoals of that fish, when they issue forth through the Straits of Kertch into the open sea, make at once for the shores of Asia Minor, where they are captured in great quantities. The forests, also, with which the sea-slopes of that country were clothed—the pines of Pontus, which Horace has celebrated[1], and the box-trees of Cytorus in Bithynia, which called forth the praises of Catullus and Virgil[2], were at hand to furnish an inexhaustible supply of wood. In the

Colonies on the Euxine.

Dangers and Attractions of that Sea.

---

[1] Hor. *Od.* 1. 14. 11;   Pontica pinus,
                        Silvae filia nobilis.

[2] Catull. 4. 13; Cytore buxifer:
   Virg. *Georg.* 2. 437; Et juvat undantem buxo spectare Cytorum.

interior, behind this woodland region, the elevated plateaux of Phrygia and Cappadocia, which are still famous for the Angora wool which they produce, supported innumerable flocks of sheep and goats, whose fleeces and hides were brought down to the coast, and formed a valuable article of export.　It was just at the middle point of this southern shore of the Euxine, where the broad mass of Paphlagonia projects into **Sinope, *circ.* 770 B.C.** its waters, in a position closely resembling that which Carthage occupied in the Mediterranean, that the Milesians founded their colony of Sinope about the year 770 B.C.　In its neighbourhood was the mouth of the Halys, the most important river in Asia Minor; and owing to this, and to the other facilities which it offered for commerce, the same place had been from old days the chief *entrepôt* for the trade of the interior of Asia.　The prosperity of the new Greek settlement at once justified the choice of its founders.　So rapid was its development, that in the middle of the same century its citizens were able to establish a daughter-colony of their own further to the east on the same coast, at Trapezus (Trebizond)—another point of great commercial importance, for there, notwithstanding that it is backed on the land side by lofty mountain ranges, the chief trade-route from Persia by way of Armenia reaches the sea.　Nor were the lines of communication between the cities on the Pontus and the mother country neglected.　The Hellespont was secured by the occupation of Abydos, and almost contemporaneously with Sinope the colony of Cyzicus was founded to command **Cyzicus on the Propontis.** the Propontis, which piece of water, as its name implies, was the vestibule of the Euxine.　The sites of these two places bore a marked resemblance to one another. Sinope was built so as to occupy a narrow isthmus, which joins a triangular peninsula to the mainland; while at Cyzicus in place of the peninsula there was an island joined by bridges to the shore close to the city.　At the present day the correspondence between the two is still more complete, for at Cyzicus also, in consequence of the accumulation of sand, an isthmus has been formed between the island and the coast.　Each of these towns had two ports; and in the case of Cyzicus it was partly, no doubt, due to this, that at a later period the city ranked as one of the

three which were most famous for their arsenals and manu-
factories of arms, Rhodes and Massilia being the other two[1].

The progress of colonisation in this direction was for a while
interrupted in consequence of movements on the
Colonies on
the North   part of the Cimmerian peoples, and Sinope itself
Coast of the required to be founded anew by Miletus a hundred
Euxine.
              and fifty years after its first establishment; but in
the course of time a fresh advance was made along the western
and northern coasts of the Euxine, until at last the whole of that
sea was encircled with a belt of Greek cities. The mouths of
the great rivers which pour their waters into it offered a special
attraction to the settlers on account of the means of intercourse
which they provided with the natives of the interior; and the
positions of several of their trading stations are at once recognised by their bearing the names of the streams with which they
were associated—Istros being the port for the Danube, Tyras
for the Dniester, Tanais for the Don, and Phasis for the Rion.

The most important of all was Olbia, or the "city
Olbia, 645   of wealth," which was founded in 645 B.C. near
B.C.
              the *embouchure* of the Hypanis (Bug), somewhat
below the site of the modern Nicolaief, and in the vicinity
of the mouth of the Borysthenes (Dnieper). The temptations
held out by the immense export and import trade, which soon
sprang up throughout this region, overcame the repugnance which
the Greeks must at first have felt to a country and a climate so
unlike their own: for here, instead of the varied aspect and
genial skies of Greece, they met with a monotonous expanse of
dreary steppes, which were exposed to winters of extraordinary
rigour. As they advanced further towards the east these dis-
couragements were intensified. There they found themselves
opposed by the Tauri of the Crimea, the memory of whose
barbarous customs has been perpetuated in the story of Iphigeneia
and Orestes, and by the savage Sarmatian tribes, who dwelt on
the northern side of the Palus Maeotis. But, notwithstanding

---

[1] Strabo, 14. 2. 5; speaking of Rhodes he says, κἀνταῦθα δὲ, ὥσπερ ἐν
Μασσαλίᾳ καὶ Κυζίκῳ, τὰ περὶ τοὺς ἀρχιτέκτονας καὶ τὰς ὀργανοποιίας καὶ θησαυ-
ροὺς ὅπλων τε καὶ τῶν ἄλλων ἐσπούδασται διαφερόντως, καὶ ἔτι γε τῶν παρ'
ἄλλοις μᾶλλον. Cp. also 12. 8. 11,

this, they planted their colony of Panticapaeum (Kertch) on the western shore of the Bosporus Cimmerius, the narrow strait by which that sea is entered, while Panticapaeum
(Kertch). on the opposite side another warder was established by the foundation of the sister city of Phanagoria. At last they penetrated to the inmost recesses of those shallow waters, which were ice-bound during several months of the year, and formed a settlement in the delta of the Tanais. The eastern coast of the Pontus, again, was occupied by the cities of Phasis and Dioscurias, where the Greeks were brought in contact with the wild races of the Caucasus, and Dioscurias. the warlike Iberian nation, that dwelt between the Euxine and the Caspian. In this way lines of traffic were opened out in various directions—by the Borysthenes to the north of Scythia, by the Tanais towards the Ural mountains, and through Dioscurias into Armenia. Thus it came to pass that, at the expiration of two centuries from the first sending out of the settlers to Sinope, Miletus found herself the mother of about eighty colonies.

Meanwhile another Ionian city on the opposite side of the Aegean had been extending Hellenic influence along the coast of Thrace. This was Chalcis, the Chalcidic
Colonies in
Thrace. situation of which place on the narrow strait of the Euripus, with spaces of sea extending from it in two directions, marked it out from the first as a starting-point for maritime enterprise. The neighbouring and rival city of Eretria in Euboea had already established a colony at Methone, on the Pierian shore of the Thermaic gulf, but the chief field of the activity of the Chalcidians was that strange peninsula which advances into the north of the Aegean—at first in a broad mass of hilly country, and afterwards in three narrow projections that resemble the prongs of a trident—and which from them has received the name of Chalcidice. Here and in the neighbouring region they found extensive forests to supply timber, and metals beneath the soil; and in order to obtain these, and at the same time to provide themselves with a refuge from the wild storms of the Thracian coast and the no less ill-famed barbarians of Thrace, they built and fortified a number of towns in convenient places by the shore. Of these Torone, which lies towards the extremity of the central peninsula of the three, Sithonia, was the most considerable. So great was their success, that in the course of the eighth century they had gained possession of the entire district, and at last the number of the Chalcidic colonies amounted

Megarian
Colonies in the
Propontis:

to thirty-two. It now fell to the lot of a Dorian state to carry on the work, and the Megarians distinguished themselves by occupying a number of important posts on the Propontis, until in the course of their advance they crossed the path of the Milesians. First Astacus was founded by them in the recesses of the gulf of Ismid, where at a later period the great city of Nicomedia was built; and after-

Byzantium,
658 B.C.

wards Chalcedon and Byzantium, on either side of the Bosporus, at the point where that piece of water joins the Sea of Marmora. Finally, about a century later, they established Heraclea on the south coast of the Euxine, and that place in turn reached out an arm across the sea, and built the town of Chersonesus, on a site close to that of the modern Sebastopol.

When we turn our attention towards the lands to the west-

Greek
Colonies in
Italy,

ward of Greece, we find that no less energy pre- vailed on the part of the Greek states in extend- ing their influence in those regions. In Italy the first colony was planted by the same city which we have just seen engaged in Hellenising the north of the Aegean. At an

Cumae,

unknown, though very early date Cumae was founded by the Chalcidians on the coast to the northwards of the bay of Naples, upon a rocky hill which rises steeply from the shore. The undertaking was a not less ad- venturous one than that of the first explorers of the Euxine, for the treacherous Ionian sea had to be crossed, and the dangers of Scylla and Charybdis to be faced, before the western basin of the Mediterranean could be reached: and there the emigrants were confronted by the naval power of the Tyrrhenians, which was strong enough to compete with that of the Carthaginians, and would not tamely brook any interference with their commerce in those waters. Notwithstanding this, the new foundation main- tained itself, and became the centre of a remarkable civilisation, which extended over the neighbouring districts of Campania; and its influence was perpetuated by its still more famous daughter-city of Neapolis, which in Roman times continued to be a focus of Hellenic culture, and which, Neapolis, alone of all the cities of Italy, retained a large Greek population throughout the middle ages, and possesses a considerable number of Greek inhabitants even at the present day. The success of these settlements was due to their felicitous position, for in this neighbourhood all the conditions were present which we have enumerated as being most eligible in the eyes of the Greeks—harbours, like those of Misenum and Puteoli, sheltered by promontories and fringed by islands, a soil of extraordinary fertility, the volcanic nature of which was especially favourable to the growth of the vine, and the whole area of Campania to serve as a field for trade. To secure the approaches from Greece to these remote Chalcidian colonies the same measures were adopted as in the case of the Thracian and the Cimmerian Bosporus, for the passage of the Straits of Messina was secured by the establishment of two strongholds, one on Rhegium and Messana. either side—Rhegium on the Italian shore, and Messana on that of Sicily, at a spot where a convenient harbour was formed by a curved spit of sand, which the natives had already occupied, and called by the name of Zancle, or "the Sickle."

The colonies of southern Italy were founded by the agency of other Greek states.   Before the expiration of the eighth century Sybaris and Croton, two cities Sybaris, 721 B.C. which were destined to an unenviable notoriety Croton, 710 B.C. owing to their opulence and their rivalries, were planted by the Achaeans, whose territory in the north of the Peloponnese, hemmed in as it was between the Arcadian mountains and the waters of the Corinthian gulf, afforded no means of expansion to its rapidly increasing population. By these towns in their turn a host of settlements were sent forth both to the south and the west, the most famous among which was Posidonia or Paestum on the shores Paestum. of the bay adjoining that of Naples, the productiveness of which Virgil has commemorated, where he tells of its roses that blossom twice in the year. Another colony from

Achaia was Metapontum, the source of the wealth of which is
indicated by the ear of corn, which is the emblem on
Metapontum. its singularly beautiful silver coins. In its foundation, as in that of Sybaris and Paestum, the ordinary rule which
was observed in the selection of a Greek site was disregarded, and
the city was built on low ground in the midst of a fertile plain.
Again, towards the southern extremity of Bruttium, on the Zephy-
rian promontory, the colony of Locri Epizephyrii
Locri. was founded by the Locrians. But the most delightful spot of all, the site which Horace described as "the most
charming corner of the world[1]," was reserved for the Lacedaemonians to occupy. Tarentum, the circumstances
Tarentum, 708 B.C. of the foundation of which we have already noticed
—and these were altogether exceptional, for as a
rule the unexpansive policy of Sparta prevented her from colonising—was situated in the innermost angle of the deep gulf that
intervenes between the heel and the toe of Italy; and the narrow
peninsula which it occupied was interposed like a dam between
the outer sea and a deep inlet, sixteen miles in circumference
(now called the *Mare Piccolo*), which here penetrates the land.
The fisheries, for which this inland sea is celebrated at the present
day, must always have been a source of profit; and the suitableness of the soil in its vicinity for the growth of the olive, together
with the temperate climate, could not fail to render it an attractive
locality. A further cause of the rapid progress of these cities,
besides those which have hitherto been mentioned, was the
affinity of race which existed between their inhabitants and the
natives of the country. The Oenotrian tribes, who occupied this
southern region of Italy, were more nearly akin to the Greeks
than the Sabellian and other races further to the north, and for
this reason amalgamated more readily with them, and were more
receptive of Hellenic culture. So great at last was the prosperity
which resulted from the combined effect of these various influences,
that the aggregate of the Greek colonies in that quarter was
designated by the proud title of Magna Graecia.

It was in the interval between the foundation of Cumae and

---

[1] Hor. *Od.*, 2. 6. 13.

that of Sybaris that the first Greek emigrants were despatched
to Sicily. Almost simultaneously the Ionians and
the Dorians sent out colonies to that country. In   Colonies   in
                                                      Sicily:
735 B.C. the city of Naxos was founded by the
Chalcidians at the north-eastern base of Etna, at the foot of the
hill where Tauromenium (*Taormina*) was afterwards
                                                      Naxos,
built; and the following year saw the establishment   735 B.C.
of Syracuse by the Corinthians on the island of   Syracuse,
Ortygia further toward the south. The latter place   734 B.C.
was an admirable trading station, owing to its wonderful
harbour, which received the waters of the river Anapus; and
Ortygia itself, by reason of its nearness to the shore, from which
it was separated only by a narrow channel, had all the advantages both of an island and a peninsula. These early colonies,
and also that of Megara Hyblaea, which was founded shortly
after them by the Megarians of Greece Proper, were settled on
the eastern coast, as indeed was natural, since that side of Sicily
was the nearest to the Greek seas; and there conditions were
met with equally favourable with those presented by Southern
Italy, for the soil was remarkably productive, and the Sicels,
who inhabited that part of the island, were of the same stock
as the Oenotrians, and, like them, yielded themselves readily
to Greek influences. Hence they soon rose to prosperity, as
was proved by several towns being established by them in the
neighbouring districts—Catana and Leontini by Naxos, and
Acrae and Casmenae by Syracuse. Yet a long interval of time
elapsed before they attempted to occupy positions on the
southern coast, so that Camarina, the first colony that was
founded by Syracuse in that direction, was 135 years later in
date than its parent city. The cause of this delay is to be
sought, partly in the remoteness of that seaboard—for the promontory of Pachynus appears at first to have inspired the Sicilian
Greeks with the same dread which their forefathers had felt for
Malea—and partly in the warlike character of its occupants.
The Sicanians, who inhabited the western part of Sicily—a race,
according to Thucydides[1], of Iberian extraction, but unquestionably
earlier as immigrants than the Sicels—were a hardy and stubborn

[1] Thuc. 6. 2.

people; and, in addition to this, the most easily defensible posts were in the hands of the Phoenicians. That people, who had gradually withdrawn before the advance of the Greeks, first from the Aegean, and afterwards from the east of Sicily, still maintained themselves in the west; and here they were vigorously supported by the Carthaginians, to whom the possession of this portion of the island was of the first importance, because it commanded the approach to the Tyrrhenian sea. The first adventurers who rounded Pachynus were a mixed body of Rhodians and Cretans, who built the town of Gela half a century later than the foundation of Naxos and Syracuse. Subsequently to this, the people of Hyblaean Megara erected the city of Selinus further to the west; and between these two Agrigentum, a daughter-city of Gela, was built on an elevated table of rock, retired from the sea, where the conspicuous remains of its temples still testify to its former greatness. The only colony that was founded on the northern coast, besides that of Mylae, which was near its eastern extremity, was Himera. Panormus continued to be Phoenician, though Hellenic ideas were strongly felt there— a condition of things which is illustrated by its coins, on which the emblems of both races are found in conjunction. The western angle of the island, especially the part in the neighbourhood of Mt. Eryx, long continued to be a stronghold of Semitic influence.

The establishment of these settlements in Italy and Sicily prepared the way for a still bolder advance on the part of the Ionians of Phocaea. This people, who found the rocky peninsula on which their city was built a place too strait for them, were driven by force of circumstances to take to the sea; and Herodotus tells us that they were the first of the Greeks to undertake distant voyages[1]. Embarking on their long ships of fifty oars instead of ordinary merchant vessels, they pioneered the way into the Adriatic, and along the coasts of Etruria and Spain, until they reached Tartessus, where they were hospitably received by Arganthonius, the king of the country. In the year 600 B.C., in consequence (so the story

Gela, 690 B.C.

Agrigentum, 580 B.C.

Himera, 648 B.C.

The Phocaeans at Massilia, 600 B.C.

[1] Herod. i. 163.

runs) of the preference given by the daughter of a Gaulish chieftain to a Greek over a native suitor, they founded the colony of Massilia, in a region far more remote from Greece than any which had as yet been occupied by a Hellenic settlement. The influence of that city, which itself was situated in the recesses of a spacious bay, and protected on the land side by a screen of hills, soon made itself felt in several directions. Towards the east, at the foot of the Maritime Alps, there arose a succession of prosperous towns—Antipolis (Antibes), Nicaea (Nice), and finally the Portus Herculis Monoeci (Monaco), where the appellation of the tutelary divinity, Heracles "dwelling alone," is significant of its position as the last of the Greek colonies in that direction.   Beyond that point all progress was discouraged by the close approach of the mountains to the sea; for what is now the delightful coast of the Riviera was then a wild tract, inhabited by fierce Ligurian mountaineers.   Towards the west, also, along the shores of Spain, we find the settlement of Emporiae at the extremity of the Pyrenees, and that of Hemeroscopeium, in a position convenient for traffic, opposite the Balearic islands.   But the most important field of all lay in the interior of Gaul, with which there was ready communication by means of the Rhone, since that river reached the sea in the neighbourhood of Massilia.   The other waterways, with which that country is so well provided, brought thither, not only the products of the interior, but also articles of sale from lands beyond: and ultimately, as we have seen, the tin of Britain and the amber of Frisia found their way by this route into the marts of the Mediterranean.   Owing to the same causes Massilia became also one of the most important starting-points for geographical discovery.

In one other direction, besides those which have been mentioned, the colonising spirit of the Greeks found an opening for its energy.   Africa, which from its harbourless shores and the wide space of sea which separates it from Greece elsewhere offered no inducements to settlers of that nation, at one point presented an attractive field for emigration, where the district of the Cyrenaica approaches

Colonies of Massilia.

Its Influence in Gaul.

Cyrene, 631 B.C.

most nearly to Crete and the Peloponnese. To this land a colony was sent out in the latter part of the seventh century before Christ from Thera, the southernmost of the Cyclades.

The position of the new settlement was an unusual one for a Greek city, being several miles inland, and without any port on the neighbouring shore.

Its Site and Commerce.

But this deficiency was amply compensated by the advantages of the site; for it stood on high ground, about 1800 feet above the sea, and open to the breezes from that side, while it was sheltered at the back from the hot winds of the desert; and in its midst an abundant and perennial spring welled forth, and fostered a luxuriant vegetation. Here there was opportunity for commerce with the Libyan tribes of the interior, and a brisk export trade arose, the chief article of which was the sap of the silphium tree, which was greatly valued on account of its medicinal qualities. In this instance, as elsewhere, the original foundation became the parent of other cities, among which Barca was the most conspicuous. By means of this group of colonies the element of mystery with which Africa was enveloped in the eyes of the Greeks was to some degree dispelled, and its dark-skinned natives became to them something more than the subject of fabulous stories.

In Egypt the position of the Greeks as traders and settlers was altogether different from that which they occupied when dealing with barbarians. There, instead of being the pioneers of culture, they found themselves in the presence of an ancient civilisation incomparably superior to their own, and of a well-established government, whose regulations could not be violated with impunity. Accordingly, it was only by indirect means and gradual approaches that they succeeded in obtaining a position in the country. We first hear of them in the character of mercenaries—the "bronze men from the sea," whose aid was promised to Psammitichus by an oracle at the time of his revolt in the middle of the seventh century B.C., and who appeared in the form of Ionian and Carian sea-farers clad in armour. After that leader had established himself as sovereign, he settled these strangers at Daphnae, on the easternmost or Pelusiac branch of the Nile; and about the

The Greeks in Egypt.

same time, as it would seem, he permitted the Milesians to form a trading station on the western or Canobic branch at Naucratis—the discovery of which place by Mr Flinders Petrie is one of the most interesting results of recent excavation. At the commencement of the following century, in the reign of Psammitichus II.[1], we have evidence of Greek soldiers in the service of the king of Egypt having reached the frontiers of Aethiopia, in the famous Greek inscriptions on the legs of the colossi in front of the temple of Abu Simbel in Nubia. Fifty years later, in the reign of Amasis, special privileges seem to have been accorded to Naucratis, which became an important commercial centre. From this time onwards the intercourse between Greece and Egypt, though still intermittent, was less restricted than before. Amasis himself married a Greek wife, and removed the Ionian mercenaries from Daphnae to Memphis, that they might become his bodyguard. Both Pythagoras and Thales are said to have resorted to his court, and the story of his alliance with Polycrates of Samos, and of the romantic circumstances which led to its dissolution, is familiar to every one. The point of view of the two peoples, indeed, the one looking back towards an immemorial past, the other reaching forward eagerly towards the future, presented too strong a contrast for them to be able to learn much one from another, and the jealousy of the Egyptian priesthood rendered their accumulated learning a sealed book to the outer world. At the same time, by their residence in Egypt the Greeks became acquainted with a country unique in character, and with races and products of which otherwise they would have had no cognisance.

Their Settlement at Naucratis, circ. 650 B.C.

When we compare the knowledge of the lands in the neighbourhood of the Mediterranean which had been acquired by the medium of these colonies, with that which existed in the Homeric age, we cannot fail to be struck with the marked advance that had been made in every direction. Even the Pillars of Hercules, and the limit there set to the Mediterranean sea, of which in earlier days they had only become aware

Summary.

---

[1] That the expedition took place in this reign, and not in that of Psammitichus I., is proved by inscriptions found at Naucratis: see Prof. Gardner's *New Chapters in Greek History*, p. 198.

through the Phoenicians, had come within the range of their experience; for, before the visit of the Phocaeans to Tartessus, Colaeus, a shipmaster of Samos, had already penetrated thither— through stress of weather, no doubt, and against his will, but with the result that he brought back thence a cargo of untold value. We are also led to believe that the interior of Asia was not wholly unknown at this time; thus we find Antimenidas, the brother of the poet Alcaeus, serving in the army of the king of Babylon. But, for all that, geographical knowledge was as yet confined almost entirely to the neighbourhood of the inland seas. No Greek mariner had embarked either on the waters of the Atlantic or on those of the Erythraean sea, and the remoter portions of the continents were quite unexplored.

CHAPTER IV.

EARLY GEOGRAPHICAL SPECULATIONS : HECATAEUS.

Speculations on Mathematical Geography—Anaximander, *circ.* 580 B.C.—
Spherical Form of the Earth—Theory of Zones—Speculations on Physical
Geography—Volcanic Phenomena—The Delta of Egypt—Inundation of
the Nile—Explanations of it, by Thales, Hecataeus, Anaxagoras, Hero-
dotus, Aristotle, and Eratosthenes—Invention of the Gnomon—Map-mak-
ing—Its Early Difficulties—Aristagoras and his Map at Sparta, 499 B.C.—
Delphi the Centre of the Earth's Surface—Origin of the Belief—Division
of the World into Continents—Twofold or Threefold Partition—Principles
of Demarcation—Boundary of Europe and Asia—Names of the Continents
—Their Origin—Hecataeus of Miletus (*circ.* 520 B.C.) the Father of
Geography—His Political Wisdom—His Sources of Information—His
Geographical Work — Its Arrangement — Its General Geography — Its
Contents—Europe—Asia—Africa.

HAVING thus traced the opportunities of acquiring knowledge
of distant countries which the Greeks obtained by
means of their colonial system, we may now turn
to another branch of the subject, which advanced
alongside of this, viz. their earliest enquiries into
the subject of scientific geography.   In this matter the same city,
Miletus, which, as we have seen, led the way in the work of
sending forth colonies, was the first to set on foot investigations.
The wealth which had flowed into that place through its commerce
provided a certain class of its inhabitants with leisure for study
and reflexion, and at the same time the information which was
accumulated from many quarters by their widely extended connexions supplied ample materials for the exercise of ingenious
speculation.   It was thus that the Ionian school of philosophers
arose, in whose system questions about the physical constitution
of the world held a prominent position.   These thinkers, it is
true, had not as yet emancipated themselves from the Homeric
conception of the Earth as a circular plane; but a great advance

Speculations on Mathematical Geography.

was made by Anaximander in the first half of the sixth century
B.C., who taught that the world hung free in the
midst of the universe, detached on all sides from
the circular vault of the heavens. By this, however,
it is not implied that he regarded the Earth as a sphere; his idea
rather was that it resembled in shape a section of a cylinder of
considerable thickness. At a later time, indeed, the belief prevailed that Anaximander's predecessor and teacher, Thales, had
already arrived at the idea of its spherical form; but by other
authorities it was said that he regarded the Earth as floating on
water, the movement of which was the cause of earthquakes, and
the more advanced view was probably attributed to him in order
that it might accord with other scientific ideas with which he was
credited, such as the division of the heaven into zones, with the
line of the zodiac passing obliquely across them. The first
philosophers of whom we can say with certainty
that they taught that the Earth was a globe were
the Pythagoreans; but by what process they arrived
at that doctrine we have no means of discovering. It seems more
likely, however, that it was a theoretical assumption, based on the
view that the sphere was the most perfect figure, than that it was
the result of any formal proofs, like those by which it was subsequently established. Starting from this belief,
Parmenides, the Eleatic philosopher, early in the
following century proceeded to divide the surface
of the Earth into zones—a suggestion which was fruitful in its
results, but which did not at that period admit of systematic
definition, such as it afterwards received and continues to bear
at the present day. Thus far mathematical geography can hardly
be said to have advanced beyond the region of conjecture; indeed
the limits of observation did not as yet warrant any more definite
conclusions: but it contained a germ of great promise for the
future, because whatever facts were ascertained at a later time
could be regarded in relation to these central questions.

Another branch of the subject in which the philosophers of
the Ionian school appear to have interested themselves was physical geography. We learn from
Strabo that Xanthus, a Lydian historian, who was

Marginal notes:

Anaximander, *circ.* 580 B.C.

Spherical Form of the Earth.

Theory of Zones.

Speculations on Physical Geography.

about contemporary with Herodotus, devoted much attention to the volcanic phenomena which are so marked a feature of Western Phrygia—the craters of the Katakekaumene or "Burnt Country," the earth- quake shocks which frequently caused great damage to buildings throughout the neighbouring parts of Lydia, and the mephitic vapours which issued from the ground at many points[1]. In that passage together with Xanthus other ancient writers are mentioned as authorities on this point; and from this we may conclude that the subject had for some time before occupied the minds of the learned. But it was by means of the communication which existed between Miletus and Egypt through the trading settlement at Naucratis that speculation on geographical subjects was especially promoted. It was remarked in the Augustan age that the first thing about which strangers enquired on arriving in Egypt was the Nile and its peculiar features[2]; and this must always have been the case, on account of the mystery which surrounded the unknown sources of that stream, its immense volume when com- pared with the rivers of Greece and Italy, the strange monsters which it harboured, such as the hippopotamus and the crocodile, and above all its extraordinary geographical phenomena. One of these was the absence of all tributaries during its entire course of eleven hundred miles through Nubia and Egypt from the point where it receives the waters of the Atbara below Khartoum—a fact on which Herodotus remarked[3]. Another was the aspect of the Delta, with its remarkable expanse of perfectly level ground, intersected by the arms of the Nile. As a starting-point for speculations on the process by which this was formed, the Ionian thinkers had analogous instances of the accretion of soil close at hand, in the maritime plains and deltas at the mouths of the rivers of Western Asia— the Caicus, the Hermus, the Cayster, and especially the Maeander, which entered the sea in the neighbourhood of Miletus. The comparison between the two is made by Herodotus[4], who also

Volcanic Phenomena.

The Delta of Egypt.

[1] Strabo, 12. 8. 19.   [2] Strabo, 1. 2. 29.
[3] Herod. 4. 50; ἐς γὰρ δὴ τοῦτον οὔτε ποταμὸς οὔτε κρήνη οὐδεμία ἐσδιδοῦσα ἐς πλῆθός οἱ συμβάλλεται.
[4] Herod. 2. 10.

characterises the surface of the Delta as being level, moist and muddy[1], and notices that in approaching Egypt by water the mariner finds evidence far out at sea of the alluvium which is brought down by the Nile, since the water is comparatively shallow a day's sail from land, and mud is brought up by the sounding-line[2]. From this he concluded that what in his time was Lower Egypt was originally an arm of the sea, and that the country was "acquired, and a gift of the river." The facts which the historian here records were no doubt the result of his own observation, for he had verified them on the spot; but in all probability both these and the deductions which he drew from them date from a much earlier time: indeed, we know on the authority of Arrian that the expression "a gift of the river" had already been used of the Delta by Hecataeus[3].

But the question connected with the Nile which more than any other excited the ingenuity of the Greeks, was the cause of its inundation, which was sufficiently remarkable from its extent and its fertilising influence, but on account of its regular periodical recurrence and its taking place in the summer season was a unique phenomenon.

Inundation of the Nile.

Explanations of it, by Thales,

Herodotus has recorded the various explanations of it which had been propounded before his time, together with his own[4]. The first of these, which subsequent writers agreed in attributing to Thales, the founder of the Ionian school, was that it arose from the Etesian winds, which blew from the north during the summer, coming from the Euxine and the coasts of the Aegean, and caused the water of the river to overflow by preventing it from running off into the sea. Herodotus rightly remarks on the insufficiency of this explanation, inasmuch as other rivers which flow in an opposite direction to these winds are not affected in the same manner, and the rising of the Nile takes place even when they do not blow. The second view — which, though the

Hecataeus,

---

[1] Herod. 2. 7.   [2] Herod. 2. 5.

[3] Arrian, *Anab.* 5. 6. 5; Αἴγυπτόν τε Ἡρόδοτός τε καὶ Ἑκαταῖος οἱ λογοποιοί, ἢ εἰ δή του ἄλλου ἢ Ἑκαταίου ἐστὶ τὰ ἀμφὶ τῇ γῇ τῇ Αἰγυπτίᾳ ποιήματα, δῶρον τοῦ ποταμοῦ ἀμφότεροι ὡσαύτως ὀνομάζουσι.

[4] Herod. 2. 19—25.

historian does not name its author, is unquestionably that of
Hecataeus—though more than half a century later in date than
the preceding, is far more primitive in its character. According
to this, the increase of the volume of water was due to the
connexion of the Nile with the circumfluent river Oceanus, from
which in the southern part of its course it was supposed to be
derived; and the sweetness of its water was accounted for by the
supposition that its saline ingredients evaporated owing to the
heat of the sun in its passage through the torrid regions[1].
Herodotus rightly dismisses this explanation without further discussion, as depending on an antiquated theory.
He treats with hardly greater consideration the
Anaxagoras,
third view, which is assigned by Diodorus and others to Anaxagoras, that it proceeded from the melting of snow during the
summer on the mountains in the interior of Libya. Notwithstanding the reasonableness of this as a conjecture, the historian
at once dismisses it, on the ground, which we now know to be
erroneous, that it was impossible for snow to lie in so hot a
country. After disproving these views to his satisfaction he propounds his own, which has very
Herodotus,
little to recommend it; namely, that, as in the winter-time the
sun withdraws towards the upper parts of Libya, the streams
which feed the rivers there will naturally shrink during that
season, in consequence of the scorching heat of his rays. This
suggestion might serve as a possible explanation of the lowering
of the level of the water in winter, but leaves untouched the
question of its overflow in summer. It was reserved
for Aristotle and Eratosthenes to suggest the true
Aristotle and
Eratosthenes.
cause, in the tropical rains which fall during the
spring and early summer on the highlands about the upper
waters of the Blue and White Nile; and this was afterwards
confirmed by Agatharchides through information obtained from
natives of the interior of Africa.

We must here notice two inventions, generally attributed by

---

[1] See Diodor. I. 40. 4; μαρτυρεῖν δὲ τούτοις καὶ τὴν ὑπερβολὴν τῆς γλυκύτητος
τοῦ κατὰ τὸν Νεῖλον ὕδατος· διὰ γὰρ τῆς κατακεκαυμένης αὐτὸν ῥέοντα καθέψεσθαι,
καὶ διὰ τοῦτο γλυκύτατον εἶναι πάντων τῶν ποταμῶν, ἅτε φύσει τοῦ πυρώδους πᾶν
τὸ ὑγρὸν ἀπογλυκαίνοντος.

ancient writers to Anaximander, which were of the first importance for the study of mathematical geography.
Invention of   One of these was the gnomon, a primitive kind
the Gnomon.
of sun-dial, consisting of a perpendicular staff or
pillar, the length of the shadow of which, corresponding to the
progress of the sun, could be measured by feet marked on the
spot where it fell.   The discovery of this was extremely valuable,
because by means of it latitudes could be determined, and it long
continued to be the only instrument available for that purpose.
Herodotus, indeed, states that the use of the gnomon was learnt
by the Greeks from the Babylonians[1], and this was probably the
case; so that Anaximander should be regarded rather as having
introduced than as having originated it.   The other
Map-making.
invention with which he was credited is that of
map-making, and there seems to be no doubt that he was the
first person who attempted to represent the surface of the Earth,
with the boundaries of the countries upon it, and their leading
features.   We can readily understand how many
Its Early   difficulties the man had to encounter who first
Difficulties.
set to work to frame a scheme of geographical
expression of this kind, which now for the first time was rendered
possible by the discovery of such facts as that the Mediterranean
and the Euxine were enclosed spaces of water.   Information had
to be collected from sailors about distances by sea, and the
outlines and directions of coasts; and from traders and other
travellers by land concerning the countries that lay at the back
of the newly-established colonies, and the routes of commerce
that led through them : and all this, and still more the reports
that were brought of distant regions beyond, required to be sifted,
and the accounts of different narrators had to be compared and
reconciled.   The positions thus ascertained needed to be placed
in their due relations one to another; and when this had been
accomplished for each country, the same process had to be
repeated on a larger scale, in order to arrange the various lands
and seas in their proper grouping.   It was only after these
preliminaries had been effected that lines could be drawn to

[1] Herod. 2. 109.

describe these features on a level surface, and names appended
to explain what was designated by them.

The first mention that we meet with of the employment of
such a map is in Herodotus, where the historian is   Aristagoras
recounting the circumstances of the Ionian revolt   and his Map at
against Persia.   Aristagoras, tyrant of Miletus, he   Sparta, 499 B.C.
tells us, who was the leader of that rising, visited Sparta in order
to persuade Cleomenes the king to lend his assistance to their
undertaking.   In the course of the interview that followed, in
order to set forth the advantages to be gained by an expedition
against Persia, he described the wealth of the lands which lay
between the sea-coast of Asia Minor and that country : and that
he might explain this more clearly, he produced "a bronze
tablet whereupon the whole circuit of the Earth was engraved,
with all its seas and rivers[1]."   On this he pointed out to the king
with his finger the position of the different peoples that lay on
the way, at the same time descanting on the riches which they
possessed.   Cleomenes for the time postponed his reply, and at
their next conference enquired how many days' journey it was
from the Ionian sea to Susa.   In an incautious moment
Aristagoras answered that it was a journey of three months;
whereupon Cleomenes, discouraged by the magnitude of the
undertaking, at once dismissed him from Sparta.   The map that
was exhibited on this occasion by the tyrant of Miletus was in all
probability an adaptation of that which had been designed by
his fellow-countryman Anaximander, and afterwards improved by
Hecataeus.

A point, the determination of which must have gone some
way towards regulating the shape and arrangement
of the early maps, was the position of the centre of   Delphi the
                                                          Centre of the
the Earth's surface.   This was fixed at Delphi for   Earth's
                                                          Surface.
the Greeks by religious associations, in the same
way as at a later time Jerusalem became the central point of the
world in the minds of Dante and his contemporaries.   The
popular belief on this subject gave rise to the fable which Pindar
relates, that two eagles which were let go by Zeus, the one from
the east, the other from the west, met at Delphi[2].   Apollo himself

---

[1] Herod. 5. 49.   [2] Strabo, 9. 3. 6.

was reputed to have selected this spot as the chosen seat of
his worship, and the fame of the wealth of its
temple and the wisdom of its oracle dated from the
earliest period of Greek history, for both of these
are mentioned in the Homeric poems. In the *Iliad* Achilles
speaks of the riches that were stored at Pytho as being com-
parable to the possessions of Ilium[1]; and in the *Odyssey*
Agamemnon is related to have obtained thence an oracular
response before proceeding to Troy[2]. By degrees it became
more and more the political as well as the religious centre of the
country, for its influence was exerted in the direction of holding
the Greek states together and counteracting their centrifugal
tendencies, and its wide outlook and practical sagacity in all
matters which affected the Hellenic community caused it to be
generally resorted to for the sake of the good counsel which it
supplied. This was especially the case at the time of the
foundation of the Greek colonies, for the influence which the
oracle exercised in regulating that movement was so great, that
when the Spartan Dorieus met with disaster in endeavouring to
found a colony in Libya, his failure was attributed to his having
neglected to consult the god beforehand[3]. The national position
which Delphi thus obtained caused it to be regarded, not only
metaphorically, but locally, as the middle point of Greece —
a character which it might fairly claim from its geographical
situation ; and since Greece was considered by its inhabitants to
occupy a central position among the countries of the world, this
place came to be called "the navel of the Earth," and the idea

Origin of the Belief.

---

[1] *Il.* 9. 401—5;

> οὐ γὰρ ἐμοὶ ψυχῆς ἀντάξιον οὐδ' ὅσα φασὶν
> Ἴλιον ἐκτῆσθαι, εὖ ναιόμενον πτολίεθρον,
> τὸ πρὶν ἐπ' εἰρήνης, πρὶν ἐλθεῖν υἷας Ἀχαιῶν,
> οὐδ' ὅσα λάϊνος οὐδὸς ἀφήτορος ἐντὸς ἐέργει,
> Φοίβου Ἀπόλλωνος, Πυθοῖ ἔνι πετρηέσσῃ.

[2] *Od.* 8. 79—81;

> ὡς γάρ οἱ χρείων μυθήσατο Φοῖβος Ἀπόλλων
> Πυθοῖ ἐν ἠγαθέῃ, ὅθ' ὑπέρβη λάϊνον οὐδὸν
> χρησόμενος.

[3] Herod. 5. 42.

thus established was formally expressed on the maps, so that
Delphi became the starting-point in their construction[1].

A further point which presented itself for solution at an early
time to the geographers and map-makers was the   Division of
division of the world into continents. On this   the World into
subject a diversity of opinion existed, both as   Continents.
regards the principle of division, and the limits at which the
boundaries were to be fixed. The triple system   Twofold or
of partition into Europe, Asia, and Africa, which Threefold
ultimately carried the day, was at first the least Partition.
popular, for most of the authorities divided the world into two
parts, Europe and Asia—Africa (or, as the Greeks called it,
Libya) being regarded as part of the latter. This seems to
have been the case with Hecataeus, for where he is cited by
subsequent writers as an authority for the position of places
in Africa, the part of his work thus referred to is quoted in
some instances as a treatise on Asia, in others on Libya; from
which circumstance we may infer that the latter of these was a
subdivision of the former. Now as Africa was not unknown to
the Greeks of that time, an explanation seems to be required
of its omission in the division of the world into continents: and
this we may probably discover in the view that the principle of
partition turned on the cold and heat of the regions toward the
north and the south respectively, Europe—in which all that we
now call Russia in Asia was comprehended—being the colder
section, and Asia, including Libya, the warmer. This is confirmed
by our finding that Eratosthenes, who at a later time returned to
the twofold division, did so expressly on the ground of the
difference in temperature between those parts of
the globe[2]. The dividing line between Europe and   Principles of
Africa was clearly marked by the straits at the   Demarcation.
Pillars of Hercules, while the geographical features which were

[1] Agathemerus, *Geogr.* I. 2. Speaking of the early attempts at map-
making, he says—Οἱ μὲν οὖν παλαιοὶ τὴν οἰκουμένην ἔγραφον στρογγύλην, μέσην
δὲ κεῖσθαι τὴν Ἑλλάδα, καὶ ταύτης Δελφούς.

[2] Varro, *De re rust.*, I. 2. 3: Primum cum orbis terrae divisus sit in duas
partes ab Eratosthene maxime secundum naturam ad meridiem versus et ad
septentriones. See Berger, *Geschichte der Erdkunde,* I. p. 53.

chosen for the delimitation of Asia were rivers—the Phasis on the side towards Europe, and the Nile in the direction of Africa. A stream of water at all times suggests itself at first sight as the most natural boundary between tracts of land, though a chain of mountains or an isthmus forms a far more certain and definite limit. Hence the Caucasus, though it is mentioned by Aeschylus as the highest of mountains[1], and therefore must have been known to the Greeks before his time, was ignored as the dividing line between Europe and Asia; and the Isthmus of Suez, which forms the natural line of separation between Asia and Africa, was passed over in like manner. At a later time the importance of isthmuses from this point of view was brought prominently forward; so much so, that the land which intervenes between the Euxine and the Caspian was treated as an isthmus, and was regarded as the boundary of Asia on that side[2]; but this principle of division implies a wider survey of the field of geography than was possible at an early age. By some the Phasis continued to

Boundary of Europe and Asia.   be treated as the limit even in the time of Herodotus[3]; but in the meanwhile the advance of the Greek colonies in the direction of the Palus Maeotis had initiated another view, and that piece of water together with the Cimmerian Bosporus at its entrance and the Tanais which flowed into it were regarded as separating the two continents— an opinion which ultimately prevailed. It appears to have been adopted by Hecataeus, for he treats the town of Phanagoria, which lay on the eastern side of the Cimmerian Bosporus, as being in Asia[4]; while in Aeschylus both views are represented, for in the *Prometheus Vinctus* the dramatist describes Io as passing from

[1] *Prom. Vinct.* 719:

πρὶν ἂν πρὸς αὐτὸν Καύκασον μόλῃς, ὁρῶν
ὕψιστον.

[2] Strabo, 1. 4. 7: τοὺς δὲ τοῖς ἰσθμοῖς [διαιρεῖν τὰς ἠπείρους], τῷ τε μεταξὺ τῆς Κασπίας καὶ τῆς Ποντικῆς θαλάσσης, καὶ τῷ μεταξὺ τῆς Ἐρυθρᾶς καὶ τοῦ Ἐκρήγματος.

[3] Herod. 4. 45: οὐρίσματα αὐτῇ Νεῖλός τε ὁ Αἰγύπτιος ποταμὸς ἐτέθη, καὶ Φάσις ὁ Κόλχος· (οἱ δὲ Τάναϊν ποταμὸν τὸν Μαιήτην καὶ Πορθμήϊα τὰ Κιμμέρια λέγουσι).

[4] Hecat., *Fragm.* Nos. 164, 165, in Müller's *Fragmenta Historicorum Graecorum*, I. p. 11.

Europe into Asia when she crosses those straits[1], and in the *Prometheus Solutus* he definitely states that the Phasis is the boundary[2]. This curious contradiction, taken in connexion with Herodotus' mention of the same two opinions, shews how greatly men's minds fluctuated on the subject.

The names by which these continents came to be designated seem to have been in use before the continents themselves were known. This arose from their being first applied to coast lands or limited districts, *Names of the Continents.* while afterwards their application was gradually extended, so as to include the whole of the area of country that lay behind. This is clearly seen in the case of Europe, which name first occurs in the Homeric Hymn to the Pythian Apollo[3] in conjunction with that of Peloponnese, which also is used there for the first time: and in that passage it is evidently employed of the mainland of Greece as distinguished from that peninsula and the islands, and not in any wider acceptation, for the Greek nation is there divided into "those who dwell in fruitful Peloponnese, and those who inhabit Europe and the seagirt islands." Both this appellation and that of Asia came from the East, though probably not from Phoenicia, as has been *Their Origin.* commonly thought, but from Assyria, where the words *açû* 'sunrise' and *irib* or *ereb* 'darkness' frequently occur in inscriptions. They may have been brought to the Aegean by way of Lydia, the Heracleid kings of which country were according to their traditions connected with Assyria[4]. The neighbourhood of the Aegean must in any case have been the locality in which these words came to be used with a descriptive significance, to represent

[1] *Prom. Vinct.* 729 foll.:

ἰσθμὸν δ᾽ ἐπ᾽ αὐταῖς στενοπόροις λίμνης πύλαις
Κιμμερικὸν ἥξεις, ὃν θρασυσπλάγχνως σε χρὴ
λιποῦσαν αὐλῶν᾽ ἐκπερᾶν Μαιωτικόν·
.........λιποῦσα δ᾽ Εὐρώπης πέδον
ἤπειρον ἥξεις ᾽Ασίδ᾽............

[2] *Prom. Sol.*, Fragm. 1:

τῇ μὲν δίδυμον χθονὸς Εὐρώπης
μέγαν ἠδ᾽ ᾽Ασίας τέρμονα Φᾶσιν.

[3] l. 73.

[4] Kiepert, *Lehrbuch d. a. Geographie*, p. 26.

respectively the lands towards the east and towards the west, for there is no other position on the borders of the two continents where they could have had that force. Libya, on the other hand, which, as we have already seen[1], is mentioned in the *Odyssey*, received its name from the principal native race with which the Greek settlers were brought into contact, in the same way as Italy was so called from the tribe of Itali in the southern part of that country, and Sicily from the Sicels. The name of Africa, which was given to it by the Romans, was borrowed by them from the Carthaginians, who thus designated the part of the continent in which their city was placed.

The knowledge of the world which was possessed by the Ionians of this time was embodied in the work of Hecataeus of Miletus, who was the first person to write a treatise on that subject, and for that reason may rightly be called the Father of Geography, as Herodotus is termed the Father of History.   In the character of a politician he is conspicuous at the time of the Ionian revolt, on account of the prudent and patriotic advice which he gave to his fellow-country-

Hecataeus of Miletus (circ. 520 B.C.) the Father of Geography.

His Political Wisdom.

men on that occasion. When Aristagoras by specious repre-sentations tried to induce the Ionians to rise against the Persians, Hecataeus, we are told, stood alone in endeavouring to dissuade them by pointing out to them the magnitude of the resources of Darius; and when he failed in this, he urged them to provide themselves with a naval force, and for this purpose to make use of the treasures laid up in the temple at Branchidae, which other-wise would certainly fall into the hands of their opponents[2]. This advice also was rejected. Again, when the commencement of the insurrection was unfavourable to the Ionians, and there was a prospect of the Persian fleet appearing off their coasts, while Aristagoras was in favour of emigrating to Sardinia or to Myrcinus in Thrace, Hecataeus advised that they should occupy the neighbouring island of Leros, and watch from thence the progress of events; but he was no more successful in inciting them to bold measures, than he had previously been in restraining their head-

---

[1] *supra*, p. 26.   [2] Herod. 5. 36.

MAP II.

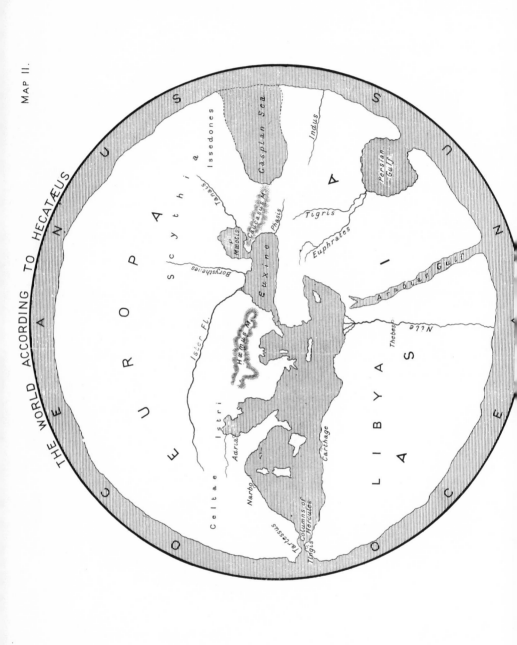

THE WORLD ACCORDING TO HECATÆUS

strong enthusiasm[1].   In all these proceedings he appears in the
character of a clear-sighted statesman—a faculty which may have
been in great measure the result of his study of past events, for by
the ancients he was known as an "annalist," on account of his
historical work which was entitled *Histories* or *Genealogies*.   He
is often supposed to have travelled extensively, and
Herodotus makes mention of a visit of his to Thebes   His Sources
in Egypt[2]; but with regard to other countries there   of Information.
is no sufficient ground for this belief, for it rests mainly on the
acquaintance which he shews with various lands, such as Spain
and the coasts of the Euxine.   This however is amply accounted
for by his residence at Miletus, the colonies of which place on the
Black Sea would furnish their native city with abundant information
about the countries in their neighbourhood; and the same thing
would happen with regard to Spain by means of the trading
stations founded by Massilia on its shores, from which intelligence
would be transmitted to the parent state in Ionia, Phocaea.   A
confirmation of this view is found in the closeness with which
Hecataeus' geographical knowledge corresponds to the position of
the Greek colonies.   Thus, while he names a number of insignificant Illyrian and Liburnian tribes, an acquaintance with which
might have been gained by the cities of Epidamnus and Apollonia
on the Adriatic Sea, there is no mention in his writings of any
place on the Italian and Ligurian coasts between Campania and
the Portus Herculis Monoeci, evidently on account of the absence
of Greek settlements throughout that region.

The geographical work of Hecataeus was called a *Periodos*, or
General Survey, of the inhabited world as known at   His Geo-
that time; and since, from the nature of the case, a   graphical
great part of it was taken up with an account of   Work.
places and districts bordering on the sea, it must have borne a
considerable resemblance to what was afterwards called a *Periplus*,
or Coasting Survey.   It has only come down to us in fragments,
and the majority of these are of the briefest description, having
been preserved in the epitome of the work of Stephanus of
Byzantium, which gives little more than the names of places with
the countries to which they belonged.   It is clear however that

[1] Herod. 5. 125.   [2] Herod. 2. 143.

the 'Survey' was not confined to dry statements like these, but contained notices, occasionally of some length, of remarkable objects which were found in different localities. Thus we learn from Porphyry that the accounts of the phœnix, the hippopotamus, and the hunting of crocodiles in the second book of Herodotus were taken almost bodily from Hecataeus[1]. The work was divided into two parts, the former of which treated of Europe, the latter of Asia, under which Libya was included. These parts must have been sub-divided into sections, for in the quotations in Stephanus some places are referred to under special headings, such as Helles-pontus, Aeolica, Aegyptus, and Libya. Hecataeus maintained the traditional view of the Ionian philosophers, that the Earth was a circular plane surrounded by the stream of Ocean; and the land which was thus enclosed was divided into two equal portions, the continent of Europe towards the north, and that of Asia to the south. This view, which Herodotus ridicules, is not, indeed, attributed by him to Hecataeus by name, but it is highly probable that he is one of those to whom the historian refers as having held it[2]. The division between the two continents was formed, first by the Mediterranean, the Euxine and the Palus Maeotis, and afterwards by the Tanais, and perhaps the Caspian Sea, for there is some reason to believe that the Ionians treated that sea as a bay of the eastern ocean[3]. These geographical features he regarded as forming nearly a continuous line running from west to east. The map of the world on which these objects were represented was considered to be an advance on that of Anaximander[4].

Its Arrangement.

Its General Geography.

The contents of Hecataeus's work on geography, so far as we have the means of judging of it, correspond in the main to what we have seen to be the range of

Its Contents.

---

[1] Hecat. *Fragm.* Nos. 292—4, in Müller's *Fragm. Hist. Gr.*, I. p. 21, with the editor's notes.

[2] Herod. 4. 36.

[3] Berger, *op. cit.*, I. p. 33.

[4] Agathem. I. 1: Ἀναξίμανδρος ὁ Μιλήσιος, ἀκουστὴς Θάλεω, πρῶτος ἐτόλμησε τὴν οἰκουμένην ἐν πίνακι γράψαι· μεθ' ὃν Ἑκαταῖος ὁ Μιλήσιος, ἀνὴρ πολυπλανὴς, διηκρίβωσεν ὥστε θαυμασθῆναι τὸ πρᾶγμα.

knowledge of that time. With the northern coasts of the Mediterranean, especially those of Greece, Sicily and southern Italy, he shews himself familiar; and he Europe. mentions not only the islands of Sardinia and Corsica, but also that of Aethale (Elba), which was even then famous for its iron mines. On the other hand, he is unacquainted with any sea to the north of Europe, and indeed with any lands or peoples north of the parallel of the Alps, except the Scythians far away towards the north-east, and other tribes—two of which, the Melanchlaeni and the Issedones, we also read of in Herodotus—and the chain of the Caucasus in the same direction. He knows that the Iberians are the inhabitants of Spain, and the Celts of Gaul: and in the former of these countries he mentions Tartessus, though he does not notice Gades; and in the latter the town of Narbo (Narbonne), which he characterises as a commercial centre. In Italy, which was not yet known by that name, he notices the principal races which occupied various regions—the Tyrrhenians towards the north, the Ausonians in the centre, and the Oenotrians in the south; and also a number of native towns in the neighbourhood of the colonies of Magna Graecia, but neither Rome nor any of the great cities of Etruria. At the head of the Adriatic he places the Istri, and also the town of Adria, which was situated between the mouths of the Po and the Adige, where he remarks on the extraordinary fertility of the soil.

In the other section of the work, which treats of Asia and Africa, we find that the writer is intimately acquainted with Asia Minor, and further to the north the Asia. Colchians are mentioned and the Araxes. The Caspian Sea, into which that river flows, is spoken of as being surrounded by lofty wooded mountains, a description which only applies to its western shore. Media is designated as a region near the Caspian Gates, and the Persian Gulf is named, but no notice is taken of Babylon or the other great cities in that region. But the knowledge of India—that is, of the district of that country west of the Indus—which Hecataeus possessed, is certainly remarkable, especially when we remember that that province was annexed to the Persian empire within his lifetime. The name of that land occurs for the first time in this treatise, and he makes special mention of

Caspapyrus or Caspatyrus, the town on the banks of the Indus from which Scylax of Caryanda was reputed to have started at the command of Darius on his voyage of exploration down that river. Several places are also noticed in Phoenicia, Syria and Arabia, and especially in Egypt, as we might expect from his having himself visited that country. The Nile was for him the boundary

Africa. of Libya on its eastern side, and, as we have already seen, he regarded that river as flowing from the southern ocean; akin to which primitive view is his reckoning such mythical peoples as the Pygmies and the Sciapodes among the inhabitants. The remainder of the treatise, to judge from the extracts, dealt with the Mediterranean coast of Africa as far as the Straits; and even beyond that limit occurs the name of Thinge, the modern Tangier.

Map III.

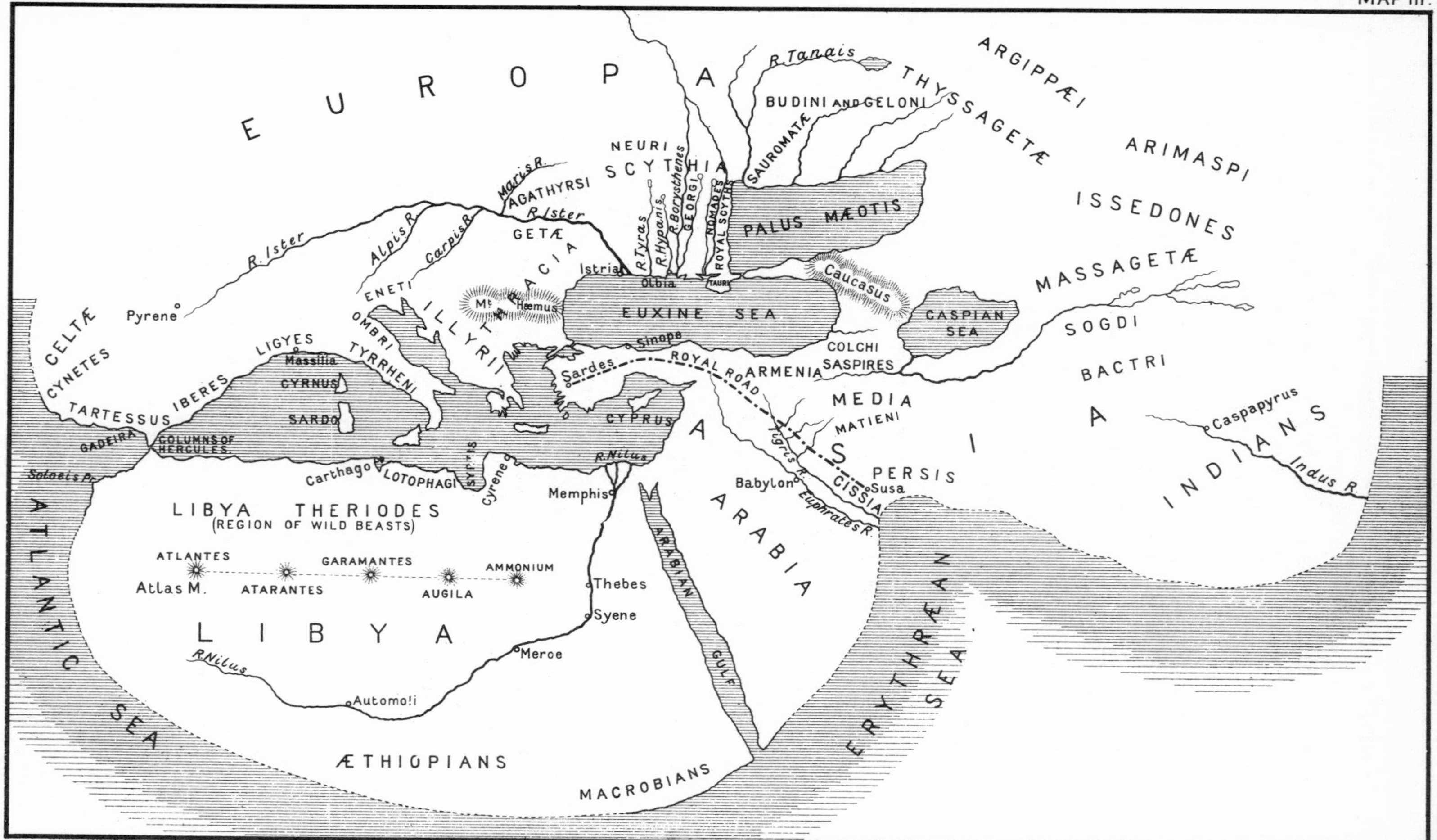

THE WORLD ACCORDING TO HERODOTUS

University Press Cambridge.

Edwin Wilson Cambridge.

CHAPTER V.

HERODOTUS.

Importance of Herodotus to Geography—His Life, and Travels—His General Views of Geography—His Primitive Cosmical Beliefs—Symmetrical Correspondences—Courses of the Nile and the Ister—Attempts at Drawing a Meridian—His Conception of the Map of the World—No Northern Sea—Continuity of the Southern Ocean—Inlets from the Ocean—The Caspian an Inland Sea—Size of the Palus Maeotis—The Three Continents—Boundaries between them—His Confusion about the Araxes—His Actae, or Projecting Tracts—Central and Western Europe—His Imperfect Knowledge of them—Scythia—His Acquaintance with it—Its Shape, and Inhabitants—Peoples to the North of Scythia—The Agathyrsi, Neuri, Budini, and Geloni—Lands to the North-east—Gold of the Ural Mountains—The Argippaei—The Issedones—Asia—Sources of his Information—Scanty Notices of the Geography—Error about Asia Minor—Ignorance of the Mountain Chains—Knowledge of the Rivers—The Royal Road—Its Course through Asia Minor, Cilicia, Armenia, Matiene and Cissia—India—Its Races, and Products—The Nile Valley—Meroë—The Two Branches Unnoticed—The Automoli—The Macrobian Aethiopians—Northern Coast of Africa—Eastern Portion—Western Portion—Dumb Commerce—Interior of Africa—The Three Tracts—The Oases—The Garamantes—The Troglodyte Aethiopians—Expedition of the Nasamones—Narrative of Herodotus.

THOUGH Hecataeus was, as we have seen, the Father of Geography, as being the first to systematise that subject, and to overcome the difficulties that presented themselves in the early stages of such a science, yet a far greater stimulus was given to the study by Herodotus, because of the vast amount of geographical material which he accumulated, and the varied aspects under which he regarded it. This was the result of his extensive travels, which were pursued in an enthusiastic spirit of enquiry, with the " hungry heart" of one who was eager for knowledge, and the keen eye which could distinguish the objects which were worth observing, and could perceive their bearings upon other questions. It is true that the work of Herodotus was primarily historical, and that geography is

Importance of Herodotus to Geography.

nowhere methodically introduced into it, in consequence of which important places and countries, concerning which he could hardly have failed to possess valuable information, are but slightly noticed in his pages, because his History was not directly concerned with them. Thus the mention of the native kingdoms in Italy, about which any intelligence would be welcome to us, is almost confined to passing references to the naval power of the Tyrrhenians, though the writer must have had it in his power to communicate much more than this, since the later part of his life was spent in Magna Graecia. Still, Herodotus' work was designedly episodical, and in this way room was found for digressions relating to general geography, to the shapes of continents and the courses of rivers and mountain chains, to climatic influences, to the products of the soil and objects of commerce. Above all, he was especially attracted by a branch of research which lies intermediate between the study of geography and that of history—the investigation of the various tribes that inhabited the countries of which he treated, with their physical characteristics, and their manners and customs. The facts which are thus brought together form a rich store, from which the materials for a more complete and systematic treatment of the subject may be gleaned, and the geographical notices are seldom uninteresting, because they are combined with illustrative remarks, such as an observant traveller can make.

Of the life of Herodotus few details have come down to us.
His Life,   We know, however, that he was born at Hali-
carnassus early in the fifth century before Christ, and that in middle life he removed to Athens; afterwards, though from what motive we are not told, he joined the colony which was sent out from Athens to Thurii in South Italy in 443 B.C. There is reason also to suppose that he revisited Athens at a later time, for in one part of his History he implies that he had seen the Propylaea of the Acropolis[1], and that building was not completed until the commencement of the Peloponnesian war. The greater part of his work was probably written before he migrated to Thurii, but various indications shew that he completed and

---

[1] 5. 77; speaking of a votive offering which was dedicated to Pallas by the Athenians, he says—τὸ δὲ ἀριστερῆς χερὸς ἕστηκε πρῶτον ἐσιόντι ἐς τὰ προπύλαια τὰ ἐν τῇ ἀκροπόλι.

retouched it after his settlement in that place. More important for our present purpose is the question of the extent $\quad$ and Travels. of his travels, and the only data by which this can be determined are to be found in his writings. The subject is one about which much exaggeration has prevailed, but even after every deduction has been made, they appear to have been very extensive. He was familiar with the coast-lands on all three sides of Asia Minor; also with the islands of the Aegean, the mainland of Greece, and the neighbouring shores of Thrace, including places as remote, and as far removed from one another, as Dodona and Byzantium. As regards more distant countries—we find that he visited the coast of Scythia between the mouths of the Ister and the Borysthenes, for he speaks in two passages of having obtained information from the natives there[1]: in Colchis he compared the appearance and customs of the inhabitants with those of the Egyptians, to whom he believed them to be related[2]. Babylon he describes as a professed eye-witness[3]; he made a voyage to Tyre with the express purpose of enquiring about the temple of Heracles there[4]; he travelled far and wide in Egypt, and ascended the Nile as far as Elephantine[5]: and, finally, in Libya he visited Cyrene, where he describes a statue from his own inspection[6]. In all these, and in other instances, unless we discredit his statements as false, it is proved, either by positive statement on the historian's part, or by direct implication from his words, that he had seen the countries which are named; and this involves still more extensive journeys through the intervening lands.

[1] 4. 76; ὡς δ' ἐγὼ ἤκουσα Τίμνεω, τοῦ Ἀριαπείθεος ἐπιτρόπου. 4. 81; ἔλεγον οἱ ἐπιχώριοι.

[2] 2. 104; φαίνονται μὲν γὰρ ἐόντες οἱ Κόλχοι Αἰγύπτιοι· νοήσας δὲ πρότερον αὐτός, ἢ ἀκούσας ἄλλων, λέγω. ὡς δέ μοι ἐν φροντίδι ἐγένετο, εἰρόμην ἀμφοτέρους.

[3] 1. 181—3.

[4] 2. 44; καὶ θέλων δὲ τούτων πέρι σαφές τι εἰδέναι ἐξ ὧν οἷόν τε ἦν, ἔπλευσα καὶ ἐς Τύρον τῆς Φοινίκης, πυνθανόμενος αὐτόθι εἶναι ἱρὸν Ἡρακλέος ἅγιον.

[5] 2. 29; ἀλλὰ τοσόνδε μὲν ἄλλο ἐπὶ μακρότατον ἐπυθόμην, μέχρι μὲν Ἐλεφαντίνης πόλιος αὐτόπτης ἐλθών, τὸ δ' ἀπὸ τούτου ἀκοῇ ἤδη ἱστορέων.

[6] 2. 181; ἡ δὲ Λαδίκη ἀπέδωκε τὴν εὐχὴν τῇ θεῷ. ποιησαμένη γὰρ ἄγαλμα ἀπέπεμψε ἐς Κυρήνην, τὸ ἔτι καὶ ἐς ἐμὲ ἦν σόον, ἔξω τετραμμένον τοῦ Κυρηναίων ἄστεος. It has been doubted whether the historian's words here imply autopsy, but the mention of the position and aspect of the statue, 'facing outwards from the city,' is strong evidence in favour of it.

As Herodotus was an adherent of the Pythagorean School of His General Views of Geography. Philosophy, we cannot be surprised if we find him disagreeing with some of the geographical views of the Ionian School. This point has already been noticed in speaking of Hecataeus, where we have seen that the historian derides the notion, which was still maintained by that school, that the Earth was a circular plane surrounded by the ocean stream[1]. Yet the cast of his own mind was essentially unphilosophical, and while he expresses incredulity about the opinions of his predecessors, he shews strange simplicity in his own His Primitive Cosmical Beliefs. conceptions of the order of nature. Nothing indeed can well be more childish than his belief that the sun was driven southward out of its regular course by the winds at the approach of winter[2]. For this reason it is the less strange that he should not have adopted the Pythagorean tenet of the sphericity of the Earth, notwithstanding the persuasiveness of that doctrine when it had once been propounded, and the numerous difficulties which it seems to solve. That he held fast to the belief that the world is a plane surface seems probable from his saying that in India the greatest heat of the day was in the morning hours, and not as in other countries in the middle of the day ; for this idea on his part seems to have arisen from the belief that the sun was nearer to the Earth at that time[3]. He was wedded also to a certain class of *a priori* views with regard to the Symmetrical Correspondences. symmetrical arrangement of land and water and inhabited districts on the Earth's surface, especially in comparing its northern and southern portions. Thus, when speaking of the stories that were current concerning the Hyperboreans, he remarks, as if it were an indisputable proposition, that if there are ' dwellers at the back of the North wind,' there must also be 'dwellers at the back of the South wind[4].' A Courses of the Nile and the Ister. still more marked instance of supposed correspondence is the parallel which he draws between the Nile and the Ister. Speaking of the Nile, which in

---

[1] 4. 36.

[2] 2. 24; τὴν χειμερινὴν ὥρην ἀπελαυνόμενος ὁ ἥλιος ἐκ τῆς ἀρχαίης διεξόδου ὑπὸ τῶν χειμώνων, ἔρχεται τῆς Λιβύης τὰ ἄνω.

[3] 3. 104.   [4] 4. 36.

the upper part of its course, he says, follows a direction from west to east[1], he remarks that by some it was identified with a river which had been discovered by the Nasamones far away in the interior of Africa. He then adds, "reason favours that view, for the Nile certainly flows out of Libya, dividing it down the middle, and as I conceive, judging the unknown from the known, rises at the same distance from its mouth as the Ister. This latter river has its source in the country of the Celts near the city Pyrene, and runs through the middle of Europe, dividing it into two portions. The Celts live beyond the Pillars of Hercules, and border on the Cynesians, who dwell at the extreme west of Europe. Thus the Ister flows through the whole of Europe before it finally empties itself into the Euxine at Istria, one of the colonies of the Milesians[2]." With regard to the correspondence in position of the mouths of the two rivers he further says :—" Egypt lies almost exactly opposite the mountainous portion of Cilicia, whence a lightly-equipped traveller may reach Sinope on the Euxine in five days by the direct route. Sinope lies opposite the place where the Ister falls into the sea. My opinion therefore is that the Nile, as it traverses the whole of Libya, is of equal length with the Ister[3]." In another passage he speaks of the Ister as falling into the sea with its mouth facing the south-east[4], and from this it has sometimes been inferred that he intended to find a resemblance between this change in the direction of its course and the bend which he regarded the Nile as making from east to north in the neighbourhood of Meroë ; but perhaps we are hardly justified in deducing so much from his words. In the passage just quoted about the mouths of the rivers we may find an illustration of the more scientific side of Herodotus's mind ; for in attempting to draw an *Attempts at Drawing a Meridian.* imaginary line from Egypt to Cilicia, and thence by way of Sinope to the Ister, he is evidently feeling his way towards a meridian of longitude. Here the geographer's instinct for determining the relative position of places, quickened by the map-maker's habit of arranging them, is asserting itself. A similar rude essay in mathematical geography is found in his describing the situation of

[1] 2. 31.   [2] 2. 33.
[3] 2. 34.   [4] 4. 99.

a town in the interior of a country by means of its relation to
another on the nearest coast; as where he speaks of Pteria in
Cappadocia as being " over against Sinope[1]," that place being due
north of it.

In one of his digressions Herodotus has communicated to us
His Concep-
tion of the Map
of the World.
his conception of the general features of the world[2],
and by a comparison of this with other passages we
can form a tolerably clear idea of his views on the
subject. In respect of the limits of the northern continent, while
endeavouring to confine himself to ascertained facts in opposition
to the guesswork of his predecessors, he really deviated further
No Northern
Sea.
from the truth than they had done, for he professes
his scepticism as to the existence of a sea either to
the north or to the east of Europe. He could not
discover the evidence, he says, of anyone having visited the
supposed northern sea ; and for the same reason he disbelieved in
the Cassiterides islands, from which tin was reported to come, and
in a river Eridanus, from which amber was brought[3]. On the
Continuity of
the Southern
Ocean.
opposite side of the world, however, he considered
that the ocean extended continuously from the coast
of India to that of Spain ; this he regarded as
sufficiently proved by two expeditions, which had accomplished
between them the entire circumnavigation of the intervening continent. One of these was the voyage of Scylax of Caryanda, who
had sailed by the orders of Darius from the mouth of the Indus
to the Red Sea ; the other was the expedition which was despatched
by Necho from Egypt to explore the coast of Africa, and had succeeded in reaching the Pillars of Hercules by the southern route.
The first part of this sea to the eastward of Africa, which we now
call the Indian Ocean, was known to him as the Erythraean sea,
while that to the west he names the Atlantic—an appellation
which here occurs for the first time, though he implies that it
was already in familiar use[4]. He only believes in two great

[1] I. 76; κατὰ Σινώπην πόλιν τὴν ἐν Εὐξείνῳ πόντῳ μάλιστά κη κειμένη.
[2] 4. 36—45.
[3] 3. 115.
[4] I. 202 ; ἡ ἔξω στηλέων θάλασσα ἡ 'Ατλαντὶς καλεομένη.

inlets as penetrating into the land from this outer ocean, namely, the Mediterranean and the Red Sea, or, as he designates it, the Arabian Gulf. With the Per- Inlets from sian Gulf he shews no acquaintance, for he not the Ocean. only omits all mention of it, but he describes the Tigris and Euphrates as falling into the Erythraean sea, without any suggestion of the existence of an intervening space of water. With respect to another point, however, he is more accurate than either his predecessors or those who came after him in geography. He regarded the Caspian as an inland sea[1], whereas in all probability the Ionians at an The Caspian an Inland Sea. earlier time, and certainly the writers of the period subsequent to Alexander the Great, treated it as being connected with the ocean. But he was in error with regard to the Palus Maeotis, the size of which he greatly overrates. "The Pontus," he says, "has also a Size of the Palus Maeotis. lake belonging to it, not very much inferior to itself in size. The waters of this lake run into the Pontus: it is called the Maeotis, and also the mother of the Pontus[2]." In reality the Sea of Azov is not much more than one-twelfth of the size of the Euxine, so that, even if we make a considerable allowance for the contraction of its area since classical times by the alluvium brought down by the Don, the historian's estimate of its extent is still greatly exaggerated. His conception of its position also is inexact, for he regarded it as running from north to south, so that it formed the eastern boundary of Scythia[3].

The division of the world into three continents, together with the names of Europe, Asia, and Libya, which were assigned to them, Herodotus accepts with a protest The Three Continents. as being sanctioned by custom, though he can discover no principle which would justify such a partition: but he speaks of Europe—including under that name the whole of the northern continent from west to east—as being equal in length

---

[1] I. 203 ; ἡ δὲ Κασπίη ἔστι ἑτέρη ἐπ’ ἑωυτῆς.

[2] 4. 86.

[3] 4. 99 ; ἔστι γὰρ τῆς Σκυθικῆς τὰ δύο μέρεα τῶν οὔρων ἐς θάλασσαν φέροντα, τήν τε πρὸς μεσαμβρίην, καὶ τὴν πρὸς τὴν ἠῶ, κατάπερ τῆς Ἀττικῆς χώρης.

to the other two combined, and much broader than they were.
Though he was well aware that the Arabian Gulf
Boundaries between them. was a long and narrow sea to the eastward of
Africa, he maintained that the western frontier of
Egypt formed the true boundary of that continent on the side
towards Asia[1]. He admits that the Nile was the limit usually
accepted by the Greeks, but objects to it on the ground that
on this supposition Egypt, through which that river flows, would
be partly in Asia and partly in Libya. Again, while he mentions the view that the Cimmerian Bosporus and the Tanais
were to be regarded as dividing Asia from Europe, he himself
would draw the line at the Phasis, the Caspian Sea, and the
Araxes, in a direction running due east[2]. The mention of the
last-named river introduces one of the most puzzling questions
His Confu- of Herodotean geography. He seems indeed to
sion about the have confused together two streams called
Araxes. Araxes—one the modern Aras, which discharges
its waters into the western side of the Caspian, for he says that
the Araxes rose in the land of the Matieni, *i.e.* in the north
of Armenia, where the sources of the Aras lie ; the other—
which Cyrus had to cross in order to attack the Massagetae,
and which is described as a great river, not much inferior to
the Danube—the Jaxartes, which flows into the sea of Aral ;
but as that piece of water was unknown to the ancients, it is
not surprising that Herodotus represents it as reaching the
Caspian[3]. But the difficulty does not end here, for in his
description of the boundary line between Europe and Asia he
says definitely that the Araxes, which lies beyond the Caspian,
flows *towards* the rising sun[4]; that is to say, in a direction
exactly opposite to the course of the Jaxartes, and away from
the Caspian. Unless we accept Canon Rawlinson's somewhat
drastic suggestion that the writer here made a *lapsus*, and
described the river as running east, when he meant to say that
it ran west, the confusion appears to be inextricable.

In his account of the geography of Asia Herodotus introduces

[1] 2. 17.   [2] 4. 40, 45.   [3] 1. 202.
[4] 4. 40; ὁ Ἀράξης ποταμὸς, ῥέων πρὸς ἥλιον ἀνίσχοντα.

an idea of the conformation of that continent which is peculiar to
himself, by dividing it into *Actae*, or tracts of land
of a somewhat peninsular character. After noticing
the four races which occupy the belt of country
that intervenes between the southern sea on the hither side of
India and the Euxine—the Persians, the Medes, the Saspires and
the Colchians—he says that the land to the west of this may be
regarded as forming two separate areas. The northernmost of
these, starting from a line drawn through the Phasis and the gulf
of Issus, is bounded on the north by the Pontus and the Hellespont up to Sigeium, and on the south by the coast as far as the
Triopian promontory in Caria : it corresponds therefore nearly to
Asia Minor. The southern area, on the other hand, embraces
Persia, Assyria, and Arabia on the side towards the Erythraean sea,
and Phoenicia, Palestine, and Egypt in the direction of the
Mediterranean. Libya, notwithstanding the width to which it
spreads on the further side of Egypt, he regards as an appendage
to the second of these Actae[1]. It is not altogether easy to divine
the object which the historian had in view in this grouping of
countries, but it reveals to us the imperfection of his knowledge of
the relative size of these districts, and it suggests also, what was
undoubtedly the case, that he greatly underrated the size both of
Asia and of Africa. He was in ignorance, too, of the southward
extension of both those continents, for he does not include in his
survey the peninsula of Hindostan—an omission which continued
to prevail until long after his time—and he believed that the
African coast began to trend due west at no great distance from
the mouth of the Red Sea.

As geography is a subject not systematically introduced into
Herodotus' work, but only as subordinate to history,
except so far as he indulges in digressions on the
countries which are noticed in his narrative, we
cannot be surprised if his description of the centre and west of
Europe is scanty as compared with that of Asia, since those
regions were unconnected with the struggle between Greece and
Persia, which it was his purpose to commemorate. Yet, even

His Actae,
or Projecting
Tracts.

Central and
Western
Europe.

[1] 4. 37—9.

allowing for this, the inaccuracy of the details which he from time
to time introduces would seem to shew that the acquaintance of
the Greeks with those lands had made but little advance since the
time of Hecataeus.   He knows that Gades or
Gadeira is "without the Pillars of Hercules upon
the Ocean[1]," but he is unaware that the western
coast of Spain is bounded by the sea.   He mentions the Ombrici
or Umbrians in Northern Italy, and the Eneti or Venetians at the
head of the Adriatic, but he does not imply that there was any
great mountain barrier which enclosed them towards the north.
The names, indeed, of three of the principal chains in Europe
occur in his writings, but curiously travestied in their application.
That of the Pyrenees appears in the city of Pyrene, far away to the
west in the land of the Celts near the sources of the Ister[2]; while
the Alps and the Carpathians are represented by two streams
called Alpis and Carpis, which are tributaries of that river, flowing
in a northerly direction[3].   He enumerates also a number of its
other affluents in the lower part of its course ; but the Iron Gate
of the Danube near the modern Orsova, with its formidable rapids,
which formed a bar to further navigation, seems to have been the
limit of accurate information in that quarter.   With regard to
Thrace, however, he has more to communicate, and he extended
the limits of that country as far north as the Ister, including the
Getae, who dwelt in that neighbourhood, among the Thracian
tribes.   This accounts for his exaggerated idea of the numbers of
that race, for he speaks of them as exceeding in multitude every
other people in the world, with the exception of the Indians[4].

In strong contrast to the imperfect acquaintance with the rest
of Europe, except the parts about the Mediterranean
Sea, which Herodotus thus betrays, is the elaborate
account which he has given of Scythia.   The subject was one in
which he knew that his readers would be interested, partly because
of the number of their fellow-countrymen who were engaged in
trade with that region, but still more on account of the attention
that had been attracted to it by the inroad of the Cimmerians from
Scythia into Asia Minor, and by the expedition of Darius against

His Imper-
fect Know-
ledge of them.

Scythia.

---

[1] 4. 8.   [2] 2. 33.   [3] 4. 49.   [4] 5. 3.

the Scythians and its disastrous conclusion. The historian had
himself visited the country, where he took up his
abode at Olbia near the mouth of the Hypanis;   His Acquaint-
                                                ance with it.
and he tells us that he proceeded up that stream for
four days' voyage as far as a place called Exampaeus or "the
Sacred Ways[1]." Hence he shews a familiar acquaintance with the
features and products of the neighbouring districts ; he expatiates
on the ice of the Palus Maeotis and the Cimmerian Bosporus,
which became as proverbial in antiquity as a ' Crimean winter ' has
become in the present century; and he mentions the capture and
salting of the sturgeons, which were found in great numbers at the
mouths of the rivers[2]: these at the present day are the great source
of *caviare*, which is made from the roe of that fish.   The Crimea
itself, or Tauric Chersonese, he knew to be a projecting tract of
land, but he was not aware that it was joined to the continent
behind by a narrow isthmus, for he compares its   Its Shape,
shape to that of the extremity of Attica and to the
heel of Italy[3].   He conceived of Scythia as forming a square, the
southern side of which was bounded by the Euxine between the
mouth of the Ister and the Palus Maeotis, and the eastern side by
the last-named sea[4]; so that it represents the area which is inter
sected by the lower courses of the rivers of South Russia—the
Dniester, the Bug and the Dnieper. These he describes with
considerable accuracy, but his account of the streams eastward of the Dnieper is incorrect.   Within the territory which is
thus defined he places the various Scythian tribes
in their respective positions—the agricultural part   and Inhabit-
                                                      ants.
of the population in the rich plains on either
side of the Borysthenes, further to the east the nomad Scythians,
and beyond them again, bordering on the Maeotis, the royal tribe.

[1] 4. 52, where the distance of the place from the sea is given; 4. 81, where
his presence there is implied in his statement that an object which he describes
had been shewn to him there.

[2] 4. 53.

[3] 4. 99.

[4] 4. 101. As regards the Ister Mr Macan remarks with some probability
(*Herodotus*, vol. II. p. 32), "It seems more than possible that a confusion
between the Pruth and the Danube has taken place, and that the Pruth marks
the western limit of Scythia in the fifth century B.C."

The information which Herodotus proceeds to communicate

Peoples to the North of Scythia. about the peoples who were settled to the northward of Scythia is extremely curious and interesting. The historian no doubt derived this from the Greek traders who penetrated into the interior of the country; and it bears the impress of its origin, for it treats of such subjects as would naturally attract the attention of persons engaged in commerce—the peculiar types of physiognomy and customs of those with whom they were brought into contact, and especially their differences in respect of language, which at once affected the intercourse of the Greeks with them. The territory which was occupied by these races formed a wide tract, extending from the Ister to the Maeotis; and within this, following a line which extended from west to east, he enumerates successively seven peoples—the Agathyrsi, the Neuri, the Androphagi, the Melanchlaeni, the Geloni, the Budini and the Sauromatae. Of these, the Andro-phagi, as their name implies, were a cannibal tribe, and the Melanchlaeni or "Black-cloaks" were distinguished by their dark dress, while the Sauromatae are generally identified with the Sarmatians, who afterwards migrated westwards, and ultimately settled in Poland. The four remaining peoples are marked by more distinctive peculiarities. Of the

The Aga-thyrsi, Agathyrsi, who lived the farthest to the west, we are told that they wore an abundance of gold ornaments[1]; and from this trait, taken in connexion with the geographical position assigned to them, it has been conjectured that they occupied the modern Transylvania, where there are gold

Neuri, mines at the present day. With the Neuri was associated a widely spread belief, that periodically each member of the tribe changed into the form of a wolf, but after the lapse of a few days resumed his natural shape[2]. This fancy Herodotus regards with incredulity, but his mention of it is none the less valuable, for the were-wolf is a figure which constantly

Budini, appears in modern folk-lore. The Budini, a nomad race inhabiting a forest and lake district, are described as being distinguished from the others by their blue eyes and red

[1] 4. 104.   [2] 4. 105.

hair[1], which characteristics seem to suggest that they belonged
either to a Germanic or a Slavonic stock.   Among   and Geloni.
them the Geloni were settled, but these were quite
distinct from them in their mode of life, for they dwelt in a city,
and their occupations were agricultural.   The historian adds, that
they were by origin Greeks, having migrated thither from one of
the Greek settlements, and that they had set up Greek temples and
altars, and spoke a mixed dialect of Greek and Scythian.   It would
not be difficult to find similar instances of civilised communities,
when isolated, falling away into a state of semi-barbarism.

Of the lands to the northward of these races Herodotus could
learn nothing, but this was not the case with those
that lay to the north-east.   The reason of this is to   Lands to the
North-east.
be found in the existence of a trade-route, by means
of which there was communication between the Greek settlements
in the neighbourhood of the Maeotis and the tribes far away in
the interior to the northward of the Caspian.   The article of
commerce was gold, of which, he tells us, a very   Gold of the
large quantity existed in the north of Europe[2]; and   Ural Mountains.
the place from which it came was no doubt the
Ural mountains, which are at the present day the great gold-field
of Russia.   These he describes as a lofty chain, which formed the
limit of the habitable world in that direction[3], and the gold that
was found there was fabled to be guarded by griffins[4].   That this
precious metal was brought thence to the coast is proved by
the abundance of it that has been discovered in the Scythian
tombs.   Two of the tribes that inhabited that distant
region, the Argippaei and the Issedones, deserve   The
Argippaei.
especial notice.   The former of these, who dwelt close
under the southern side of the mountains just mentioned, to judge
from the description of their peculiar physiognomy—their flat
noses, projecting jawbones, and bald heads—appear to have been
Kalmucks, though the baldness in reality only applies to the
sacerdotal caste of that tribe; and this view is confirmed by the
description given by Herodotus of their principal article of food,

[1] 4. 108, 109.   [2] 3. 116.
[3] 4. 25.   [4] 3. 116; 4. 27.

which also is in use among the Kalmucks. This was a kind of cake, prepared from the fruit of a tree (the bird-cherry); and the juice, which was strained off in the process of making it, was drunk mixed with milk[1]. The Issedones, who, as

The Issedones.

they were situated eastward of the Argippaei and northward of the Massagetae[2], must have lain to the north-east of the Caspian, are noticeable on account of the historian's statement that among them women had equal rights with men: by which is probably meant that they practised "Mutterrecht" and inheritance in the female line. In the midst of all this curious information we are struck by one remarkable omission. The great river of these parts, the Volga, which the trade-route just mentioned must have crossed, is altogether un-noticed.

The account which Herodotus has given of Asia is in many

Asia.

respects different, and follows different lines, from his notices of the other continents. The amount of information which he has to communicate is ample, but where-as elsewhere he usually treats of the people, whom he mentions, in connexion with the features of the countries which they in-habited, in this part of his work ethnography becomes altogether predominant and geography falls into the background. The

Sources of his Informa-tion.

reason of this is not far to seek. The region of Asia to which his description is limited is its western portion, and, with the exception of Arabia, nearly the whole of this area was at that time included in the Persian empire. Concerning these districts a large amount of intelligence was obtainable, and it is this which Herodotus has introduced into his History. In his third book he gives us an account of the twenty satrapies into which that kingdom was divided; and this notice, we can hardly doubt, was based on a Persian record of a statistical nature, drawn up primarily with a view to taxation, since it enumerates the various nations that occupied those satrapies, together with the amount of tribute that they paid[3]. The details concerning the inhabitants of western Asia which are

[1] 4. 23; cp. Bunbury, *History of Ancient Geography*, I. p. 197.
[2] 4. 25; I. 201.   [3] 3. 89 foll.

thus communicated to us can be checked by a comparison with
the list of tribes that furnished contingents to the army of Xerxes
which is contained in the seventh book[1]; and additional light has
been thrown upon them by various monuments that have been
discovered in modern times, especially by the famous Behistun
inscription of Darius—the same which has furnished us with the
key for interpreting the cuneiform writing. But
from the nature of the case these documents contributed little to the knowledge of geography, and
this deficiency is reflected in Herodotus' narrative. We have
already seen how rude was his conception of the conformation of
this part of the continent in his description of the Actae, or tracts,
into which he divided it. In the latter of these tracts it is hardly
surprising that he shews a very limited acquaintance with Arabia,
which was comprehended within it, because that land, as we have
said, did not form part of the Persian empire, and has at all
times opposed great obstacles in the way of travellers. But in
the former, which comprised Asia Minor, it is
remarkable that he should so greatly underestimate
the width of the country between the northern and
the southern coasts, for he speaks of it as being five days' journey
for a good walker[2], whereas it is in reality about 300 miles across
in a direct line. He also shews no knowledge of the strongly
marked physical characteristics of that land, and especially of the
elevated table-land in its interior, with its severe climate in
winter and its sparse vegetation—features which in every age
have greatly affected its history. Still more strange
than this is his ignorance of the mountain chains
of Asia, for the Caucasus is the only one of these
that he mentions. Even the Taurus—which to subsequent geographers became the most important of all ranges, and was made
to include the Himalaya and other chains by which Asia is
intersected—is not named in his writings. With the
rivers, however, especially those which were crossed
by the main line of communication between the
Aegean and Persia, he shews an adequate acquaintance. He

Scanty Notices of the Geography.

Error about Asia Minor.

Ignorance of the Mountain Chains.

Knowledge of the Rivers.

[1] 7. 61 foll.   [2] 1. 72.

knows that the Halys is the western limit of the Cappadocians in Asia Minor, and mentions the bridges by which its stream was passed[1]. He is conversant, too, with the courses of the Tigris and Euphrates, and knows that they flow from the highlands of Armenia; and with the confluents of the Tigris—the Greater and Lesser Zab, which he rightly distinguishes as separate rivers, though bearing the same name—Zabatus, which however he omits to mention; the Gyndes, which, according to the story, Cyrus had caused to be divided into 360 channels; and the Choaspes, which flowed by the city of Susa[2].

The line of communication which has just been noticed—the Royal Road, as it was called—leading from Sardis to Susa, is described by Herodotus in considerable detail. He introduces it in connexion with the story of the visit of Aristagoras of Miletus to Sparta, in order to justify the statement of that personage that it required three months to reach the Persian capital from Ionia: and he computes the distances across the intervening countries both by stages or day's journeys and by parasangs—here again evidently following an official document[3]. The numbers which he gives, as they have come down to us, are in some cases clearly inaccurate; still, when taken in connexion with the countries and places that are named, they enable us to determine with a fair amount of certainty the direction which the road followed. Its course through Asia Minor cannot have been the same as that of the Graeco-Roman road of a later period, which proceeded due eastwards from the valley of the Maeander and the city of Apameia through southern Phrygia by Iconium to the lowlands of Cilicia; this route is excluded from consideration by its lying at some distance to the south of the Halys, which was crossed by the Persian road. In order to reach that stream from Sardis it was necessary to follow a much more circuitous route towards the north of Phrygia, so as to avoid the barren tracts and salt lakes which occupy the centre of that province. The direction of this was by Pessinus to Ancyra (Angora), and thence, after crossing the Halys, to

The Royal Road.

Its Course through Asia Minor,

---

[1] 1. 75.　　　　　[2] 5. 52.　　　　　[3] 5. 52, 53.

Tavium, in the neighbourhood of which place must have been the point of junction with the line of traffic from Upper Asia to the Black Sea by way of Sinope[1]. The most reasonable explanation of the preference given by the Persians to this devious course is the supposition that it followed an older line of communication, which existed under previous rulers of the country, when the position of the governing centre of that period caused it to be the natural road[2]. Of the succeeding portion of the route Herodotus tells us, that after a long *Cilicia,* stretch through Cappadocia the gates were reached by which Cilicia is entered: by these, however, he cannot mean the well-known pass of the Cilician Gates, which led to Tarsus and the sea, for he estimates the width of Cilicia as no more than three days' journey, and this statement can only apply to the mountainous north-eastern portion of that province, where it is enclosed within narrow limits. The pass here intended is probably one of those which cross the Taurus in the region of Commagene between Melitene and Samosata[3]; at the latter of those places the road would be met by the Euphrates, which the historian rightly speaks of as the boundary of Armenia on that side. *Armenia,* After this, though the limits that he assigns to the various countries traversed are not easy of explanation, the route itself presents no great difficulty. It passed from the upper course of the Euphrates to that of the Tigris in the south of Armenia, reaching the latter stream not far from the modern Diarbekir; and after crossing it traversed the hilly country of Matiene and Cissia on its left bank *Matiene and* *Cissia.* which is intersected by the affluents of the Tigris that have already been mentioned, until it reached the Persian capital.

The accounts that Herodotus received of India, which formed. the remotest satrapy of the Persian empire, seem to *India.* have made a great impression upon him, for he speaks of the Indians as the most numerous of all nations then known, and of the tribute that they paid in gold-dust as being

[1] *v. supra,* p. 47.

[2] Ramsay, *Historical Geography of Asia Minor,* p. 27.

[3] See Mr Hogarth's remarks in Macan's *Herodotus,* vol. II. pp. 300 foll.

enormous[1]. At the same time, his knowledge of that country was very limited; it did not in fact extend beyond the Indus. The lands further to the east he regarded as sandy wastes, which were uninhabited[2]—an idea which may have arisen from exaggerated reports of the desert tract which lies beyond that river. The Indians with whom he was acquainted were of different races, speaking different languages, and some of them were nomads. Hence it is evident that he included among them the aborigines as well as the Hindus, and this would account for the barbarous customs which he ascribes to some of them. On the other hand, the abstinence from animal food which he attributes to certain tribes, and their unwillingness to put any live animal to death, are tenets of the Brahmans[3].

Its Races,

Among the products of the country, besides gold, he mentions cotton, which he describes as a kind of wool that grows wild on trees, and is superior in beauty and quality to the wool of sheep, and is used by the natives for making clothes[4]. He had also heard that crocodiles were found in the Indus, which he believed to be the only river in the world besides the Nile that produced them[5]; yet, strange to say, he omits all mention of elephants.

and Products.

We have already seen that Herodotus had thoroughly explored Egypt, and had ascended the Nile as far as Elephantine, which lies immediately below the First Cataract. The cataract he describes without exaggeration, saying that, owing to the rising of the ground, "it is necessary to attach a rope to the boat on each side, as men harness an ox, and so proceed on the journey[6]." At that point, however, anything like an accurate knowledge of the Nile valley on his part comes to an end, for the information which he gives was obtained by hearsay. The next important station which he mentions was the city of Meroë, the capital of the Aethiopians, the ruins of which have been discovered to the northward of Khartoum, between that place and Berber. Notwithstanding its remote position, it was known to

The Nile Valley.

Meroë.

---

[1] 3. 95.　　　　　　[2] 3. 98.　　　　　　[3] 3. 100.
[4] 3. 106.　　　　　　[5] 4. 44.　　　　　　[6] 2. 29.

the Egyptians and formed part of their dominion at an early period, as is shewn by monuments which remain on the site. The pointed cliffs jutting out of the water and sunken rocks beneath the surface, which Herodotus describes as obstructing the river at one point between the First Cataract and Meroë, so that travellers were forced to quit the stream and follow the bank for a period of forty days, are to be recognised as those which occur in the great arc which the Nile makes at one point in this part of its course, the chord of which is cut off by the track across the desert that is usually taken at the present day; and it is not an improbable suggestion, that the sudden bend towards the west which is made by this loop was the origin of the idea that the river flowed from west to east in the upper part of its course. The account of the lands and tribes beyond Meroë is still more vague and shadowy. *The Two Branches Unnoticed.* The most marked feature of the Upper Nile valley, the confluence of the two great branches of the river, the White and the Blue Nile, at Khartoum, is not even mentioned. One people, however, whom he places on the banks of the Nile far away in the interior of the continent, possess a historical interest. These were the Automoli or " deserters," who in the native language were called Asmach, and were re- *The Automoli.* puted to have deserted from Psammitichus on account of the hardness of their service, and to have withdrawn into Aethiopia, where the king of the country provided them with lands[1]. By later writers they are called Sembritae or "foreigners," and from them we learn that their position was not as remote as that which Herodotus assigns to them, but in the modern district of the Sennaar, immediately south of Khartoum, between the two branches of the Nile[2]. In the extreme south of Africa, on the shores of the ocean, and therefore at a distance from the course of the Nile, lay the Macrobian Aethiopians—a half fabulous people in respect of their habits and mode of life, reflecting some of the traits of the Homeric *The Macrobian Aethiopians.* Aethiopes[3]—against whom Cambyses undertook an expedition which ended in disaster[4].

[1] 2. 30.　　　[2] Strabo, 17. 1. 2.　　　[3] *v. supra*, p. 26.
[4] Herod. 3. 17—25.

The northern coast of Africa, which borders on the Mediterranean Sea, is rightly divided by Herodotus into an eastern and a western portion, the former of which was low and sandy, and inhabited by nomads, while the latter was hilly and well wooded, and maintained an agricultural population[1]. The determining feature of the country, to which the difference which is thus characterised is due, is the chain of the Atlas, which extends through the western part, sending off spurs towards the sea, and maintaining a high average of fertility, but sinks when it reaches the longitude of Carthage.

Northern Coast of Africa.

It is the eastern portion, between that city and the Egyptian frontier, with which the historian shews himself to be familiar, and he has put on record a large amount of curious information about the customs of the wandering tribes in that neighbourhood: this no doubt he obtained at Cyrene at the time of his visit to that city. He places the Great Syrtis—or, as he calls it, the Syrtis, for he recognises only one—to the westward of Cyrene[2]; and he notices, in contrast to the prevailing barrenness, the extraordinary productiveness of the plain in which the river Cinyps flowed[3]—a feature which has also attracted the attention of modern travellers. He also assigns to the Lotophagi their correct position in the neighbourhood of the lake Tritonis, though it is doubtful whether he rightly distinguished that piece of water from the Lesser Syrtis[4]. His notices of the people to the west of this contain a considerable element of the marvellous; and beyond the Straits the only place which he definitely names is the promontory of Soloeis (probably Cape Spartel), of which he would have heard through the Carthaginians[5]. To that people also is due his account of the "dumb commerce" which was practised on the Atlantic coast of Africa; and this, as it exactly corresponds with what occurs at the present day in places where the natives are in fear of being kidnapped by traders, deserves to be quoted.

Eastern Portion.

Western Portion.

"There is a country in Libya, and a nation, beyond the Pillars

[1] 4. 191; cp. 186, 187.   [2] 4. 169.   [3] 4. 198.
[4] 4. 177, 178.   [5] 2. 32; 4. 43.

of Hercules, which the Carthaginians are wont to visit, where they no sooner arrive but forthwith they unlade their wares, and, having disposed them after an orderly fashion along the beach, leave them, and, returning aboard their ships, raise a great smoke. The natives, when they see the smoke, come down to the shore, and, laying out to view so much gold as they think the worth of the wares, withdraw to a distance. The Carthaginians upon this come ashore and look. If they think the gold enough, they take it and go their way; but if it does not seem to them sufficient, they go aboard ship once more, and wait patiently. Then the others approach and add to their gold, till the Carthaginians are content. Neither party deals unfairly by the other: for they themselves never touch the gold till it comes up to the worth of their goods, nor do the natives ever carry off the goods till the gold is taken away[1]."

Dumb Commerce.

The historian's information also concerning the interior of Africa to the southward of the countries that border on the Mediterranean contains a surprising amount of truth, when we consider how difficult it has been in all ages to penetrate that region. He divides the entire area into three tracts or zones, stretching across from west to east; the first of these was the inhabited tract in the neighbourhood of the sea-coast; the second a region infested by wild beasts; the third an uninhabited tract of sandy desert[2]. The first zone is that which has been already described, reaching as far inland as the chain of the Atlas and the low hills that form its easterly continuation; the second, or "wild beast tract," which lies to the southward of this towards the interior, was, at least in its western portion, the Gaetulia of the Romans, and was called by the Arabs the "Land of Dates"; the third region, which lay beyond this again, is the true Sahara desert. In addition to this general outline of the country, Herodotus

Interior of Africa.

The Three Tracts.

---

[1] 4. 196, Rawlinson's translation; to which work I am indebted in other passages which I have quoted.

[2] 2. 32; 4. 181—185. Mr Macan observes that these 'zones' suit the western part of this district of Africa better than the eastern: *Herodotus*, vol. I. pp. xcviii and 130.

notices one feature of a more special character in the oases,

The Oases.

which he speaks of as lying at intervals of about ten days' journey from one another, so as to form a belt on the edge of the "wild-beast tract" towards the desert. Here we find the love of symmetry which is characteristic of his mind asserting itself, for these patches of fertile land, though they are found in this part of Africa, and from the nature of the case determine the lines of communication, are much more irregular in their occurrence than he describes them to be. The same combination of truth with exaggeration is found in his account of their details. He speaks of them as salt-hills, with springs of fresh water issuing from the midst of the salt, while in their neighbourhood palm-trees and grazing ground are found; and this is so far true, that all the oases abound in salt, and that in places, as he says, masses of it are used for building purposes. On the other hand, instead of being hills, the oases are in reality depressions in the surface of the desert, and the water which collects in them is the cause of their fertility. Some of the stations which he mentions in the early part of the caravan route along them, to the westward of Egypt, can be identified; for the second of them, which he calls

The Garamantes.

Augila, still bears the name of Aujileh, and the next is in the country of the Garamantes, who occupied the district now called Fezzan, which lies at a distance of thirty days' journey from the coast, due south of

The Troglodyte Aethiopians.

Tripoli. In connexion with that people he introduces the Troglodyte Aethiopians, against whom they were wont to make raiding expeditions. These are easily recognised in the Tibboos of the interior of Africa by the peculiarities which Herodotus attributes to them—their squeaking voices, their remarkable fleetness of foot, and their habit of dwelling in caves—all of which are found in that race.

Expedition of the Nasamones.

Concerning the countries which lie beyond the great desert Herodotus furnishes us with one intimation, which occurs in the story of the Nasamones already referred to. This was communicated to him by natives of Cyrene, who had been told it by Etearchus, king of the Ammonians, while he in turn had received it from the Nasamonian travellers themselves. These were certain young men of that

tribe in the neighbourhood of the Syrtis, who, being seized
with a desire for adventure, determined to explore the deserts
of central Africa.   Their narrative is thus given by the historian :
"The young men, despatched on this errand by their comrades with a plentiful supply of water and pro-
visions, travelled at first through the inhabited   Narrative of
                                                       Herodotus.
region, passing which they came to the wild beast
tract, whence they finally entered upon the desert, which they
proceeded to cross in a direction from east to west.   After
journeying for many days over a wide extent of sand, they came
at last to a plain where they observed trees growing; approaching
them, and seeing fruit on them, they proceeded to gather it.
While they were thus engaged, there came upon them some
dwarfish men, under the middle height, who seized them and
carried them off.   The Nasamonians could not understand a
word of their language, nor had they any acquaintance with the
language of the Nasamonians.   They were led across extensive
marshes, and finally came to a town, where all the men were of
the height of their conductors, and black-complexioned.   A great
river flowed by the town, running from west to east, and containing crocodiles[1]."

The dwarfs who are here mentioned are the same race which
we have identified with the Pygmies of Homer[2].   The river was
regarded by Herodotus himself as being the Nile in its upper
course, which he supposed to flow from western Africa.   This
view we know to be erroneous, but the story itself, owing to the
circumstantial manner in which it is narrated, appears to be
deserving of credit.   On such a subject as the identification of
this river it is hazardous to speak with confidence, but the direction which was followed by the Nasamones suggests the probability that the stream which they reached was the Niger, which
lies to the south-west of the Sahara.

[1] 2. 32.   [2] *v. supra*, p. 29.

CHAPTER VI.

EXPEDITIONS BEFORE THE TIME OF ALEXANDER.

Real and Fictitious Expeditions—Circumnavigation of Africa under Necho—The Story derived from the Egyptians or Phoenicians—Argument from the Sun being seen on the Right Hand—Criticism of it—Improbability of the Voyage—Expedition of Scylax of Caryanda—Objections to its Authenticity—Voyage of Sataspes—Reasons for believing in it—Expedition of Hanno—His Narrative of it—Island of Cerne (Herne)—Promontory of Soloeis (C. Cantin)—River Lixus (Wady Draa)—River Bambotum (Senegal River)—(Cape Verde and Gambia River)—The Western Horn (Bay of Bissagos)—Flaming Mountain-sides—Explanation of the Phenomenon—Mt. Theon Ochema (Mt. Sagres)—The Southern Horn (Sherboro Sound)—Capture of Gorillas—Expedition of Himilco—The 'Ora Maritima' of Avienus—Account of the Oestrymnides—Of the Mid-Atlantic—Of the Sargasso Sea—The Retreat of the Ten Thousand—Character of Xenophon's 'Anabasis'—Geographical Features of Armenia—Its Mountains and Rivers—Sources of the Euphrates and Tigris—Lake of Van—The March from Cunaxa to Armenia—The Zabatus (Greater Zab)—Land of the Carduchi (Kurdistan)—The Centrites (River of Sert)—Source of the Tigris—The Teleboas (Kara-su)—Eastern Euphrates (Murad-su)—Highlands of Armenia—Underground Dwellings—The Phasis (Aras)—The Harpasus (Tchoruk)—Gymnias—Trapezus (Trebizond)—The first view of the Sea—The Poisonous Honey—The 'Periplus' of Scylax—Its probable Date—Its Contents—Doubts as to its Genuineness—Interesting Notices in it.

WE have now to consider a series of expeditions into regions
Real and Fictitious Expeditions. as yet unexplored, which professed to have been made between the beginning of the sixth and the middle of the fourth century before Christ, and the narratives of which, whether real or fictitious, have in one form or another been transmitted to us. Of the reality of one of these—the Retreat of the Ten Thousand under Xenophon—there never has been any question; for, owing to the upright character of its narrator, and the trustworthiness of his record, which bears on its face the stamp of truth, it stands out as one of the best ascertained facts of history. Indeed, an apology might seem to be required for introducing it along with a number of less well-

authenticated expeditions—especially as the others were made by sea, and were undertaken in the first instance with a view to investigation—were it not that the circumstances of the case rendered it a notable example of adventurous exploration, which contributed largely to the extension of geographical knowledge. The claims to our acceptance which are put forward by the remainder will call for a careful examination, for the truth of each in turn has at different times been questioned, and several of them still continue to be subjects of debate.

The first of these in order of date is the circumnavigation of Africa, said to have been executed by Phoenician sailors at the command of Necho, king of Egypt, about 600 B.C. Our knowledge of this is derived from Herodotus, who gives the following account of it :— *Circumnavigation of Africa under Necho.*

"As for Libya, we know it to be washed on all sides by the sea, except where it is attached to Asia. This discovery was first made by Necho, the Egyptian king, who on desisting from the canal which he had begun between the Nile and the Arabian Gulf, sent to sea a number of ships manned by Phoenicians, with orders to make for the Pillars of Hercules, and return to Egypt through them, and by the Mediterranean. The Phoenicians took their departure from Egypt by way of the Erythraean sea, and so sailed into the southern ocean. When autumn came, they went ashore, wherever they might happen to be, and having sown a tract of land with corn, waited until the grain was fit to cut. Having reaped it, they again set sail; and thus it came to pass that two whole years went by, and it was not till the third year that they doubled the Pillars of Hercules, and made good their voyage home. On their return, they declared—I for my part do not believe them, but perhaps others may—that in sailing round Libya they had the sun upon their right hand. In this way was the extent of Libya first discovered [1]."

Herodotus does not inform us from what source he obtained this story, but we may assume with some confidence that it was either from the Egyptians or the Phoenicians. The preciseness of statement with which it is delivered, as far as it goes, is in its *The Story derived from the Egyptians or Phoenicians.*

[1] Herod. 4. 42.

favour, but it is unfortunate that no details should be forthcoming
which would serve to corroborate it, such as notices of the
countries that were visited, of the climate that was experienced,
or of the strange sights and remarkable tribes that were met with.
We might at least have expected to hear something of the disappearance of the northern constellations in a southern latitude,
since it was by them that the Phoenicians were wont to steer.
Still more remarkable is the omission of all notice of the great
southward extension of the continent of Africa, which must have
made a greater impression than any other feature on one that
sailed round it, and yet remained altogether unknown to the
geographers of a later time, who believed, with Herodotus, that
the coast of Africa trended away to the west shortly after passing
Cape Guardafui.   The ignorance which existed among the ancients
on this point, we may observe, facilitated their belief in the
accomplishment of the task, because the chief difficulty which
stood in the way of it was unknown to them.   In modern times,
the point which has been regarded as lending the
strongest support to the truthfulness of the narrative, is the statement of the navigators that in
passing round Africa they had the sun on their
right hand.   Such no doubt would be the case when they were
within the southern hemisphere; and this fact, taken in connexion with the incredulity of Herodotus on the subject, seems at
first sight an instance of that kind of evidence which has been
noticed above[1], as most convincing in establishing the truth of
a story—viz. the mention of a phenomenon, which appeared
marvellous to the men of a former age, but is easily explained by
the knowledge of modern times.   Such a statement, it may be
said, could not have been invented.   In reality, however, this
principle does not apply in the present instance,
for the question turns on the acquaintance with
astronomy which was possessed, not by Herodotus,
or even by the Greeks, his contemporaries, but by the Phoenicians or the Egyptians, from whom Herodotus derived the tale.
Now the learned among the Egyptians were well aware that
Syene was under (or close to) the tropic—that is to say, that the

Argument from the Sun being seen on the Right Hand.

Criticism of it.

[1] *v. supra*, p. 18.

sun was vertical at that place at the summer solstice; and from
this it was a simple inference, that the inhabitants of the countries
further to the south would at that season have the sun to the
northward of them, and for an increasingly long period in proportion as they approached the equator.　This conclusion could
be verified through personal observation by anyone who advanced
along the Nile in the direction of Meroë; and the same thing
would come to the knowledge of the Phoenician sailors who
reached that part of the Red Sea which lies within the tropic
of Cancer.　In consequence of this, when once the story of the
circumnavigation of Africa had come into existence, the statement
that the voyagers had the sun on their right hand during the
passage would be easily attached to it as a corollary.　On the
whole we may conclude, that the execution of so
great an undertaking at that early period, though
in no sense impossible, is highly improbable; and

*Improba-
bility of the
Voyage.*

that, in order to accept it as a fact of history, we need stronger
evidence than is furnished by the story in Herodotus, unsupported
as it is by the authority of any other ancient writer[1].

In the same part of his work in which the account of Necho's
expedition is given, the historian mentions two
other voyages of exploration, which were said to
have been undertaken at the command of the kings

*Expedition
of Scylax of
Caryanda.*

of Persia—that of Scylax of Caryanda in the time of Darius,
about a century later than the Egyptian expedition, and that of
Sataspes during the reign of Xerxes.　The former of these, he
tells us, had for its object the investigation of the shores of Asia
from the mouth of the Indus to the head of the Red Sea.　By
the order of Darius a party, among whom was Scylax, a Greek of
Caryanda, in Caria, started on shipboard from Caspatyrus, a town
on the upper course of the Indus, the exact position of which is
unknown to us, though the name—or rather that of Caspapyrus,
by which the same place is meant—occurs in Hecataeus[2].　They
followed the stream of the Indus "towards the east and the
rising sun" as far as the sea, after which they turned westward

[1] See Bunbury, *History of Ancient Geography*, vol. I. pp. 289—296, where
the question of the circumnavigation is fully and fairly discussed.

[2] *v. supra*, p. 74.

and at the expiration of thirty months reached the place from which Necho had despatched the Phoenicians to sail round Libya. "After this voyage was completed," he adds, "Darius conquered the Indians, and made use of the sea in those parts[1]." This story, for which Herodotus is again our only authority, is very briefly recorded, and furnishes fewer details even than that of the circumnavigation of Africa. The intrinsic improbabilities which it involves are no doubt much less great, because the voyage was shorter and less uncertain, and the difficulties which it presented were not of equal magnitude. The circumstance also that Caryanda, the birthplace of Scylax, was in the immediate neighbourhood of Halicarnassus, where Herodotus resided, seems to favour its authenticity, because of the facility with which the

Objections to its Authenticity.

writer could have obtained information on the subject. But this very fact, when examined more closely, tends to excite our suspicions, on account of the ignorance which Herodotus displays of the geographical features of the route which he supposes Scylax to have followed. He speaks of the Indus as flowing towards the east; he is unaware of the existence of the Persian Gulf[2]; and he describes the Red Sea as being so narrow, that it could be crossed in its widest part in half a day[3]. Mistakes such as these clearly prove that, if an account of the expedition of Scylax ever existed, Herodotus could not have seen it; nay, we may go further, and affirm that Scylax, if he made the voyage, could not have returned to Caryanda, for in that case more accurate knowledge would have been in circulation on the subject than that which Herodotus possessed. When we add to this, that there is no subsequent trace of any such communication having existed between Persia and India as the historian implies when he says that Darius made use of the sea in those parts; and also that, when Alexander sailed down the Indus, and despatched a fleet under the command of Nearchus to the head of the Persian Gulf, he and his companions were wholly unaware of any previous expedition of the kind having been made; we cannot but feel that the story rests on a very insecure foundation.

[1] Herod. 4. 44. [2] v. supra, p. 81.

[3] Herod. 2. 11.

The other expedition which Herodotus mentions in this connexion is associated with a somewhat dramatic
incident. Sataspes, a Persian of high rank, was　　Voyage of
　　　　　　　　　　　　　　　　　　　　　　　　Sataspes.
condemned by Xerxes to be impaled in conse-
quence of his having offered violence to a noble lady; but his
sentence was remitted, on the intercession of his mother, who was
a sister of Darius, on condition of his circumnavigating Africa
from the Mediterranean to the Red Sea.　Accordingly he provided
himself with a ship and crew in Egypt, and after passing the
Pillars of Hercules, and rounding the promontory of Soloeis
(Cape Spartel), proceeded southward along the Libyan coast.
After sailing for several months, however, he became disheartened,
and seeing no end to his voyage, returned by the same route, and
ultimately presented himself once more at the Persian court.
There he pleaded in excuse of the non-fulfilment of his undertaking, that his ship stopped and was unable to make any way;
and he mentioned also that, at the furthest point which he reached,
the country was inhabited by a dwarfish race, who wore dresses
made of palm leaves[1].　These statements did not satisfy Xerxes,
who ordered him to be put to death in accordance with the
sentence originally passed upon him: but they may justify us in
accepting his account as true, since they correspond to what is observed at the present day.　The　Reasons for
　　　　　　　　　　　　　　　　　　　　　　　　believing in it.
alleged impossibility of making further progress
may have been due to the trade-winds, which blow on the coast
of Guinea without cessation during the summer months in the
face of vessels southward bound: and the pygmies are the same
race whom we have already noticed as being mentioned by
Homer and Herodotus among the inhabitants of Africa[2].　Thus,
while the historical character of the occurrences that led up to
Sataspes' voyage is proved by the circumstantial manner in which
they are related, including the names of the persons affected,
the voyage itself is rendered probable by the intimations that
it contains of things which were unknown at that time, and could
hardly have been invented.

About the same time that Sataspes was engaged on this

---

[1] Herod. 4. 43.　　　　　　[2] v. supra, pp. 29, 97.

ineffectual voyage, or not long after, two remarkable expeditions
were despatched to the Pillars of Hercules by
the Carthaginians, to explore the Atlantic coasts
of Africa and Europe respectively. The names

Expedition of Hanno.

of the commanders of these were Hanno and Himilco, and the
object with which they were sent was not so much to discover
unknown lands, as to establish colonies and trading stations in
those regions, and to reinforce those already existing there. The
Hanno here spoken of has been with some probability identified
with the son of that Hamilcar who invaded Sicily in 480 B.C.,
and was defeated and slain at the battle of Himera[1]; and on this
supposition we may fix the date of his expedition approximately at
470 B.C. After his return to Carthage he composed
a brief account of his voyage, which was inscribed
on a bronze or marble tablet, and dedicated in the

His Narra- tive of it.

temple of Cronos (Moloch) in that city; and by great good
fortune a Greek version of this has come down to us, under the
title of the *Periplus* or Coasting Survey of Hanno. From this we
learn that he sailed from Carthage with a company of men and
women to the number of thirty thousand—who were evidently
intended to be left at the trading stations, and must have been
conveyed on board of transports, though this is not stated—and
with a fleet of sixty penteconters, which formed the escort. The
first half of their voyage after they passed the Straits, in the course
of which they established the settlements which were their primary
object, was occupied in reaching an island named
Cerne. The determination of this place is the most
important point in connexion with the geography of

Island of Cerne (Herne).

the expedition, and it has been fixed with some certainty at an
island now called Herne, the similarity of name forming one
element in the process of identification. The last-named island is
small, and lies in the recesses of a deep bay—at the mouth of the
Rio de Ouro—both which features are attributed by Hanno to
Cerne; its distance from the Straits of Gibraltar also corresponds
better than that of any other place which has been suggested
with the reckoning of the Carthaginian, who says that they found

---

[1] See C. Müller's Prolegg. to his *Geogr. Gr. Minores,* vol. I. pp. xxi, xxii.

the voyage between those two points to be of equal length with that from Carthage to the Pillars of Hercules[1]. Moreover it accords satisfactorily with the distances that are given in the subsequent part of the voyage, in which several of the places reached can be determined with confidence.

The two most noticeable geographical features which the voyagers passed on their way from the Straits to the island of Cerne were the promontory of Soloeis and the river Lixus. The promontory here in- **Promontory of Soloeis (C. Cantin).** tended is not Cape Spartel to the westward of Tangier, to which, as we have seen[2], Herodotus gave that name—possibly he may have confused the accounts he received of the two[3]—but Cape Cantin, which lies considerably further to the south, in the same latitude as Madeira. The Lixus, which is described in the *Periplus* as "a great river, flowing from Libya[4]," can be none other than the Wady Draa, which is quite the largest stream in this part of Africa, so that its **River Lixus (Wady Draa).** course is said to be longer than that of the Rhine; it reaches the sea opposite the Canary Islands. This identification is confirmed by the Carthaginian's remark, that the coast along which they sailed to the southward of this was desert[5], for it is at the Wady Draa that the desert commences. The information is added, that the mountains far in the interior, from which the Lixus flowed, were inhabited by men of strange aspect, who were cave-dwellers, and were said to be fleeter of foot than horses[6]. In these we discover a branch of the same race in central Africa which Herodotus characterises by these peculiarities, and which we have already recognised as the Tibboos[7].

From the island of Cerne, where their last colony was established, the Carthaginians made two successive expeditions to the

---

[1] Hannonis *Periplus*, § 8, in Müller, *op. cit.*, p. 6; see also his Prolegg. p. xxvi. The valuable notes to this edition have done more than any other work towards determining the positions mentioned by Hanno. Dr Müller, for his part, handsomely acknowledges his debt to Rennell.

[2] *v. supra*, pp. 94, 103.

[3] Bunbury, *History of Ancient Geography*, I. p. 163 note.

[4] *Periplus*, § 6.   [5] § 8.

[6] § 7.   [7] *v. supra*, p. 96; Herod. 4. 183.

southward along the coast, returning in the interval to their starting-point, though for what reason we are not informed. In the former of these, which was also the shorter, the most noteworthy incident was their reaching a broad river, full of crocodiles and hippopotami[1].

River Bambotum (Senegal River).

The name of this river is given by Pliny[2]—on the authority of Polybius, who explored this coast at a later time, and took note of the animals here mentioned—as Bambotum; but there can be little doubt, as Bochart has remarked[3], that this is a corruption of Bamothum, for *bamoth* or *behemoth* is the Semitic name for the hippopotamus, so that the meaning would be Hippopotamus river. It is the Senegal River of modern times. On the second voyage they sailed along the same coast, and after passing that river reached a mountainous promontory covered with a dense vegetation of aromatic trees: when they had rounded this they found a very deep inlet with level land on either side of it[4]. Here the promontory is undoubtedly Cape Verde, which is now recognised as the western-most point of Africa, though of that fact the ancients were not aware: in its elevation, and the forests from which it has obtained its name, it corresponds, as no other point on this coast does, to the description just given. The inlet is the mouth of the Gambia River, which forms a broad estuary with flat shores. The next place which they reached to the southward of this was an extensive bay, known to their native interpreters as the Western Horn, in which lay an island so formed that it embraced a harbour with another island within it. On this they disembarked, but in the course of the night they were so terrified by the sight of numerous fires in the woods, and the sound of cymbals and drums and voices, that

(Cape Verde and Gambia River.)

The Western Horn (Bay of Bissagos).

---

[1] *Periplus*, § 10; ἐκεῖθεν πλέοντες εἰς ἕτερον ἤλθομεν ποταμὸν μέγαν καὶ πλατὺν, γέμοντα κροκοδείλων καὶ ἵππων ποταμίων.

[2] *H. N.*, 5. 10; flumen Bambotum crocodilis et hippopotamis refertum.

[3] See Müller, *op. cit.*, p. 9.

[4] *Periplus*, §§ 12, 13; τῇ δ' οὖν τελευταίᾳ ἡμέρᾳ προσωρμίσθημεν ὄρεσι μεγάλοις δασέσιν· ἦν δὲ τὰ τῶν δένδρων ξύλα εὐώδη τε καὶ ποικίλα. Περι-πλεύσαντες δὲ ταῦτα ἡμέρας δύο ἐγινόμεθα ἐν θαλάττης χάσματι ἀμετρήτῳ, ἧς ἐπὶ θάτερα πρὸς τῇ γῇ πεδίον ἦν.

they quitted the spot incontinently[1]. The bay here mentioned is
that of Bissagos, which lies between the Gambia and Sierra Leone
at the mouth of the Rio Grande; and one of the numerous
islands which lie about it and in front of it—that called Harang or
Orango—exactly corresponds to what Hanno describes, having a
land-locked port with a smaller island in its middle. The sights
and sounds, which awoke the superstitious fears of the navigators,
may well have been the accompaniments of a native festival.

As it approaches its close, the story of the explorers becomes
almost sensational. We hear of country-sides blazing in the night-time with flames which sent forth   Flaming
Mountain-
an aromatic odour, of torrents of fire rushing   sides.
down towards the sea, and, in particular, of a burning mountain
which towered above all[2]. We cannot wonder if this part of the
narrative has awakened incredulity, and yet the accounts of modern
travellers in Africa provide us with an easy explanation of it, if we
allow for the impression produced on men who   Explanation
viewed it from a distance and were ignorant of its   of the Phenomenon.
cause. The following is Mungo Park's description
of the spectacle which he saw in Western Africa, at the season
when the dry grass is set on fire with the view of producing a fine
crop for the following year. "The burning of the grass in
Manding exhibits a scene of terrific grandeur. In the midst
of the night I could see the plains and mountains, as far as my
eye could reach, variegated with lines of fire; and the light
reflected on the sky made the heavens appear in a blaze[3]."
Similar testimony is borne by other African travellers, and the

---

[1] § 14; ἤλθομεν ἐς μέγαν κόλπον, ὃν ἔφασαν οἱ ἑρμηνέες καλεῖσθαι Ἑσπέρου
Κέρας· ἐν δὲ τούτῳ νῆσος ἦν μεγάλη, καὶ ἐν τῇ νήσῳ λίμνη θαλασσώδης, ἐν δὲ
ταύτῃ νῆσος ἑτέρα, εἰς ἣν ἀποβάντες ἡμέρας μὲν οὐδὲν ἀφεωρῶμεν ὅτι μὴ ὕλην,
νυκτὸς δὲ πυρά τε πολλὰ καιόμενα καὶ φωνὴν αὐλῶν ἠκούομεν κυμβάλων τε καὶ
τυμπάνων πάταγον καὶ κραυγὴν μυρίαν.

[2] §§ 15, 16; ταχὺ δ' ἐκπλεύσαντες παρημειβόμεθα χώραν διάπυρον θυμιαμάτων
μεστήν· μέγιστοι δ' ἀπ' αὐτῆς πυρώδεις ῥύακες ἐνέβαλλον εἰς τὴν θάλατταν·
ἡ γῆ δ' ὑπὸ θέρμης ἄβατος ἦν. Ταχὺ οὖν κἀκεῖθεν φοβηθέντες ἀπεπλεύσαμεν.
Τέτταρας δ' ἡμέρας φερόμενοι, νυκτὸς τὴν γῆν ἀφεωρῶμεν φλογὸς μεστήν· ἐν
μέσῳ ἦν ἡλίβατόν τι πῦρ, τῶν ἄλλων μεῖζον, ἁπτόμενον, ὡς ἐδόκει, τῶν ἄστρων.
Τοῦτο δ' ἡμέρας ὄρος ἐφαίνετο μέγιστον, Θεῶν ὄχημα καλούμενον.

[3] Mungo Park's *Travels in the Interior of Africa*, I. pp. 259, 260.

same sight may be seen on a smaller scale on the plains in Greece
during the autumn.   The burning mountain of
which Hanno speaks, and which, he says, was
called Theon Ochema, or the Chariot of the Gods,
was no volcano, as Mela and Pliny supposed it to be, but simply
a lofty summit whose slopes were on fire.   It is now called
Mt. Sagres, and is described as a conical mountain of great height,
forming the marked feature of this part of the coast, which otherwise is perfectly flat[1].

Mt. Theon Ochema (Mt. Sagres).

A voyage of three days to the southward of this brought the
Carthaginians to the Southern Horn, a bay which
in certain points bore a peculiar resemblance to the
Western Horn, for it contained a similar island,
with an enclosed space of water surrounding a smaller island[2].
This bay, which now bears the name of Sherboro Sound, lies
a little to the south of Sierra Leone; and the larger island here
mentioned is called Macauley Island, and on its western coast
embraces a smaller island on three sides.   The narrative concludes with the following remarkable incident, of which the last-
named island was the scene.   "The place," it says, "was full
of savage people, but the majority of them were
women, whose bodies were covered with hair; these
our interpreters called Gorillae.   When we pursued
them, we were unable to catch the men, all of whom escaped,
since they were accustomed to precipitous places and defended
themselves with stones.   Three women, however, we secured,
but these refused to accompany us, and scratched and bit those
who conducted them.   So we killed them and flayed them, and
brought their skins to Carthage[3]."   It is through this passage
that the name Gorilla has been introduced into natural history,
and it seems probable that the creatures which are here described were large anthropoid apes, such as are still found near
Sierra Leone.   Beyond the Southern Horn the explorers did not

The Southern Horn (Sher-boro Sound).

Capture of Gorillas.

---

[1] See Rennell, *Geography of Herodotus*, p. 734.

[2] *Periplus*, §§ 17, 18; τριταῖοι δ’ ἐκεῖθεν πυρώδεις ῥύακας παραπλεύσαντες ἀφικόμεθα εἰς κόλπον Νότου Κέρας λεγόμενον. Ἐν δὲ τῷ μυχῷ νῆσος ἦν, ἐοικυῖα τῇ πρώτῃ, λίμνην ἔχουσα· καὶ ἐν ταύτῃ νῆσος ἦν ἑτέρα.

[3] *Periplus*, § 18.

advance, the reason being, Hanno tells us, that their stock of provisions failed them. It was also the furthest point reached by any ancient navigator. We may remark in corroboration of the views that are here expressed as to the position of the places named in the *Periplus*, that the distances between them correspond in the main to those which are there assigned to them. It is an interesting question whether Herodotus was acquainted with Hanno's expedition. There is no difficulty in the way of the supposition on the ground of their respective dates, and certain points which the historian mentions, especially the description of "dumb commerce" which has been given above[1], may not improbably have been derived from this source. At the same time it must be allowed that such information may have been obtained through earlier visits of the Carthaginian traders.

The second of the two great Carthaginian expeditions was that which was sent forth under the command of Himilco. Pliny informs us that this took place Expedition of Himilco. at the same time as that of Hanno, and that its object was to explore the western coast of Europe[2]; but it must have fallen strangely into oblivion, for this is the only notice of it that occurs until quite a late period of literature, though some of the observations on the wonders of the open ocean that were made in the course of it are shewn to have obtained a wide circulation from the mention of them in various writers. Possibly this forgetfulness may have been due to the greater fame of the subsequent voyage of Pytheas in the same direction, which eclipsed the achievements of the earlier navigator. As it is, the only information which we possess concerning it The 'Ora Maritima' of Avienus. is derived from Avienus, a Latin author of the fourth century of our era, who in his geographical poem entitled *Ora Maritima* bases a number of his statements and descriptions on the narrative of Himilco, whom he mentions by name. This narrative, we may reasonably suppose, was

---

[1] *v. supra*, p. 95.

[2] *H. N.*, 2. 169; Et Hanno Carthaginis potentia florente circumvectus a Gadibus ad finem Arabiae navigationem eam prodidit scripto, sicut ad extera Europae noscenda missus eodem tempore Himilco.

originally inscribed on a tablet in the same way as that of Hanno;
but in what form, or through what medium, it reached Avienus
we have no means of knowing. The *Ora Maritima* is a work of
little merit and highly uncritical; and the passages for which
Himilco is referred to as the authority are so confusedly introduced that it seems impossible to form a clear idea of the course
which he followed, so that it is better to treat what they narrate
as a number of separate episodes[1]. He seems to have sailed
along the coast of Spain from Gades onwards, and
to have reached a group of islands called the
Oestrymnides, and a cape of the same name, which

Account of
the Oestrym-
nides.

in a former chapter[2] we have identified with the extremity of the
Armorican peninsula and the islands in its neighbourhood. The
inhabitants of these islands he speaks of as hardy navigators, who
were accustomed to cross the sea in boats like coracles, covered
with hides[3]; and he implies that they visited Ireland and the
intermediate island of Albion[4]. The last point is confirmed by
Caesar, who remarks in his account of Armorica that in consequence of this they had complete command of the traffic in those
parts[5]. Himilco adds, that both the Carthaginians and the in-

---

[1] The *Ora Maritima* will be found in vol. v. of Wernsdorf's *Poetae Latini
Minores*: the passages from it which bear on Himilco's voyage are given in
Elton's *Origins of English History*, pp. 418—420; also in vol. I. of
Müllenhoff's *Deutsche Altertumskunde*.

[2] *v. supra*, p. 36.

[3] *Ora Marit.*, ll. 103—7:

> Non hi carinas quippe pinu texere
> Acereve norunt, non abiete, ut usus est,
> Curvant faselos; sed rei ad miraculum
> Navigia junctis semper aptant pellibus
> Corioque vastum saepe percurrunt salum.

[4] *Ibid.* 108—12:

> Ast hinc duobus in Sacram, sic insulam
> Dixere prisci, solibus cursus rati est.
> Haec inter undas multa caespitem jacet,
> Eamque late gens Hiernorum colit.
> Propinqua rursus insula Albionum patet.

[5] *B. G.*, 3. 8, quoted on p. 36.

habitants of Gades used to make voyages thither—no doubt in connexion with the tin trade[1].

After visiting these northern regions it would seem that the explorers sailed, or were driven by stress of weather, far out into the Atlantic, for in the second passage *Of the Mid-Atlantic.* of Avienus in which Himilco is quoted[2] we hear of a wide expanse of sea in the distant West, unvisited before by any mariner, where dead calms and dense fogs prevailed. The mention which occurs in various Greek writers of features like these, which could not have fallen within the experience of ordinary voyagers, must almost certainly have been derived from the Carthaginian narrative[3]. Finally, a third passage, which is the most remarkable of all, and with which a part of the first passage must be associated, describes that astonishing phenomenon, which is well known to navigators of the Atlantic, *Of the Sargasso Sea.* the Sargasso Sea. The following is Humboldt's account of it. "At the point where the Gulf Stream is deflected from the banks of Newfoundland towards the east, it sends off branches to the south near the Azores. This is the situation of the Sargasso Sea, or that great bank of weeds, which so vividly

---

[1] *Ora Marit.*, 113—19:

> Tartesiisque in terminos Oestrymnidum
> Negotiandi mos erat ; Carthaginis
> Etiam coloni et vulgus inter Herculis
> Agitans columnas haec adibant aequora,
> Quae Himilco Poenus mensibus vix quattuor,
> Ut ipse semet rem probasse retulit
> Enavigantem, posse transmitti adserit.

[2] *Ibid.* ll. 380—89 :

> Porro in occiduam plagam
> Ab his columnis gurgitem esse interminum,
> Late patere pelagus, extendi salum,
> Himilco tradit : nullus haec adiit freta;
> Nullus carinas aequor illud intulit,
> Desint quod alto flabra propellentia,
> Nullusque puppim spiritus caeli juvet :
> Dehinc quod aethram quodam amictu vestiat
> Caligo, semper nebula condat gurgitem,
> Et crassiore nubilum perstet die.

[3] See the reff. in Berger, *Geschichte der Erdkunde*, II. p. 58.

occupied the imagination of Christopher Columbus, and which
Oviedo calls the sea-weed meadows (*Praderias de yerva*). A host
of small marine animals inhabits these gently moved and ever-
green masses of *Fucus natans*, one of the most generally dis-
tributed of the social plants of the sea[1]." It is this prodigious
mass of tangle which is described in the poem—for nothing else
can be meant—when we are told, that in the midst of the currents
an abundance of sea-weed is found, which checks the vessel's
course as if it were brushwood ; that there was no depth of water,
and as the ships crept through it with difficulty, they were surrounded by sea-monsters[2]. "These things Himilco the Carthaginian stated that he saw with his own eyes, and had experience
of on the surface of the ocean[3]."

A similar account of this phenomenon—which, if it is not
derived, as it well may be, from Himilco, at least confirms his
statements—is given in the pseudo-Aristotelian treatise *On
Wonders*. It runs thus :—"They say that the Phoenicians of
Gades, sailing before an east wind for four days from the Pillars
of Hercules, reach a desolate spot, full of tangle and sea-weed,
which floats with the ebb, and sinks with the flow of the tide, and
on it is found an immense multitude of tunnies, incredibly large
and fat[4]."

The enterprise which next claims our attention, the Retreat of
the Ten Thousand, though the preciseness of the
record in which it is related communicates to it in
the reading something of a matter-of-fact character,

The Retreat
of the Ten
Thousand.

---

[1] Humboldt's *Cosmos* (Otté's Trans.), I. p. 313.

[2] *Ora Marit.*, ll. 122—9 :

> Adjicit et illud, plurimum inter gurgites
> Exstare fucum, et saepe virgulti vice
> Retinere puppim: dicit hic nihilominus
> Non in profundum terga demitti maris,
> Parvoque aquarum vix supertexi solum:
> Obire semper huc et huc ponti feras,
> Navigia lenta et languide repentia
> Internatare belluas.

Compare also ll. 408—11.

[3] *Ora Marit.*, ll. 412, 413.

[4] *De Mirabilibus Auscultationibus*, § 136 (ed. Apelt).

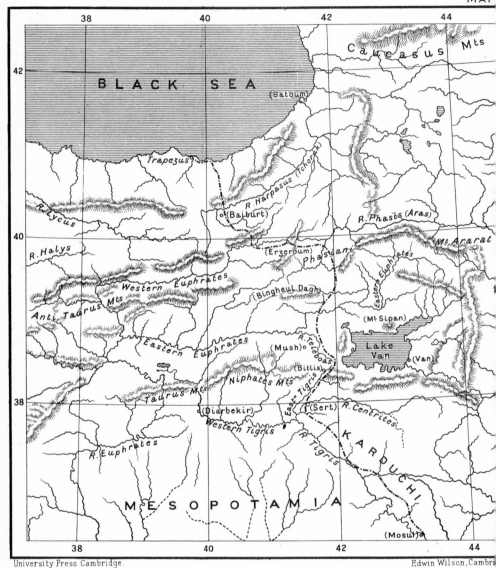

University Press Cambridge.
Edwin Wilson, Cambri

XENOPHON'S ROUTE ACROSS ARMENIA

must yet, on account of the strange vicissitudes to which those engaged in it were exposed, and the heroism which they displayed, be ever reckoned among the first of "moving accidents by flood and field." In the history of geography it forms an important episode, because it added considerably to the knowledge of that subject which the Greeks already possessed, especially as regards Armenia, a region at all times difficult to traverse and but little explored. It is to the portion of their journey which lay through that country that our attention shall here be confined. It should be borne in mind, however, that though Xenophon, the historian of the expedition, noticed, as far as the circumstances permitted, with the eye of an intelligent campaigner the characteristics of the regions through which he passed, and the mode of life of their inhabitants, yet his primary object in writing was not geography but history, and consequently we cannot be surprised, if points about which we desiderate information are left unnoticed. To this we may add that, in order to arrive at any conclusion concerning his route and the places which he mentions, it is necessary in this part of his narrative to ignore almost entirely the distances which he gives, whether computed by measurements or by day's marches— a circumstance which, perhaps, will hardly excite surprise if we take into account the difficulty of the ground, the inclemency of the weather, and the opposition on the part of the natives which was from time to time encountered. Fortunately for us, the features of the region which he and his companions traversed are so peculiar, and the circumstances of their journey, taken in connexion with the goal for which they were making, determine so well their natural line of march, that we may speak with some confidence of the route which they actually pursued. In order to make this more clear, it may be well, before entering into details, to describe briefly the geography of Armenia.

Character of Xenophon's 'Anabasis.'

That country has been called, in consequence of its elevation and of the streams that descend from it in several directions, the roof of Western Asia. It occupies a great part of the triangle which lies between three seas—the Mediterranean, the Euxine, and the Caspian. It also forms a link to join the great plateaux of Central Asia with the

Geographi- cal Features of Armenia.

uplands of Anatolia. Its height above the sea is very great, reaching 6,000 feet in the plains which intervene between Erzeroum and Ararat in the northern part of the district, and consequently the climate during many months of the year is very severe. It is bounded and intersected by vast ranges of mountains, the most important of which are the Taurus towards the south, dividing it from Mesopotamia, and the Anti-Taurus towards the west; besides these, it attains a great altitude in the volcanic summits of Bingheul-dagh—the 'mountain of a thousand lakes,' *i.e.* fountains—in the centre of the country, of Sipan above the lake of Van, and of Ararat in the east, which rises to a height of more than 17,000 feet. From its northern side the Araxes (Aras), which rises in the Bingheul-dagh, finds its way to the Caspian, and the Acampsis to the Euxine, while in the opposite direction the Euphrates and the Tigris carry their waters to the Persian Gulf. Both the last-named rivers rise from two sources in distant parts of the country, and flow for a considerable distance in separate streams. The western branch of the Euphrates, which retains the ancient name in that of Frat, starts from the plains near Erzeroum, and divides Greater from Lesser Armenia; the Eastern, or Murad-su, flows from the neighbourhood of Ararat, and after passing between the Bingheul-dagh and Sipan, and skirting the northern foot of the Taurus range, joins its brother stream before descending to the lowlands of Mesopotamia. It is in this range, and therefore in the south of Armenia, that the sources of both branches of the Tigris lie, though they are distant as much as a hundred miles one from another. The easternmost of these, which is the more important for our present purpose, is situated in the midst of those lofty summits of Taurus which bore the name of Niphates, near where the town of Bitlis now stands; the river which it forms descends steeply towards the lower country, where it is joined by the western stream. To the eastward of Bitlis, but on the high plateau, lies the Lake of Van, an expanse of brackish water larger than the Lake of Geneva, deeply sunk among the mountains, and without an outlet.

We may now return to the Ten Thousand, whose march, it

will be seen, undertaken as it was in mid-winter through the
country which has just been described, was a task of
appalling difficulty.   After the battle of Cunaxa on
the banks of the Euphrates in 401 B.C., in which the
younger Cyrus was defeated and slain, the Greeks who had accompanied that prince as part of his army from Asia Minor by way of
the Cilician Gates and Mesopotamia, found themselves in a position of great difficulty, since they were in the midst of an enemy's
land at a great distance from their native country, and feared to
return by the route which they had previously taken on account
of the desert which had to be crossed, and their inability to defend
themselves against the Persian cavalry in the plains.   Accordingly,
having obtained from the Persian king, Artaxerxes, a promise of
safe conduct on condition of their quitting the country, they
crossed the Tigris, and marched upward along its left bank, until
they reached the stream of the Zabatus (Greater
Zab), which flowed from the Median mountains.
Here Clearchus and the other generals were treach-
erously seized at an interview by Tissaphernes, the Persian commander, who was professing to escort them, so that the Greeks
were left without a leader.   It was at this crisis that Xenophon
who up to that time had accompanied the army as a volunteer,
offered to undertake the perilous task of leading them back to
Greece, and was accepted as their general.   They now crossed
the Zabatus, and continuing to advance along the Tigris, though
harassed by the Persians, they passed the neighbourhood of
Nineveh, and thus reached the mountain region
inhabited by the Carduchi, the ancestors of the
modern Kurds.   These were a warlike race, and as
the passes which led through their country were of the most rugged
description, and were vigorously defended, the Greeks found in
them a more serious foe than the Persians had previously been.
At length however they struggled through this difficult region, and
crossed the Centrites, on the farther side of which
Armenia commenced.   This river, which is now
called the River of Sert from the name of the chief
town on its banks, is a tributary of the eastern Tigris, which it
joins between the head-waters of that stream near Bitlis and its

The March from Cunaxa to Armenia.

The Zabatus (Greater Zab).

Land of the Carduchi (Kurdistan).

The Centrites (River of Sert).

union with its western branch. From this point the route by which they reached the high plateau of Armenia is clearly determined by the nature of the ground. Xenophon informs us that they passed the source of the Tigris, and beyond that came to a river of no great size, called the Teleboas, after which they forded the Euphrates, which was reported to rise not very far off[1]. Now the pass which crosses the Taurus range immediately above Bitlis bifurcates at the point where the source of the Tigris lies, one branch leading eastwards to the Lake of Van, which is only a few miles distant, though out of sight, the other westwards to the plain of Mush; and as no mention is made of the lake, it is clear that the latter route is the one that they followed. The Teleboas of Xenophon must be the Kara-su, which rises almost at the same spot as the Tigris, and runs in the opposite direction to it, until it reaches the Murad-su, or Eastern Euphrates, in the further part of the plain of Mush[2].

Source of the Tigris.

The Teleboas (Kara-su).

Eastern Euphrates (Murad-su).

The Greek force had now arrived at the upland levels of this bleak country—the plain of Mush is between four and five thousand feet above the sea—and at once discovered the severity of an Armenian winter. The historian describes the sufferings of his soldiers as they plodded through the deep snow, some of whom lost their eyesight, others their toes, while a certain number died from exhaustion. He also dwells with satisfaction on the shelter afforded by the dwellings of the inhabitants—which, like those of the same region at the present day, were half underground, and contained the cattle as well as human beings—and on the plentiful provision of food, and especially of beer, which they contained[3]. The next feature of the country which is mentioned after the Euphrates is the river Phasis, in the neighbourhood of which they met with a tribe called Phasiani[4]. Now as the plain in which the Araxes

Highlands of Armenia.

Underground Dwellings.

The Phasis Aras).

[1] *Anab.*, 4. 4. 3 ; 4. 5. 2.
[2] See the Author's *Turkish Armenia*, pp. 292, 299.
[3] *Anab.*, 4. 5. 25—27; *Turkish Armenia*, p. 287.
[4] 4. 6. 4, 5.

(Aras) flows bears the name of Pasin at the present day, there is a presumption in favour of identifying that stream in this part of its course with the Phasis of Xenophon, especially as it lies to the northwestward of the valley of the Euphrates, and that would be the direction which the Greeks would naturally follow in endeavouring to reach their home.   The argument last advanced applies also to the next stage of their course, for the configuration of the ground in this part of the country is such, that the only practicable route towards the west lies through a valley, which leads by an easy pass to the plain of Erzeroum.   There they would find the head-waters of the western Euphrates (Frat); and as it would have defeated their object to follow that stream, they would be almost forced to make their way over the mountains to the northwest, which intervene between this region and the Euxine.   After this, the two principal points which are mentioned in their route are a large river called Harpasus, and an important town named Gymnias[1]. The former of these is   The Harpasus (Tchoruk). probably to be identified with the Tchoruk—usually called the Acampsis by ancient writers—which flows from these parts, and reaches the sea near Batoum.   The posi-   Gymnias. tion of the latter may have been at no great distance from the modern town of Baiburt, which is situated on the banks of that stream.   The ranges which intervene between that place and the sea are so steep and so intricate, that they may almost as well be crossed at one point as at another; so that it is probable that the Greeks followed as nearly as might be a direct course, and at last descended by a river valley which   Trapezus (Trebizond). reaches the coast some way to the east of their destination, Trebizond[2].

The famous first view of the sea, which aroused the enthusiasm of the weary soldiers, was, even independently of the circumstances under which it was seen, a sight to awaken   The first View of the Sea. thrilling feelings of delight. Though we cannot speak with confidence of the exact spot where the scene which Xenophon describes occurred, yet for a considerable distance along the mountain ridges in this part the impression would

[1] 4. 7. 18, 19.
[2] *Turkish Armenia*, pp. 406, 432.

be the same.   Here from a height of between 7,000 and 8,000 feet
above the sea, the eye which has been accustomed to the treeless
uplands and monotonous plains of Armenia looks down upon
forest-clad mountains and delicately cut ridges, separated from
one another by ravines, and gradually descending towards Trebizond; while, away to the north-east, cape after cape is seen
extending into the Euxine, backed by ranges which run up to the
snow-topped mountains of Lazistan, and the whole is completed
and harmonized by the soft blue expanse of water.   The entire
view, from its delicacy and multiplicity of form, and its combination of sea and mountains, strikingly resembles the coasts of
Greece.   When suddenly presented to the eye of a Greek, it must
have spoken to him of home in every line.   Another point in
Xenophon's narrative on which modern observation
The Poison-   has thrown light, is his account of the poisonous
ous Honey.
                 honey of this region, after partaking of which his
soldiers displayed all the symptoms of intoxication and frenzy[1].
This is now known to have been due to the moisture that distils
from the flowers of the *Azalea pontica*, which grows in profusion
in the valleys at the back of Trebizond; this is poisonous, and
affects the honey of the bees that feed upon it.   A similar circumstance is related by Strabo with regard to Pompey's forces during
his campaign in these parts; only in that case the honey seems to
have been obtained immediately from the trees[2].

Before concluding this chapter, it may be well to notice a
treatise belonging to the period before Alexander,
The 'Periplus'   which, though not actually a record of any expedi-
of Scylax.
                 tion, yet contains a summary of information which
must have been obtained in the first instance by means of numerous coasting voyages.   This is the work which is known as the
Periplus of Scylax of Caryanda, but which is of much later date
than the reign of Darius, in which that explorer was supposed to
have lived, and appears to have had his name attached to it in

---

[1] *Anab.*, 4. 8. 20.

[2] Strabo, 12. 3. 18; οἱ δὲ Ἑπτακωμῆται τρεῖς Πομπηίου σπείρας κατέκοψαν
διεξιούσας τὴν ὀρεινήν, κεράσαντες κρατῆρας ἐν ταῖς ὁδοῖς τοῦ μαινομένου μέλιτος,
ὃ φέρουσιν οἱ ἀκρεμόνες τῶν δένδρων· πιοῦσι γὰρ καὶ παρακόψασιν ἐπιθέμενοι
ῥᾳδίως διεχειρίσαντο τοὺς ἀνθρώπους.

order to attract attention by its celebrity. The date of its composition can be determined within narrow limits by
internal evidence, for it mentions the foundation   Its probable
Date.
of the Athenian colony at Neapolis on the Thracian
coast, which took place in 360 B.C., and, on the other hand, it
speaks of Olynthus, which was destroyed in 347 B.C., as still existing; whence we may infer that it was written in the interval
between those two events[1]. This coasting survey
starts from Gades and the Pillars of Hercules, and   Its Contents.
follows the sinuosities of the coast all round the Mediterranean,
the Euxine, and the other seas connected with them, commencing
with the northern shores, and returning by the way of Asia Minor,
Syria and Northern Africa; it continues also beyond the Pillars of
Hercules along the African coast as far as the island of Cerne.
The work is composed in the main of notices of the islands,
harbours and rivers, and of the towns and tribes which border on
the sea; the distances also from point to point are carefully given.
Here and there further information is added, but such remarks
are of somewhat rare occurrence. It is well, how-   Doubts as to
ever, at once to intimate that serious doubts have   its Genuineness.
been raised as to the genuineness of the greater part
of this narrative. Several of the most eminent authorities on the
subject, including Carl Müller and Berger, are of opinion that,
though the original *Periplus* was composed about the time already
mentioned, yet this was epitomised about the third or fourth
century of our era, and what we now possess is this epitome, after
it had been further altered and interpolated at a subsequent
period[2]. This view is chiefly based on the corrupt and mutilated
condition in which the work has come down to us, and on the
style of the Greek in which it is written, which is certainly later
than the time of Philip of Macedon. From the last point we
may at least infer that, if the *Periplus* is genuine, it must have
been recast by a later hand. Still, these difficulties have not
prevented other good judges, like Kiepert and Bunbury, from
accepting it in substance as a work of the earlier period[3]; and it

---

[1] Bunbury, *Hist. of Anc. Geography,* I. pp. 404, 405.

[2] Müller, *op. cit.,* Prolegg., p. xlix; Berger, *op. cit.,* 2. p. 79.

[3] Kiepert, *Lehrbuch d. a. Geographie,* p. 3; Bunbury, *op. cit.,* I. pp. 405, 406.

is certainly in favour of this conclusion, that it contains no reference to Alexandria, or any of the other great cities which afterwards arose, for these would undoubtedly have been introduced by one who was writing for a subsequent generation. If the former of the suppositions here mentioned is correct, it would seem to be almost a hopeless task to endeavour to distinguish those parts of the work, as we possess it, which are original and genuine. On the other hand, if the earlier date is the true one, its contents are of great value, because of the general view that they present to us of the Greek world at that time.

The most interesting notices which this *Periplus* contains are
those which relate to the Italian peninsula. Here
Interesting Notices in it. for the first time in any extant author the name of
Rome occurs[1]; but it is introduced incidentally, and it is remarkable that, whereas the writer elsewhere pays especial attention to the rivers, in this connexion he makes no mention of the Tiber, nor does he notice any of the coast-towns between that point and Massilia. A much fuller enumeration, also, is found here of the tribes that inhabited Italy than in any previous writer, for the Latins, Volscians, Samnites, Umbrians and Celts are all named, and are assigned to their rightful localities. The mention of the Celts is especially remarkable, inasmuch as before this time no notice occurs in any writer of peoples of that race being found south of the Alps, for Hecataeus and Herodotus place them in the west of Europe. They are here spoken of as occupying a narrow tract of North Italy, and reaching to the Adriatic; and as having been "left behind from their expedition," by which is meant the invasion of Italy in the course of which they captured Rome[2] (390 B.C.). Scylax also is the first author in whom is found the confusing view, which afterwards obtained wide acceptance, that the Ister divided into two branches, one of which entered the sea at the head of the Adriatic, the

---

[1] Scylacis Caryandensis *Periplus*, § 5, in C. Müller's *Geogr. Gr. Minores*, vol. I.

[2] § 18. It is not intended by what is here said to exclude the view, which is maintained chiefly on archæological grounds, that the earlier inhabitants of the valley of the Po were of Celtic extraction. See Bertrand and Reinach, *Les Celtes dans les vallées du Pô et du Danube.*

other on the shores of the Euxine. The idea of an Adriatic
branch seems to have arisen from a confusion between the name
of the river and that of the tribe of Istri at the head of that sea,
whom in fact Scylax mentions in this connexion[1]. Again, on the
opposite side of the Mediterranean, the coast which lies between
Cyrene and Carthage—including the two Syrtes, the land of the
Lotophagi, and the lake Tritonis—is described with unusual
fulness and much interesting detail[2]. And generally, a comparison of the contents of this work with the notices of the same
coasts which are found in Herodotus suggests the conclusion,
that a great advance had been made in the knowledge of them
during the intervening period of less than a century.

[1] § 20; Μετὰ δὲ 'Ενέτους εἰσὶν "Ιστροι ἔθνος, καὶ ποταμὸς "Ιστρος. Οὗτος ὁ
ποταμὸς καὶ εἰς τὸν Πόντον ἐκβάλλει.
[2] §§ 108—110.

CHAPTER VII.

ALEXANDER'S EASTERN EXPEDITION.

Effects of Alexander's Conquests—His Political and Social Aims—Development of Geography—Novel Aspects of Nature—Narratives of the Expedition—The Expedition originated by Philip—His Death, 336 B.C.—The Project renewed by Alexander—Battle of the Granicus, 334 B.C.—Battle of Issus, 333 B.C.—Siege of Tyre, 332 B.C.—Occupation of Egypt—Visit to the Temple of Zeus Ammon—March to the Tigris, 331 B.C.—Battle of Arbela—March to Persepolis—Depôt at Ecbatana (Hamadan) 330 B.C.—Description of Iran or Ariana—Flight of Darius into Parthia—The Caspian Gates (Sirdar Pass)—Death of Darius—Hecatompylus in Parthia—The Hyrcani and Mardi—The Caspian Sea—Artacoana (Herat)—Drangiana (Seistan)—Arachosia (Candahar)—Paropamisus Range (Hindu Kush)—Alexandria ad Caucasum—Invasion of Bactria, 329 B.C.—The Oxus (Jihoun)—Its Ancient Course—Maracanda (Samarcand)—The Polytimetus (Zerafshan)—Alexandria Eschate—Mistakes concerning the Jaxartes and the Caspian—March to the Indus, 327 B.C.—Campaign in the Punjab, 326 B.C.—The Hydaspes (Jhelum)—The Hyphasis (Bias)—Descent of the Indus—Pattala (Hyderabad) 325 B.C.—Bore of the Indus—Indian Trees—Return March of Craterus through Drangiana, of Alexander through Gedrosia—Arrival at Persepolis—Embassies from the West—Death of Alexander, 323 B.C.—The Voyage of Nearchus—Alexandri Portus (Karachi)—Harmozia (Ormuz)—Pearl Fishery—Encounter with Whales—Arrival at Susa.

THE conquest of Western Asia by Alexander the Great is the highest military achievement which the world has seen. The extraordinary gifts of the commander by whom it was accomplished—his personal prowess, which impelled him whenever occasion offered to encourage his soldiers by his own heroic daring; his unrivalled genius, both in organising strategical combinations on a grand scale, and in disposing his troops and handling them in the field; and his unfailing foresight in providing for contingencies, and arranging beforehand the conditions which might secure the success of his undertakings—caused him to appear to his contemporaries a superhuman being, and still excite our wondering

Effects of Alexander's Conquests.

admiration. The overthrow of the great Persian empire, and the downfall of its monarchy, which had come to be regarded as an embodiment of earthly grandeur, startled mankind from end to end of the then known world. Within the short period of twelve years an area of country as large as Europe had been sub-jugated, and its regulation, at least in embryo, provided for. Nor were the political results of these campaigns of less importance than their success from a military point of view. Though the early death of the great con- His Political and Social Aims. queror prevents us from speaking with the confidence which we could wish of the scheme that was in his mind for reorganising the world, yet the system which he had already introduced had so far taken root that, notwithstanding the dismemberment of his empire after his death, it was generally carried out by his suc-cessors. This consisted in the establishment of Greek colonies with political rights throughout the countries which he subdued, and the introduction through them of Greek ideas and Greek civilization among the native populations. Unlike the majority of conquerors, whose object has been to maintain their power by placing one race in subjection to another, Alexander evinced the greatest consideration for the customs, whether political or religious, of those who passed under his sway, while at the same time he endeavoured to develop a new form of unity by fusing them with the Greeks. Owing to the extent to which this scheme was prosecuted by the monarchs who succeeded him, these influences became the leading factor in determining the condition of Western Asia, and subsequently, by the power which they exercised over society, modified the harshness of the Roman dominion; indeed, their effect continued to be felt until a new order of things was inaugurated by the rise of Mahomet and the conquests of the Arabs.

In the field of geography a similar extraordinary expansion was produced by Alexander's expedition. It is not too much to say, that by means of it the knowledge of that subject on the part of the Greeks was Develop-ment of Geo-graphy. doubled. The country that lay between the Tigris and the Hyphasis (Bias), and between the Jaxartes (Sir Daria) and the Indian Ocean, was traversed in several directions by a Greek army, and the southern shores of the Caspian, and the northern shores of the Persian Gulf, were explored. But the revelation of this vast area was not, perhaps, in itself the most important result that accrued to geographical study from these campaigns. An even greater stimulus was communicated to it by the novel and striking natural features with which the Greeks now became acquainted.

Novel Aspects of Nature. In the course of their marches they passed over desert plains and salt-steppes alternating with luxuriantly fertile districts, and through snowy mountain-chains exceeding in elevation anything that they had hitherto conceived, among which the Hindu Kush reaches the height of 18,000 feet. The variety of configuration of the ground which was thus presented to them, together with the differences of climate and the unwonted size and strange appearance of the vegetation, suggested innumerable points of comparison and contrast with the objects that they were familiar with in Europe. All these characteristics were carefully recorded by accurate observers, for Alexander on this occasion had associated with him so large a number of men of great attainments, that his enterprise might claim the character of a scientific expedition.

Narratives of the Expedition. Unfortunately not one of the narratives of these campaigns, which were composed by Aristobulus, Onesicritus and others of his companions, has come down to us, and we are compelled to trust for our knowledge of them to histories written under the Roman empire—especially to those of Arrian in Greek and Curtius in Latin. By these, however, we are to some extent indemnified for the loss of the original authorities, because the facts which they contain are largely drawn from their writings.

The Expedition originated by Philip. The expedition which Alexander so successfully executed was not in reality originated by him. It was designed in the first instance by his father, Philip of Macedon, after he had broken the power of the independent states of Greece, as a means of facilitating and consolidating his hegemony, by uniting the Greeks in the common object of assailing the traditional enemy of their country, the king of Persia. He was making preparations for this invasion, and a part of the requisite forces had been assembled, when the project was

suddenly arrested by his assassination in 336 B.C. His successor,
Alexander, who was at that time twenty years of age,
was as yet but little known, though the part which   His Death,
336 B.C.
he played in the battle of Chaeroneia had proved
that he was a dashing soldier; but in the course of the two years
that followed he gave ample evidence both of his capacity and of
his overpowering force of character, by subjugating the wild tribes
in the neighbourhood of Macedonia, and by crushing with merci-
less determination the attempts of the Greek cities to regain their
independence. He was thus in a position in the   The Project
spring of 334 B.C. to renew the project which had   renewed by
been interrupted by the death of Philip; and to the   Alexander.
execution of this he brought, not only a military ability superior
even to that of his predecessor, but an intellect imbued with an
eager love of knowledge and scientific enquiry through the influence of his instructor Aristotle.

The Persian king Darius, meanwhile, had made no preparations for resisting the threatened attack, and the invader was
allowed to transport his army across the Hellespont unopposed.
The circumstances of the commencement of the campaign were
of a nature to awaken all the enthusiasm of an ardent temperament such as that of Alexander. Steeped as his mind had been
from early days in veneration for the Homeric poems, so that his
great desire was to rival, or rather to identify himself with, the
heroes of that tale, he now found himself on the Plain of Troy, in
the presence of the inspiring memories of the conflicts of the
Greeks and Trojans, and he proceeded to commemorate the
occasion by sacrificing to Athena at Ilium, and celebrating rites at
the tomb of Achilles. It was in this spirit that he shortly afterwards encountered the army which the Persian   Battle of the
satraps of Asia Minor had brought up to oppose   Granicus,
334 B.C.
him on the banks of the Granicus; on which
occasion he led his cavalry in person across that stream in the
face of the enemy, thus deciding the fortune of the day, though
his life was exposed to imminent peril. By means of this victory,
especially in consequence of the death of the leading commanders
on the Persian side on that occasion, Alexander found the whole
of Asia Minor open to him. It was only at certain points that

resistance was offered. On the western coast, first Miletus and afterwards Halicarnassus—which were defended by Memnon, the leader of the Greek mercenaries in the service of Darius, and by a Phoenician fleet that had arrived off the coast—delayed him for some time; but Ephesus and the other chief towns in that neighbourhood submitted, and during the following winter Alexander with a picked body of troops made his way through the southern districts—Caria, Lycia and Pamphylia—receiving the submission of the inhabitants, and finally over the Taurus range in Pisidia to the uplands of Phrygia. During this part of his progress occurred the famous passage of Mount Climax on the Lycian coast, when he conducted a detachment of his troops between the precipices and the sea, though the water at the time had risen so high as to reach their waists.

In Phrygia at the commencement of the spring of 333 Alexander was met by the main body of his army, which had wintered at Ephesus and was led thither by his general Parmenio. The next part of his route lay through Cappadocia and the Cilician Gates, by which pass the Taurus was crossed into Cilicia. So difficult is this line of transit, by which at the present day the exports of south-eastern Asia Minor are still conveyed to the sea, that it might easily be held against a hostile force by a small body of resolute defenders; but the satrap of Cilicia, whose duty it was to secure it, abandoned it without a blow, so that the Macedonian army descended without difficulty to Tarsus. From that place Alexander advanced to the head of the Gulf of Issus, for which neighbourhood Darius also was making with an enormous host which he had summoned from all parts of his dominions. The battle of

Battle of Issus, 333 B.C. Issus, the second of the three great engagements which determined the fate of the Persian empire, was fought in the narrow space which here intervenes between the Mons Amanus and the sea—a position which was selected by Darius, but was altogether favourable to the Macedonians, because it rendered it impossible for their opponents to deploy their vast multitudes. The issue of the conflict was greatly determined by the cowardice of Darius, for when he perceived that the Macedonian lancers, led by Alexander, had broken through his left wing, and were approaching the centre where he himself was stationed, he took to flight, leaving no one in his place to issue any orders to his soldiers. From that time forward the Persian army was at the mercy of its adversaries.

The next event of importance in the campaign was the siege of Tyre. Alexander, with that circumspection which was not less characteristic of him than his promptitude in action, though his enemy was hopelessly defeated and the way to his capital lay open, determined to secure the countries in his rear before advancing into the heart of Asia. With this view he abstained from pursuing Darius, and turned southwards into Syria, and received the submission of most of the cities both of that country and of the coastland of Phoenicia. But the insular position of Tyre, and the recollection of the famous sieges which she had undergone at the hands of the Siege of Tyre, 332 B.C.

Assyrians under Shalmanezer and the Babylonians under Nebuchadnezzar, disposed her citizens for resistance; and this did not at first appear a hopeless attempt on their part, because Alexander had no fleet at his command. He was not, however, to be foiled in this manner, for he proceeded at once to construct a mole from the mainland to the nearest part of the island-city, and, notwithstanding the determined opposition of the inhabitants, in the course of seven months Tyre was joined to the continent, as it has continued to be down to the present day. But the circumstance which assured Alexander's final success was his obtaining possession of the fleets of the Phoenician and Cypriote cities, for by means of these he was able to assail the place from various sides. It was by the help of ships that the first breach was made in the walls on the southern side facing Egypt, and from this point Alexander in person stormed the city, which was taken in spite of a desperate defence. After the capture of Tyre the conqueror met with no further opposition except at Gaza, which place resisted him for three months. He then marched by way of Pelusium to Memphis, and received a ready welcome from the native population of that city, who had never been content with the Persian rule. In the Egyptian capital he reposed for some time, and then descended the westernmost branch of the Nile to Canopus, where

Occupation of Egypt.

he embarked on shipboard, and sailed along the coast as far as
the lake Mareotis, and the island of Pharos, which had associations for him owing to its being mentioned by Homer. His visit
to this neighbourhood produced results of far-reaching importance.
Alexander was struck with the suitableness of the site for a great
commercial centre, and he forthwith gave orders for the foundation of the city of Alexandria.

There now remained no obstacle to prevent the Macedonian
monarch from carrying out his original design of
subduing Asia. But before turning his face once
more eastward he was inspired with a longing to
visit the shrine of Zeus Ammon in the Libyan desert, and there
to obtain a recognition of the divine parentage which he had now
begun to claim for himself. The route by which he arrived at
that place was not the one which led westward from Memphis,
but that by way of the lake Mareotis along the coast of the
Mediterranean as far as the station of Paraetonium, from which
point the Ammonium was reached by a journey of eight days
due southwards across the desert. The difficulties which were
encountered in the course of this march have no doubt been
exaggerated by Alexander's historians; at the same time it was
a considerable feat, requiring much care and precaution, to
conduct a military force along so remote and desolate a track.
The appearance of the oasis in which the temple lay, with its
palm-groves and fountains, its deposits of salt, and the sandy
waste which surrounded it, is well described by Arrian[1]. The
response of the oracle declared that the god recognised Alexander
as his son, and promised him an unbroken career of victory.

Visit to the Temple of Zeus Ammon.

In the spring of 331 B.C. Alexander quitted Egypt, and led
his army through Phoenicia and across the northern
angle of the Arabian desert to Thapsacus, which
was at this time the usual station for the crossing of
the Euphrates. Here during the summer season which had now
been reached the stream was generally fordable, but in order
to facilitate the passage of the forces two bridges had been
previously thrown across by their leader's orders. His way now
lay through the northern part of Mesopotamia, and when he

March to the Tigris, 331 B.C.

[1] *Anab.* 3. 4.

approached the upper course of the Tigris he kept that river on
his left hand until he arrived at a point some little distance above
Nineveh, where he crossed it also. In the plains to the southward
of this, which intervene between the Tigris and the greater Zab—
or Lycus, as it is called by the historians of the expedition—
Alexander found the army of Darius drawn up to oppose him,
for that monarch had learnt from his experience at
Issus not to waste the advantage to be derived　　Battle of
　　　　　　　　　　　　　　　　　　　　　　　　Arbela.
from his vast host by confining it within a narrow
space. The place was called Gaugamela, but the battle which
ensued has received its name from the more important city of
Arbela, which lay about thirty miles off towards the east. On
this occasion, even more than in the last conflict, Alexander
relied on the dependence of an oriental army on the personal
superintendence of its sovereign to counterbalance his own immense inferiority in numbers. After strengthening his wings in
such a manner as to lessen the unavoidable risk of being out-
flanked, he pressed forward with the main body of his troops
towards the enemy's centre, and notwithstanding a vigorous
resistance on the part of the picked forces of the Persians, he
succeeded in approaching near enough to the station occupied by
the king to frighten that imbecile monarch, who fled, and by so
doing paralysed the courageous efforts of his soldiers, who were
dispersed and massacred. After this great battle Darius became
a fugitive, and the fate of the Persian monarchy was decided. At
this point also Alexander's campaigns enter on a new phase, and
one that is more intimately connected with the history of geography. The countries through which we have hitherto followed
his victorious arms were not unknown to the Greeks; but from
this time onward his progress assumed the character of an exploring expedition, and by its means new and strange lands were
revealed to the western world.

The first object of Alexander now was to make himself master
of the great cities, in which the immense treasures of the Persian
empire were stored. So powerful was the impression made by
his victory, that the two famous capitals of Babylon
and Susa at once opened their gates to him. From　　March to
　　　　　　　　　　　　　　　　　　　　　　　　Persepolis.
the latter of these places he continued his march

to Persepolis, which lies due east of the head of the Persian Gulf. In order to reach that city, it was necessary for him to traverse the mountains of Persis, the only transit through which was by a difficult pass called the Pylae Persicae or Susianae: this was occupied in force by Ariobarzanes, the satrap of the province, but by means of skilful movements Alexander succeeded in dislodging his opponents, and thus entered Persepolis, where he obtained possession of the accumulated wealth of the monarchs of that country. As it was now midwinter, he rested his army there, but early in the spring he advanced northwards through Media to Ecbatana, the capital of that district, in pursuit of Darius, the possession of whose person appeared to him to be of primary importance for the accomplishment of his purpose in securing his dominion in Western Asia. After he had occupied that city, he established there his base of operations with a view to future campaigns, and made it his principal depôt. At this point, in order to understand more clearly what follows, it may be well for us to pause a moment, and take a rapid survey of the country which we are about to enter.

Depot at Ecbatana (Hamadan) 330 B.C.

The mountains in the midst of which Ecbatana lies are part of the chain of Zagrus, which, starting from Mt. Ararat, and forming the eastern boundary of the Tigris valley, passes through Media and Persis, until it approaches the Persian Gulf. To the eastward of this chain extends an elevated table-land, on an average 4,000 feet above the sea, which occupies the centre of modern Persia, and extends in part into Afghanistan, the remainder of which country is a rugged region, forming a barrier between Persia and the valley of the Indus. This vast area, which is known as the plateau of Iran or Ariana, is for the most part a desert steppe, which is characterised by the number of rivers which lose themselves on its surface without finding their way to the sea. This feature is especially conspicuous in the neighbourhood of Lake Seistan, on the borders of Persia and Afghanistan, towards which the waters flow, both from the neighbourhood of Herat to the north, and from that of Cabul to the north-east. On the southern side this plain is separated from the Indian Ocean by the moun-

Description of Iran or Ariana.

tains of Carmania and Gedrosia, which form a continuation of
those of Persis; while in the opposite direction, between it and
the Caspian Sea, the massive chain of Elburz intervenes, which
towards its centre attains the elevation of more than 18,000 feet
in Mt. Demavend. The eastern portion of this range was known
in antiquity as the Hyrcanian mountains, and the country immediately to the south of them, though we hear but little of it at
the time of which we are now speaking, is one which rose to great
importance under the Roman empire—the land of Parthia. It
will be seen, from the position of the great desert steppe which
has been described, that the route through these regions, whether
for the passage of armies or for caravan traffic, must always in the
main have been the same.

Darius had cherished the hope that Alexander had attained
the object of his invasion by capturing the chief   Flight of
cities of Persia and the treasure which they con-   Darius into
   Parthia.
tained, and would leave him in possession of the
remainder of his dominions; and under this impression he passed
the winter of 331 at Ecbatana. But when he found that the
conqueror was still pursuing him, he quitted that place shortly
before Alexander's arrival, and fled into Parthia by way of the
Caspian Gates. That pass did not lead, as its   The Caspian
name would seem to suggest, through the Elburz   Gates (Sirdar
   Pass).
mountains to the Caspian Sea, but traversed a
lateral range, which quits the main chain to the southward of
Mt. Demavend, and runs at right angles to it. It is now known
as the Sirdar pass, and is crossed by the road which connects
Teheran and Herat. As soon as Alexander had arranged matters
at Ecbatana, he started with a small body of troops in the hope of
overtaking the fugitive, but notwithstanding that he pressed on
by forced marches, he had hardly entered Parthia
when he received the news of the death of that   Death of
   Darius.
monarch. This was the result of a conspiracy
formed against him by Bessus, the satrap of Bactria, and other
leading Persians, who felt that their cause was hopeless so long
as the supreme power remained in the hands of one so pusillani-
mous as Darius, and hoped that, when he was removed, they
might organise resistance in the outlying provinces. Alexander's

disappointment at this event was extreme, because it involved the prolongation of the war and greatly increased his difficulties;

Hecatom-
pylus in
Parthia. at the same time he had no choice but to wait at Hecatompylus, the chief city of Parthia, until he was joined by the remainder of the army. Meanwhile Bessus had escaped over the mountains into Bactria, and into that country it was necessary that Alexander should pursue him; but with the provident vigilance which he displayed in all his campaigns, that commander determined first to secure the districts which he would have in his rear, when he advanced in that direction. Owing to this, and to the treachery of the Persians who submitted to him, he spent the remainder of this year in a desultory warfare, which led him by a devious route into regions about which at all times but little information has been obtainable.

His first expedition was through the mountains at the foot of which Hecatompylus was situated, with the view of subjugating the Hyrcani and other races who occupied the country to the southward of the Caspian Sea. The people from whom he experienced the most vigorous resistance were the Mardi, a tribe who inhabited a region difficult of access on account of its ruggedness and intricacy. The description which Curtius has given of this as a mountain district clothed with dense forests[1] closely corresponds with what we know at the present day of the ground which intervenes between Mt. Elburz and the Caspian. It was at this time that the Greeks obtained a view of that sea, and, if we may believe Plutarch, Alexander's first impression on seeing this expanse of water was that it was an outflow from the Palus Maeotis[2]. The ignorance of the geography of these parts which this betrays may appear strange, but is hardly more so than other mistakes which will presently be noticed. Returning from this expedition, Alexander now marched eastwards through the north of Parthia, and

[1] Curt., *Hist. Alex.*, 6. 5. 13.

[2] Plut., *Alex.*, 44; πελάγους ἰδὼν κόλπον οὐκ ἐλάττονα μὲν τοῦ Πόντου φανέντα, γλυκύτερον δὲ τῆς ἄλλης θαλάττης, σαφὲς μὲν οὐδὲν εἶχε πυθέσθαι περὶ αὐτοῦ, μάλιστα δὲ εἴκασε τῆς Μαιώτιδος λίμνης ἀνακοπὴν εἶναι.

would have entered Bactria, but was diverted by the rebellion of
Satibarzanes, the satrap of Aria, who had shortly before submitted
to him.   He accordingly changed his course, and rapidly advancing towards the south, surprised him in his
capital city of Artacoana, which was situated on   Artacoana
(Herat).
or near the site of the modern Herat, the frontier
city of Afghanistan on the side towards Persia.   Having thus
diverged from his original design, he seized the opportunity of
subduing the province of Drangiana, now the dis-
trict of Seistan, which lies still further to the south   Drangiana
(Seistan).
about the lake of the same name.   We have al-
ready seen that from the neighbourhood of Herat the streams run
in that direction, and it was probably the valley of the Harud, the
largest of these streams, which skirts the edge of the great steppe,
that the Macedonians followed.   The year was far advanced
before these regions had been conquered, but Alexander still
pressed on, following the course of the Etymander (Helmund)
and its tributaries, which flow from the north-east
through Arachosia (Candahar) towards the same   Arachosia
(Candahar).
lake.   This route, though it lay through a rugged
mountainous district, was from the nature of the ground the only
practicable exit open to him, unless he retraced his steps; it is
the same which at the present day forms the line of communication by way of Ghuzni between Candahar and Cabul.   During the
latter part of the way the army suffered greatly from the cold and
the deep snow, for the pass between Ghuzni and Cabul reaches
the height of 8,700 feet.   In traversing it they had crossed the
watershed of these parts, for on the farther side of it the streams
begin to flow towards the Indus.   At the head of the Cabul
valley he at last halted at the foot of the great   Paropamisus
Range (Hindu
Hindu Kush range—the Paropamisus, or, as the   Kush).
Greeks of this time called it, Caucasus—which is
here interposed between Afghanistan and the regions to the north
of it.   Thus in the course of this campaign he had obtained
command of all the passes that lead into Bactria,
and of the lands through which they are approached.   Alexandria
ad Caucasum.
At this point he founded the city of Alexandria ad
Caucasum.

In the following spring (329 B.C.), as soon as the season was

Invasion of
Bactria,
329 B.C. sufficiently far advanced, Alexander crossed the Paropamisus—an operation which occupied seventeen days—into Bactria, and at once marched to the capital of the province, Bactra (Balkh), which he occupied. The general features of that region are accurately described by Curtius, who speaks of it as in most parts a sandy desert, but interspersed with districts of great fertility[1]. They

The Oxus
(Jihoun). next reached the Oxus, with which river the Greeks now for the first time became acquainted, and it seems to have made a greater impression upon them than either the Tigris or the Euphrates[2]. This river—now the Jihoun or Amu Daria—which rises away to the east in a glacier among the mountains of the Pamir[3], at the present time finds its way, like

Its Ancient
Course. the Jaxartes, into the sea of Aral: by the ancients, however, who were unacquainted with the existence of that piece of water, they were both believed to reach the Caspian. In the case of the Oxus there is every reason to believe that such was the case in the time of Alexander; and this would account for the statement of Strabo and Pliny—quoting from independent sources—that a regular trade-route existed from India to Europe by way of this river and of the Caspian and Euxine Seas[4]. After crossing the Oxus, the conqueror

---

[1] Curt., 7. 4. 26—30.

[2] Arrian, 3. 29. 2 ; ὁ δὲ Ὦξος ῥέει μὲν ἐκ τοῦ ὄρους τοῦ Καυκάσου, ἔστι δὲ ποταμῶν μέγιστος τῶν ἐν τῇ Ἀσίᾳ, ὅσους γε δὴ καὶ Ἀλέξανδρος καὶ οἱ ξὺν Ἀλεξάνδρῳ ἐπῆλθον, πλὴν τῶν Ἰνδῶν ποταμῶν. Strabo, 11. 7. 3; Ἀριστόβουλος δὲ καὶ μέγιστον ἀποφαίνει τὸν Ὦξον τῶν ἑωραμένων ὑφ' ἑαυτοῦ κατὰ τὴν Ἀσίαν πλὴν τῶν Ἰνδικῶν. Mr Curzon (Russia in Central Asia, p. 145) compares the Oxus to the Nile. "I was strangely reminded by the appearance [i.e. the brown hue] of this great river, by the formation of its bed, by the structure of its banks, and by the scenery and life which they displayed, of many a landscape on the Nile in Upper Egypt. There is the same fringe of intensely fertile soil along its shores, with the same crouching clay-built villages, and even a Bokharan counterpart to the sakkiyeh and shadoof, for raising and distributing the life-giving waters of the stream."

[3] See Mr Curzon's paper, "The Pamirs and the Source of the Oxus" in the Geographical Journal for July, 1896, pp. 44 foll.

[4] Strabo, 11. 7. 3; φησὶ δὲ [Ἀριστόβουλος] καὶ εὔπλουν εἶναι (καὶ οὗτος καὶ Ἐρατοσθένης παρὰ Πατροκλέους λαβὼν) καὶ πολλὰ τῶν Ἰνδικῶν φορτίων κατάγειν

proceeded to Maracanda (Samarcand), but before he arrived at that place Bessus, whose capture was the primary object of his expedition, had fallen into his hands. Maracanda (Samarcand). The next stream which he met after leaving Maracanda, the Polytimetus, is represented by the historians of his campaigns as flowing for some distance through The Polytimetus (Zerafshan.) a country which it fertilises with its waters, and then disappearing into the sand[1]. This description, according to the testimony of modern travellers, exactly applies to the Kohik or Zerafshan, as that stream is now called[2]. It is interesting to notice that Arrian in estimating its size takes for his standard of comparison the Peneius in Greece. At last, after traversing Sogdiana, the Macedonians reached the limit of their journey, the Jaxartes (Sir Daria), and on its banks Alexander founded another city, which after- Alexandria Eschate. wards bore the name of Alexandria Eschate, as marking the furthest point of his advance into Central Asia. It has sometimes been identified with the modern Khojend. The idea which prevailed in the minds of the Greeks concerning this river was that it was the Tanais, and that they Mistakes concerning the Jaxartes had reached the boundary which separated Europe from Asia. Surprising as this may seem, it appears to have been a widely accepted belief at this time, for Aristotle in his *Meteorologica*, when speaking of the course of the Araxes (by which he means the Jaxartes), says that at one point

εἰς τὴν Ὑρκανίαν θάλατταν, ἐντεῦθεν δ' εἰς τὴν Ἀλβανίαν περαιοῦσθαι, καὶ διὰ τοῦ Κύρου καὶ τῶν ἑξῆς τόπων εἰς τὸν Εὔξεινον καταφέρεσθαι. Pliny, 6. 52; Adicit idem Pompei ductu exploratum in Bactros septem diebus ex India perveniri ad Iachrum flumen quod in Oxum influat, et ex eo per Caspium in Cyrum subvectos, et quinque non amplius dierum terreno itinere ad Phasim in Pontum Indicas posse devehi merces.

[1] Arrian, 4. 6. 5—7; Curt. 7. 10. 1, 2.

[2] Mr Curzon says (*Russia in Central Asia*, p. 205)—"The basin of the Zerafshan river......is a veritable garden of Eden, and incomparably the most fertile part of Central Asia." The final disappearance of the stream is noticed in a passage quoted by the same writer from a paper by V. Dingelstedt in the *Scottish Geographical Magazine* for December 1888:—"Some twenty miles before reaching the Amu Daria, the now nearly exhausted, but still muddy waters of the Zerafshan flow into the marshy lakes of Denghis, Sunghur, and Karanga, which have no outlet."

it bifurcated, and that one branch of its divided stream formed
the Tanais, which fell into the Palus Maeotis[1].   Arrian, indeed,
remarks that the Tanais which Alexander reached could not be
the same river as that which Herodotus designates by this
name[2]; but this is evidently an after-criticism on his part, and
represents the views of a later age.   In this connexion we may
notice another misconception, in respect of which
the geography of this period had retrograded from
that of Herodotus—viz. the opinion that the
Caspian was not an inland sea.   This, indeed, was not Aristotle's
view, for he expresses himself with as much confidence as Herodotus in favour of the isolated position of that piece of water[3];
but it was certainly that of Alexander and his companions, for we
are told that, when that commander once more reached Ecbatana
at the conclusion of his expedition, he was planning to despatch a
fleet to explore the shores of that sea, in order to discover whether
it communicated with the Euxine or with the outer ocean towards
the east[4].   This opinion was further confirmed by the authority
of Patrocles, an officer who held a command in that part of Asia
under the Seleucidae (circ. 280 B.C.), and wrote a work, in which
he maintained the possibility of sailing round from the Indian
Ocean into the Caspian.   In fact, it was not until the time of
Ptolemy that the true view was restored.

and the Caspian. (margin note)

Though Alexander had thus traversed without serious difficulty
the low-lying regions of Bactria and Sogdiana, yet the mountainous
parts of those provinces were so difficult of access, and the hardy
tribes who inhabited them offered so stubborn a resistance to his
arms, that the whole of another year was occupied in subduing
them.   Into the details of this campaign, even if the places which
are mentioned in the course of it could be identified with any
certainty, there is no need for us to enter.   The spring of

---

[1] Arist. *Meteorol.* 1. 13. 15, 16.

[2] Arrian, 3. 30. 7—9.

[3] Arist. *Meteorol.*, 2. 1. 10; ἔτι δ' ἐπεὶ πλείους εἰσὶ θάλατται πρὸς ἀλλήλας
οὐ συμμιγνύουσαι κατ' οὐθένα τόπον, ὧν ἡ μὲν Ἐρυθρὰ φαίνεται κατὰ μικρὸν κοι-
νωνοῦσα πρὸς τὴν ἔξω στηλῶν θάλατταν, ἡ δ' Ὑρκανία καὶ Κασπία κεχωρισμέναι
τε ταύτης καὶ περιοικούμεναι κύκλῳ.

[4] Arrian, 7. 16. 1, 2.

327 B.C. was already far advanced, before he was at liberty to cross once more the Hindu Kush and commence his projected invasion of India. After halting for some time on the farther side of that range at Alexandria ad Caucasum, he marched onwards to the banks of the Cophen or River of Cabul. There he divided his army into two portions, one of which he sent forward under the command of Hephaestion and Perdiccas along the course of that river in the direction of the Indus—a route which at one point would conduct them through the famous Khyber pass. They thus reached the district called Peucelaotis, which lay near the confluence of those two streams, and proceeded to construct a bridge across the Indus, to be in readiness for the arrival of their leader. As the position of the bridge was at a little distance below the confluence, it would seem to have been close to the modern Atak, where the narrowness of the stream has in all ages provided a convenient passage. Alexander himself with the remainder of the forces undertook the more arduous task of reducing to submission the tribes which occupied the mountains from which flow the northern tributaries of the River of Cabul—the districts of Kafiristan and Chitral. The former of these is a country of such repellent wildness that there is no record of any modern explorer having entered it, until it was visited by Mr (now Sir G. S.) Robertson in 1889[1]; the latter, Chitral, which has become famous since that time in connexion with his name and the campaign of 1895, lies to the north-east of it, and is hardly less rugged. It was in this part that the famous siege and capture of the rock fortress of Aornos took place—one of the most difficult exploits of these campaigns. At last he rejoined on the banks of the Indus the forces that had preceded him, and reposed his weary troops for thirty days, in preparation for the operations of the ensuing year.

March to the Indus, 327 B.C.

Advancing from the Indus, Alexander now entered the Punjab or 'Land of the Five Rivers,' as the country is called that is traversed by the great tributaries of the Indus, which rise in the Himalaya and flow in a south-westerly direction to join it—the Hydaspes (Jhelum), the

Campaign in the Punjab, 326 B.C.

[1] See his account in the *Geographical Journal* for 1894, vol. 4, pp. 193 foll.

Acesines (Chinab), the Hydraotes (Ravi), the Hyphasis (Bias), and the Zaradrus (Sutlej). The names of these, like those of many other rivers which we have already noticed, owing to the Greek form in which they appear, produce the impression that they were at least greatly adapted by the Greeks; but it is an interesting fact, as proving the accuracy of the companions of Alexander, from whose writings the later historians obtained their information, that, with the exception of the Acesines, they correspond to those which are found in the Sanscrit writers[1]. In the

The Hydaspes (Jhelum).

neighbourhood of the Hydaspes—probably near the modern city of Jelalpur—the famous battle was fought in which the Macedonian monarch defeated the powerful Indian prince Porus; and here, on either side of its stream, he founded the two cities of Bucephala and Nicaea, the former in commemoration of his favourite horse Bucephalus, who died at this time, and the latter to celebrate his victory. He now crossed successively the two next rivers, and advanced to the

The Hyphasis (Bias).

banks of the Hyphasis; but the Sutlej he did not reach, for at this point took place the mutiny among his soldiers, who refused to proceed further towards the east, and in consequence of this he was forced to return. Disappointed in this manner of the conquest of the

Descent of the Indus.

remainder of India, he determined to visit the Erythraean sea, and with that object in view, when he arrived at his newly established cities on the Hydaspes, he gave orders for the construction of a fleet, in which he might descend that river and the Indus. On the completion of this, Alexander embarked with part of his forces, while the remainder accompanied him in two divisions which marched on either bank; and since during their passage a continual warfare was carried on against the neighbouring tribes, as much as nine months were occupied in the transit. At last they reached the head of the

Pattala (Hyderabad) 325 B.C.

Delta of the Indus at Pattala, where a naval and military depôt was established. This place is to be identified with Hyderabad, at which city a branch of the river diverges on its eastern side, which, though now it is dry except at the season of inundation, may well have been an

---

[1] See Bunbury, *Hist. of Anc. Geogr.*, I. pp. 501, 502.

important arm in former times, for in this part the course of the
Indus has been subject to many changes.   At the present day the
principal bifurcation of the stream is at Tatta, fifty miles lower
down than Hyderabad, but Tatta is too near the sea to correspond
to the position which is given by the historians of the expedition.
Alexander himself descended to the Indian Ocean, and enjoyed
the satisfaction of sailing on its waters.   On this occasion we are
told that his soldiers were affected with great terror at the unwonted sight of the tide[1].   The terms which Arrian
here uses, however, leave no doubt that what is   Bore of the Indus.
meant is not the ordinary ebb and flow of the tide,
but the bore or inrush of the flood tide, which is a remarkable
phenomenon at the mouth of the Indus, and other great
Indian rivers.   This at times rises to the height of many feet,
and produces a violent noise, when it meets the current of
the descending stream.   Their curiosity also was   Indian Trees.
excited by the unwonted vegetation of India, of
which the historians have left descriptions—especially the honey-
bearing tree (*Borassus flabelliformis*), the banyan-tree (*Ficus indica*),
with its strange mode of growth, and the cotton-tree (*Bombax
malabaricum*) with its seed-vessels bearing tree-wool[2].   The following is the account which is given of the banyan-tree:

"Onesicritus tells of certain large trees, the branches of which,
when they have grown to the height of twelve cubits, subsequently
grow downward, as if they were bent down, until they touch the
earth; after which they spread underground and take root like
layers, and then spring up and grow into a stem: after that again,
according as they grow, they are bent down, and form first one
and then another layer, and so on continuously, so that from one
tree proceeds a long sunshade, resembling a tent supported by
many poles.   He speaks also of trees which are of such a size
that five men can with difficulty clasp their trunks."

Alexander was now making preparations for his return journey.
He had already despatched a large part of his army   Return
under the command of Craterus from the point   March of
Craterus
where the Indus receives the combined waters of   through
the Punjab rivers; this detachment was to march   Drangiana,

---

[1] Arrian, 6. 19. 1, 2.   [2] Strabo, 15. 1. 21.

into Carmania by the northern route, which would lead through the difficult ravine now known as the Bolan pass into Arachosia and Drangiana, after which it would be forced to cross the desert—a journey which must have presented great difficulties, though the historians are silent concerning it.   Another portion of the troops was embarked on board the fleet, which was sent under the command of Nearchus to navigate the ocean from the mouth of the Indus to the head of the Persian Gulf—a voyage of dis-

of Alexander through Gedrosia.

covery which Alexander had much at heart.   The remainder of the army he led in person by an unexplored route from Pattala westwards through Gedrosia and Carmania, keeping at no great distance—sixty or seventy miles on the average—from the sea, his object in this being, apparently, that he might be within reach of Nearchus, so as to lend him succour in case of need.   The province of Mekran in Beluchistan, as Gedrosia is now called, forms the southern boundary of the plain of Iran, separating it from the Indian Ocean by a mountain chain; and at the present day its upland plains are known to suffer from excessive heat during the summer, and from scarcity of water, which is due to the stony and sandy nature of the soil.   It was the month of August when the march commenced, and consequently the army was exposed to the full force of these evils.   The privations of the soldiers on the way were extreme; many both of them and of the beasts of burden perished, and it was with difficulty that the diminished number was brought through.   When at last Alexander reached Carmania, he was joined by Craterus and his contingent, and during his halt in that country he was also gratified by receiving a visit from Nearchus, who in the meanwhile had arrived at the entrance of the Persian Gulf, and took the opportunity of communicating with him and reporting progress.   Nearchus, after having being highly commended and honoured, was sent back to conduct the fleet as far as the mouth

Arrival at Persepolis.

of the Euphrates, and the king continued his journey to Persepolis, at which place he arrived when the winter season had already set in.   At this point the eastern expedition, as far as it affected the discovery and conquest of new countries, may be said to have been concluded, and the year and a half which intervened between this date and the death

of Alexander at Babylon in June 323 B.C. are not of great importance from a geographical point of view.　During this time he once
more visited Susa and Ecbatana, and it was on the occasion of
his progress from the last-named city to Babylon that
he was met by embassies, which had been sent by　　Embassies
from the West.
the inhabitants of distant countries to congratulate
and to propitiate him.　No stronger proof can be found of the
extent to which the fame of his conquests was diffused than the
names which here occur; for among them we find not only the
Carthaginians and some of the tribes of Italy, but the Aethiopians
on the further side of Egypt, the Iberians and Gauls in the far
West, and the Scythians in the north of Europe[1].　The next enterprise on which his mind was set was the circumnavigation and
subjection of Arabia, and with a view to this he had already
ordered a number of ships to be constructed in Phoenicia, and,
after being transported in pieces overland to the Euphrates, to be
sent down the stream of that river to Babylon.　But this plan,
and others which he may have been designing,　　Death of
Alexander,
came to an end with the master-mind which con-　323 B.C.
ceived them, and the partition of his dominions
which followed turned men's thoughts in other directions.

It remains to speak of the voyage of Nearchus, which was not
the least arduous enterprise connected with Alexander's expedition.　The original account of this,　　The Voyage
of Nearchus.
composed by Nearchus himself, has been lost, like
the other narratives of these campaigns, but in this instance there
is the less reason to regret it, because the summary of its contents
which Arrian has given in his *Indica* is complete and full.　The
accuracy of the writer's observation and the faithfulness of his
statements have been thoroughly proved by a comparison of them
with what is known at the present day of the coasts along which
he sailed, and the places at which he touched can in a large
number of instances be identified.　As the names of these, whether
ancient or modern, would in most instances be unknown to
ordinary readers, it may suffice for our present purpose to mention
a few of the most conspicuous.　Shortly after the fleet had made its
exit from the mouth of the Indus, it was forced to seek for shelter

---

[1] Arrian, 7. 15. 4.

from the violence of the south-west monsoon which was then

Alexandri Portus (Karachi). blowing; and this was found in a harbour to which Nearchus gave the name of the Port of Alexander. This is now Karachi, the westernmost seaport of British India. After the wind had abated, they continued their course along the country of the Ichthyophagi, who occupied the narrow tract which is interposed between the mountains of Gedrosia and the sea. Owing to the barrenness of this district, its inhabitants, whose mode of life is very carefully described, were forced to subsist almost entirely, both themselves and their cattle, on fish, which they sometimes pounded into the form of meal, and used for making bread[1]. The same thing is true of the modern occupants of this region, and also of those who dwell in the corresponding territory of the Hadramaut on the southern coast of Arabia. At the entrance of the Persian Gulf Nearchus noted the lofty promontory of Maceta, now Cape Mussendum, which rises from the Arabian shore, while opposite to it, in Carmania, lay a fertile region called Harmozia, where

Harmozia (Ormuz). the crews were allowed to repose awhile after the hardships which they had undergone[2]. The name here given attained great celebrity during the middle ages, when Ormuz became a famous trading station, first of the Arabs, and afterwards of the Portuguese; but at that time it was attached, not to the district on the mainland, but to a small barren island in its neighbourhood, called by Nearchus Organa, on which the city was built. At the present day Ormuz is an insignificant place, but its former greatness is familiar to us from the mention of it in *Paradise Lost*, where Milton speaks of "the wealth of Ormus and of Ind." It was here that Nearchus' sailors found a Greek who had wandered from Alexander's army, which he reported to be at no great distance, and in consequence of this Nearchus visited his commander, as has been already mentioned. Two additional points may be noticed in connexion with this

Pearl Fishery. voyage, as confirming the truthfulness of the narrative. One of these is the mention of a pearl fishery as being carried on in an island in the Persian Gulf, which sea is

---

[1] Arrian, *Ind.*, 29.   [2] *Ibid.* 33—37.

now celebrated for the export of those gems[1]. The other is the account of their meeting with a shoal of whales in the Indian Ocean—an occurrence which sometimes Encounter with Whales. overtakes vessels in those waters in our own days. The story of the encounter of the Greeks with these animals, and their frightening them away by plashing their oars and raising a loud din with trumpets and shouting, is highly amusing and curious :—

"Nearchus relates that, when they were on their voyage from Cyiza, towards daybreak they saw water spouted up from the sea, as if it were violently carried aloft by whirlwinds; and that the men being terrified enquired of their captains what this was, and what caused it. They replied that these were whales, which spouted up the water as they traversed the sea; whereupon the sailors were seized with panic and dropped the oars from their hands. So he went up to them himself, and cheered and inspirited them, and as he passed any of them in his vessel he bade them draw up their ships in line as if for an engagement, and row forward in close array and with much noise, accompanying with loud shouts the plashing of their oars. At this they took heart, and advanced all together at a given signal; and when they came near the monsters of the deep they shouted with all their might, and blew their trumpets, and made all possible noise with their oars; on hearing which the whales, which now were seen in close proximity to the ships' bows, took fright and plunged into the depths, but not long after came to the surface again close to the sterns of the vessels, and once more spouted great jets of sea water. Then the sailors shouted aloud at their happy and un-looked-for escape, and extolled the courage and good judgement of Nearchus[2]."

At last Nearchus reached the head of the Persian Gulf, and entering the stream of the Pasitigris, which joins the Tigris near its entrance into the sea, met the army of Alexander shortly before it arrived at Susa. The entire voyage Arrival at Susa. had occupied a period of five months.

---

[1] *Ibid.* 38.　　　　　　　　　　　[2] *Ibid.* 30.

CHAPTER VIII.

GEOGRAPHY UNDER THE SUCCESSORS OF ALEXANDER.
THE VOYAGE OF PYTHEAS.

Intellectual Influence of this Period—Egypt under the Ptolemies--Position of
Alexandria—Canal from the Red Sea to the Nile—Stations on the Red
Sea—The Cinnamon Country (Somaliland)—The Upper Nile—Mega-
sthenes in India, *circ.* 290 B.C.—Envoy to Chandragupta at Pataliputra—
His Work—Verified from Native Sources—His Knowledge of India—
Its Boundaries—The Indus and Ganges—The Royal Road—The Rainy
Season—Administration of the Country—The Caste-system—Life of the
Indians—The Brahmans—The Voyage of Pytheas, *circ.* 330 B.C.—Varying
Estimates of him—His Work—Twofold Object of his Voyage—His
Scientific Attainments—His Route to Britain—The Armorican Promon-
tory (Brittany)—The British Tin Mines—Island of Ictis (St Michael's
Mount)—His Account of Britain—Customs of the Inhabitants—Evidence
in Favour of his Northern Voyage—Did Pytheas enter the Baltic?—The
Northern Sea—Thule (probably Mainland in the Shetlands)—The Arctic
Circle—"Sleeping place of the Sun"—Pytheas' Parallels of Latitude—
Wonders of the Arctic Regions—Comparison to the Pulmo Marinus—The
Amber Coast—Testimony of Pliny and Diodorus—The Word 'glaesum.'

THE kingdom which Alexander left behind included territories

**Intellectual
Influence of
this Period.**
in all the three continents, and within a short period
after his death, during which a succession of struggles
took place for the partition of his dominions, we
find Hellenic culture disseminating itself in all of them. The
spirit of enquiry, in particular, which was characteristic of the
Greeks, spread rapidly and widely, and found an ample field on
which to exercise itself in making new observations and discoveries. This result was promoted by the extended facilities of
communication, which arose from the concentration of the government in the hands of powerful rulers at definite points, and the
breaking down of the barriers of nationality and prejudice which
previously existed. At the same time the vast amount of wealth
that was thrown into circulation by the dispersal of the treasures of
the kings of Persia, furnished the means by which encouragement

might be afforded by munificent patrons, such as the Ptolemies and the Seleucidae, to men of learning, who were thus enabled to reduce to order the materials which rapidly poured in from various quarters, and to make them subservient to the purposes of science. From this point of view the moment was an auspicious one, because the methods of investigation which had recently been introduced by the philosophy of Aristotle were at hand to prevent the waste of labour which would have arisen from ill-directed speculation. But, while the spirit of research was abroad throughout the whole of this wide area, it was in Egypt that it found its most congenial home. The isolated position of that country, arising from the narrow isthmus through which alone it can be approached by land on its eastern side, caused it to be difficult to attack, and thus exempted it from the confusions which arose in the other parts of Alexander's empire owing to the contentions of rival sovereigns. The politic spirit of its rulers, who were indisposed for aggression, and anxious for the peaceful development of the land which had fallen to their lot, tended in the same direction. The three first of these, Ptolemy Soter, Ptolemy Philadelphus, and Ptolemy Euergetes, whose combined reigns extended over a century (323—222 B.C.), were also distinguished promoters of literature, and to them were due the foundation and endowment of the Alexandrian Museum and its famous library. That great institution, which became the most eminent university, or resort of learned men, that existed in antiquity, was of especial importance for geography, because it was the residence of Eratosthenes and others who were the foremost representatives of that study. The influence of those writers on scientific geography will be treated of in another chapter; for the present it may suffice to notice the additional information about countries hitherto imperfectly known which was obtained through the medium of Egypt under its early Greek rulers.

Egypt under the Ptolemies.

The newly established city of Alexandria contributed largely to the promotion of these discoveries. When its great founder selected this site for a metropolis of trade and communication, he perceived that it occupied the most central position that could be found in the

Position of Alexandria.

ancient world in respect of the three continents; and at the same
time its nearness to the isthmus of Suez opened out a wide
prospect of increased traffic by sea, whenever the shores of the
Indian ocean, both on the side of Asia and of Africa, should
become accessible to commercial enterprise. It was built at the
extremity of the Delta, just beyond the westernmost, or Canopic
arm of the Nile, on a belt of sand which separated the lake
Mareotis from the Mediterranean; and it was protected from the
violence of the sea and the north wind by the long and narrow
island of Pharos, which extended in front of it at the distance of
about a mile. As a mercantile station it was greatly improved by
the construction of the mole or Heptastadion—so called from its
length of seven stades—which was carried across from the city to
the island and connected them together. By means of this the
harbour, which previously had been exposed to the full force of
the north-east and south-west winds, was converted into two well
sheltered and commodious ports. In the reign of Ptolemy
Philadelphus this rising emporium was brought into communi-

Canal from
the Red Sea
to the Nile.

cation with the Red Sea by a canal joining the
head of the gulf of Suez with the Nile, which had
been commenced by Necho, and completed by
Darius Hystaspis, but had fallen into decay, and was now repaired
and made serviceable. The great importance of the Red Sea was
now perceived, both for purposes of commerce and of discovery.
In order still further to facilitate communication with it, and also
to avoid the dangerous navigation of the narrow gulf at its head,

Stations on
the Red Sea.

stations were established and harbours formed
considerably lower down, at Myos Hormos and
Berenice, from which merchandise was carried across
the desert to the city of Coptos, which was situated on the banks
of the Nile somewhat below Thebes. After this it was discovered
that elephants, the importance of which in warfare was beginning
to be recognised, were bred in great numbers on the banks of the
Astaboras (Atbara), the tributary of the Nile which joins that
river on its eastern side below Meroë; and as this district was
most easily reached from the Red Sea, the same king founded on
the adjoining coast, to the southward of the modern Suakin, the
town of Ptolemais Epitheras, with a view to the capture of those

animals, as its name implies.　Having advanced thus far, he at last determined to obtain the command of this sea in its whole extent, and before the end of his reign—or at latest during that of his successor, Ptolemy Euergetes—several other settlements were planted in the neighbourhood of the straits of Bab-el-Mandeb, two of which were called Berenice and one Arsinoë. At this point the line of stations came to an end, but the Greek traders continued to advance as far as the easternmost point of Africa, Cape Guardafui, the territory in the neighbourhood of which, now Somaliland, was known as the Cin- *The Cinna-* namon country, on account of the abundance of *mon Country* that valuable spice that was found there.　Beyond *(Somaliland).* that promontory they did not venture, nor does it appear that their voyages extended far along the opposite coast of Asia.　No doubt at this period a large amount of Indian wares was imported into Egypt, but it is more probable that these were obtained by the Greeks through the ports of Southern Arabia than by any actual communication with India itself.　At the same time, whether directly or indirectly, much information was collected in this way about these and other distant countries through the commercial connexions of Alexandria.　The establishment of the Ptolemies in Egypt led also, as might be expected, to a more extended knowledge on the part of the Greeks of the upper course of the Nile.　They then became *The Upper* acquainted with the two great branches of that *Nile.* stream, which are now called the Blue and White Nile, and of their junction at the point occupied by the modern Khartoum ; and they learnt the existence of the Sembritae still further to the south, whom we have already identified with the Automoli of Herodotus[1].

While the Greeks were in this manner becoming more familiar with the lands in the neighbourhood of Egypt, a *Megasthenes* remarkable addition was made to their knowledge *in India, circ.* in Further Asia.　At the time of Alexander's inva- *290 B.C.* sion of India, there existed on the banks of the Ganges a powerful monarchy, that of the Prasians, which governed the whole of the area that was drained by that river as far as its mouth.

[1] *v. supra*, p. 93.

Not long after this period, however, a revolution took place, in which an adventurous native chieftain, called Chandragupta (in Greek Sandrocottus), expelled the reigning dynasty, and obtained possession of the throne; and under his energetic rule the resources of the kingdom were greatly increased, and its boundaries extended towards the west. In this manner it came in contact with the dominions of Seleucus Nicator, who after Alexander's death, having fixed his capital at Babylon, maintained his rule over the whole of the eastern provinces of the newly-formed empire, including Bactria and India. It was inevitable that war should break out between these rival powers, and the result was that Seleucus found it expedient to cede to his opponent the whole of the Indus valley, and the neighbouring territories as far as the Paropamisus range, receiving in return a present of five hundred elephants. A durable peace was thus concluded between them, and in order to maintain the friendly relations which were now set on foot, an ambassador was sent by Seleucus to reside at the court of Chandragupta, who had fixed his capital at Pataliputra (in Greek Palibothra) on the Ganges. The agent who was selected for this office was Megasthenes (*circ.* 290 B.C.), an intelligent Greek, who made the best use of the facilities which his position furnished for the study of the country and its inhabitants. So unique was the opportunity, that the work which he wrote on the subject became the chief, and in most respects the sole, authority on India to the ancient world. Though his narrative has now perished, the most valuable part of the material contained in it has survived, being preserved in the second book of Diodorus, the fifteenth book of Strabo, and the *Indica* of Arrian. From these sources we learn what knowledge was in circulation in antiquity, not only about the geography and climate of India, but about the administration of the government, the character and mode of life of the people, and the religious system and its observances. The profound study of the ancient literature of that country, which is one of the highest glories of the present century, has opened out to us a wide field of information on the same subject, derived from the contemporary records of the Indians themselves.

Envoy to Chandragupta at Pataliputra.

His Work.

Verified from Native Sources.

To compare the statements made in the two has been the work of modern scholars, especially of Lassen, who in his *Indische Alterthumskunde* has brought together almost every thing that can throw light on the investigation. It is satisfactory to find that the issue of the enquiry has been in most instances to corroborate, even in points of minute detail, the evidence of Megasthenes.

India, as understood by that writer, comprised the wide plains in the north of Hindustan and the territories adjoining them. Of the great peninsula of Southern India, and the plateau of the Deccan in its centre, His Knowledge of India. he had no knowledge. This is clear from his remark, that "the whole of India is intersected by rivers[1]." For him, the southern coast formed a continuous and almost straight line from the Persian gulf to its eastern extremity. Of Taprobane (Ceylon) he had heard, but merely as a large island lying at a distance of seven days' voyage from the coast, in which elephants were bred, and a great abundance of gold and pearls was found[2]. He rightly regarded the northern boundary of the country as being formed by the Himalaya, which Its Boundaries. range was known to him by distinct names in different parts—that towards the west being the Paropamisus, which, as we have seen, lay to the north of Afghanistan; that towards the east, where it was supposed to sink down into the sea, the Imaus; while the central chain, in which the Ganges rose, was called Emodus. In reality the two last of these, Imaus and Emodus, are only two forms of the same native name, Haimavata or Hemota, which signifies "snowy." The western limit was found in the Indus, while on the southern and eastern sides the ocean stretched, the angle between them being formed by a projecting promontory, which represented Cape Comorin. Megasthenes accurately conceived the Indus as flowing from north to south, and reaching the sea by two mouths which enclose The Indus and Ganges. its delta; the Ganges also he rightly regarded as following the same direction at first, and afterwards bending eastwards: but of the lower course of the latter river he was clearly ignorant, for he speaks of it as reaching the eastern sea, and as

[1] Strabo, 15. 1. 13.
[2] Strabo, 15. 1. 14; Pliny, 6. 81.

having only one mouth—a statement which is in strange contrast with the reality. Pataliputra or Palibothra, Chandragupta's capital city, is described as being situated at the junction of the Ganges and the Erannaboas—near the site of the modern Patna—and as forming a parallelogram 80 stades in length by 15 in breadth, surrounded by a palisade loopholed for shooting through[1]. The main road through the country—the Royal Road,

The Royal Road.

as it was called—connected the valleys of the Indus and the Ganges. Starting from the former of these rivers it crossed the Punjab, and passing the Hyphasis (Bias) and the Zaradrus or Hesydrus (Sutlej), reached the Jomanes (Jumna), and afterwards the Ganges in its upper course : then it continued to the junction of that river with the Jumna, where Allahabad now stands, and followed the course of the stream to Pataliputra, and ultimately to its mouth[2]. As regards the climate,

The Rainy Season.

Megasthenes notices the rainy season in summer, caused by the south-west monsoon—which he calls the Etesian winds—and the inundations which then took place. As the landmarks were destroyed by these, in like manner as they were in Egypt by the rising of the Nile, regular officials were appointed to determine the boundaries of properties; and they also regulated the storage of water for agricultural purposes in canals which admitted of being closed[3].

The description furnished by Megasthenes of the administra-

Administration of the Country.

tion of the country, numerous details of which are confirmed by the ancient Hindu codes of law, gives evidence of an elaborate organisation. The various functions which it involved were divided between three departments—(1) the superintendents of public works, (2) the superintendents of the city, (3) the superintendents of the war department. All these were minutely subdivided, so that the various classes of the population, both in town and country, and the trades and occupations which they exercised, were carefully inspected, the births and deaths registered, the taxes collected, and the public buildings and institutions maintained. We learn also,

[1] Strabo, 15. 1. 36; Arrian, 10.
[2] Pliny, 6. 63 ; cp. Strabo, 15. 1. 11.
[3] Strabo, 15. 1. 13, 50.

not only that a well equipped force was kept up in all branches of the military service, including chariots and elephants, but that a fleet was employed on the rivers for purposes of war[1]. The caste-system also, which at all times has formed so prominent a feature of Indian life, is described at some length; but the division of the castes, as reported by Megasthenes, differs in many points from what we know to have been the real classification.   Instead of the four castes which constituted the primitive system in India—viz. (1) the priests, (2) the warriors, (3) the husbandmen and artisans, and (4) the serfs—he mentions seven—viz. (1) philosophers, (2) husbandmen, (3) shepherds and hunters, (4) artisans and tradesmen, (5) warriors, (6) inspectors, and (7) counsellors.   The divergence is in some cases accounted for by his treating classes, which combined to form a single caste, as if they were separate castes. Thus the Brahmans were partly priestly (philosophers), and partly secular (counsellors); and the husbandmen and artisans were associated in the same caste.   The shepherds and hunters belonged to one of the impure or mixed castes, which were outside the regular caste-system.   The inspectors did not form a caste at all.   On the other hand, he does not include the serfs; but this is hardly surprising, owing to the low position which they held.   In fact, these mistakes generally are such as an uninitiated person might easily fall into.   As regards the rules of the system, by which the castes were strictly separated from one another, so that their members might neither intermarry, nor pass from one caste to another, nor adopt the occupation of another caste, Megasthenes' story is accurate[2].

The account of the life and character of the Indians which is given by the same authority is singularly pleasing; and though his description may be somewhat idealised, a similarly favourable impression of their society at that time is derived from the ancient literature.   He speaks of it as being characterised by simplicity and honesty, the exercise of which virtues he illustrates by various practices which

The Caste-system.

Life of the Indians.

---

[1] Strabo, 15. 1. 50—52.
[2] Strabo, 15. 1. 39—41, 46—49 ; Diodor., 2. 40, 41 ; Arrian, 11, 12.

were habitual amongst them[1]; and Lassen has remarked, when noting the striking contrast which these traits present to the morals of the Indians at the present day, that it was under their Mahometan rulers that that people lost the virtues of truthfulness and honesty[2]. The repulsive custom of *suttee* or widow-burning is not mentioned by Megasthenes, but it was reported by Alexander's companion Aristobulus, though he attributes it only to one particular tribe[3]. Megasthenes accurately describes the method of catching and taming elephants—which is still in use at the present day—by means of the keddah or stockade, into which a wild herd is driven, then starved into submission, and tamed by animals already domesticated[4]. Most interesting of all is his notice of the Brahmans, whose tenets he has faith-

The Brahmans.

fully detailed. He describes the four stages of their life, as it is known to have existed in ancient times: the first stage being that of the student; the second that of the householder; the third that of the forest-dweller or hermit, who retires after his sons are grown up to lead a contemplative life in the forest; the fourth that of the religious mendicant, who renounces intellectual as well as domestic interests in preparation for his final absorption into the deity, and wanders about living on alms. In one respect, however, his account varies from that just given, namely that he speaks of those who were passing through the two last of these stages, the forest-dwellers and the mendicants, as if they formed a separate order; but this was probably to a great extent the case when he visited the country, as it is with the *fakirs* at the present day, because in the course of time those who proceeded to the higher stages greatly diminished in number[5].

We must now turn our thoughts westwards, to consider a voyage which disclosed to the ancients a world of new ideas concerning the outlying parts of Europe. Hitherto the discoveries, the course of which we

The Voyage of Pytheas *circ.* 330 B.C.

---

[1] Strabo, 15. 1. 53.

[2] *Indische Alterthumskunde*, vol. 2, p. 723.

[3] Strabo, 15. 1. 62; of the tribe of Taxili Strabo reports—παρά τισι δ' ἀκούειν φησὶ ['Αριστόβουλος] καὶ συγκατακαιομένας τὰς γυναικας τοῖς ἀνδράσιν ἀσμένας, τὰς δὲ μὴ ὑπομενούσας ἀδοξεῖν.

[4] Strabo, 15. 1. 42; Arrian, 13.   [5] Strabo, 15. 1. 59, 60.

have followed, have lain chiefly in the lands to the east of the
Mediterranean ; and it is only natural that they should have been
the first investigated, because there civilisation and wealth existed,
and these were the inducements by which conquerors and traders
were attracted.   The articles of commerce which were brought
from the far West were few, and together with the knowledge
of the countries from which they came, were in the hands of the
Phoenicians, whose narrow policy prevented them from communicating to others the information which they obtained.   The
adventurer who first broke through this monopoly, and proclaimed
to the Greeks the wonders of the ocean and the strange sights of
Northern Europe, was Pytheas of Massilia, whose voyage into
those seas took place about the same time as Alexander's expedition into Asia.   His fame has experienced strange   Varying
vicissitudes of fortune, by reason of the evil report   Estimates of
and good report through which it has passed in   him.
ancient and modern times.   The marvels which he related were
such as not easily to obtain credence, and, in consequence of this,
first Polybius, and afterwards Strabo, made his name a byword
for circulating untrustworthy statements.   In our own days he has
received more honorable treatment; and, since that part of his story
which to his contemporaries appeared incredible has now been
found to correspond to the reality, he has come to be regarded as
one of those eminent men whose only fault has been that they
lived before their time.   The work in which the   His Work.
narrative of his voyage and the results of his explorations were embodied is no longer extant, and our acquaintance
with it is mainly derived from excerpts taken from it for contro-
versial purposes, which occur in the writings of his opponents.
In addition to these a number of scattered notices of his statements
are found in various ancient authors ; and these have been pieced
together through the diligence of modern scholars, so that we now
possess sufficient material from which to determine the countries
which he visited, if not the exact route which he followed.   By
means of them, also, we are able to trace to Pytheas as its source
a large amount of information about the north-west of Europe,
which was current in antiquity from his time onward, though the
authority for it was unknown.   The question of Pytheas' voyage

and of the phenomena which he described is one of too great intricacy to be fully discussed in a notice like the present. All that can be attempted is to put the reader in possession of the main points relating to it, and to state what seem to be the best ascertained conclusions[1].

The object with which Pytheas started on his voyage appears to have been twofold. The jealousy which was felt by the traders of Massilia towards the Phoenicians, on account of their great predominance in the commerce in tin and amber from the coasts of Britain and Germany, notwithstanding a certain amount of overland traffic through Gaul which already existed[2], probably impelled them to fit out a maritime expedition to explore those regions and extend their influence there ; and the command of this they entrusted to Pytheas. This view of the public character of the expedition is not, it is true, supported by any direct evidence ; and it may not be safe to attribute much weight, as an argument in its favour, to the statement of Pytheas' habitual detractor Polybius, that he was in poor circumstances, and therefore could not have undertaken it in a private capacity[3]. But, to say the least, it was most probable that such a voyage should have been made under government auspices ; and the motive for it was ready to hand, when we find that the people of Massilia knew that tin came from countries in the far north, for they would naturally desire to find the way thither themselves. For his own part, as an eager scientific enquirer, he seized the opportunity of visiting the lands and seas to the west of Europe, as being a field which might afford a rich harvest to the explorer. Of the attainments of Pytheas in science there can be no question. He was a good astronomer, according to the standard of his age, as was shewn by his determining by means of the gnomon the latitude

Twofold Object of his Voyage.

His Scientific Attainments.

---

[1] The chief authorities on Pytheas whom I have consulted are Müllenhoff, *Deutsche Altertumskunde*, vol. 1, Elton, *Origins of English History*, and Berger, *Geschichte der Erdkunde*, Pt. 3 : the passages in ancient writers which bear on the subject have been conveniently brought together by Mr. Elton in Appendix I. to his work, pp. 400 foll.

[2] *v. supra*, p. 32.

[3] Polyb. ap. Strabon. 2. 4. 2.

of Massilia[1], on which point it has been established by modern observations that his conclusion was almost exactly correct. Indeed, no stronger proof of his eminence in this direction is needed, than the confidence with which he was regarded by Hipparchus, the greatest master of that subject in antiquity, who adopted this as a well ascertained point with a view to comparing the latitude of other places[2]. He was also the first among the Greeks to note the influence of the moon on the tides, and the correspondence between the movements of the one and those of the other. No doubt, the Phoenicians of Gades, to whom the concurrence of these phenomena must have been a matter of constant observation, could not have failed to infer the connexion of the two, but Pytheas was at least the first to report it to his fellow-countrymen[3]. In the following pages we shall have occasion to notice other contributions of his to scientific and physical geography.

Setting out from Massilia, Pytheas and his companions passed the Straits and visited Gades, after which they continued their voyage round the Sacrum Promon- His Route to torium (Cape St Vincent) and Cape Finisterre, and Britain. then followed the northern coast of Spain and the western coast of Gaul as far as the Armorican promontory[4]. In the latter part of this route they became aware of the depth to which the Bay of Biscay recedes, and of the marked angle that is formed by the projection of Brittany—an observation which Strabo discredited in his distrust of Pytheas' veracity, and consequently fell into the error of making the coast of Gaul follow an almost straight line from the mouth of the Rhine to the Pyrenees[5]. The tribe who

[1] Strabo, 2. 5. 8, 41.

[2] See the reff. in Berger, *Die geogr. Fragmente des Hipparch*, p. 58.

[3] Plutarch, *De Placitis Philosophorum*, 3. 17; Πυθέας ὁ Μασσαλιώτης τῇ πληρώσει τῆς σελήνης τὰς πλημμύρας γίνεσθαι, τῇ δὲ μειώσει τὰς ἀμπώτιδας.

[4] Strabo, 3. 2. 11; τὸ τὰ προσαρκτικὰ μέρη τῆς Ἰβηρίας εὐπαροδώτερα εἶναι πρὸς τὴν Κελτικὴν ἢ κατὰ τὸν ὠκεανὸν πλέουσι, καὶ ὅσα δὴ ἄλλα εἴρηκε Πυθέᾳ πιστεύσας. This passage has been interpreted in various ways, but the right translation of it is this—"the statement [of Eratosthenes] that the northern regions (*i.e.* coasts) of Spain offer an easier route to Celtica than if men cross the open sea, &c."

[5] Strabo, 1. 4. 5; 4. 4. 1; 4. 5. 1.

inhabited this district of Armorica he calls the Ostimii, and these

The Armori-
can Promon-
tory(Brittany).

are evidently the same as the Osismii of Caesar and Strabo. He mentions also the headland of Cabaeon, and the island of Uxisama (Ushant) with the other islands in its neighbourhood ; and if, as seems probable, these are the same as the Oestrymnides which were visited by Himilco the Carthaginian[1], his interest in them and in the neighbouring mainland would be explained, as having arisen from the communication which existed between them and Britain in connexion with the tin trade.

The British
Tin Mines.

For the same reason it is natural to assign to this part of his voyage the visit which Pytheas paid to the mining districts in the west of Britain. His account of these, which is found in Diodorus, describes the natives—who owing to their intercourse with foreigners were more civilised than the rest of the Britons—as bringing the tin, after it

Island of Ictis
(St Michael's
Mount).

had been smelted, to an island off the neighbouring coast, called Ictis, which was their commercial station. This, we are told, was connected with the mainland by an isthmus, which, though at other times covered with water, was dry at low tide, and allowed of the freight being carried across in waggons. There can be little doubt that the place which is here meant is St Michael's Mount[2].

His Account
of Britain.

With Britain and its inhabitants Pytheas became familiarly acquainted. He describes it as an island of triangular form, and distinguishes the three angles by the names of the three promontories which formed them—viz. to the north Orcas, to the south-west Belerion, the Land's End, and to the south-east Cantion, the North Foreland, near which point, he remarks, is the outlet of the sea, *i.e.* the

---

[1] *v. supra*, p. 36.

[2] Diodor., 5. 22. The evidence that the information here furnished by Diodorus was ultimately derived from Pytheas is given by Müllenhoff, *op. cit.* I. p. 472. The intermediate authority from whom Diodorus obtained it seems to have been Timaeus the historian, who is quoted by Pliny, in a passage which is confused in its details, as the authority for tin being brought from the island of Mictis (=Ictis): Pliny, 4. 104; Timaeus historicus a Britannia introrsum sex dierum navigatione abesse dicit insulam Mictim in qua candidum plumbum proveniat : ad eam Britannos vitilibus navigiis corio circumsutis navigare.

Straits of Dover. He gives his measurements of the length of the three sides of the island, and though these are greatly in excess of the truth, yet he correctly represents the southern side as being considerably the shortest[1]. He further asserted that he had made journeys in the interior; this we know on the authority of his adversary Polybius, though he only mentions the statement to express his disbelief of it[2]. It is amply corroborated, however, by the details which he furnished as to the customs of the inhabitants, for these could only have been related by an eye-witness. We have already noticed *Customs of the Inhabitants.* his mention of the use of mead as the favourite beverage[3]; and he also describes how the corn was threshed in large barns, in which the ears were collected, it being impossible to do so in open threshing-floors, as in the south of Europe, on account of the rain and the absence of sun[4]. His remarks on the decrease in the cultivation of the soil in proportion as one advances further towards the north, point strongly in the same direction[5]. Indeed, when we take all these facts into account, and consider what they involve, it is difficult to resist the conclusion that Pytheas reached the northern-most point of Britain. We must remember that as *Evidence in Favour of his Northern Voyage.* he was the first explorer of these regions, he had absolutely no data on which to go in forming a conception of their characteristic features; and when we find that he is able accurately to describe the shape and position of that island, to assign a name to its extreme headland, to remark on the changes in its vegetation—and still more, as we shall presently see, to make observations about districts further to the north, and gather information about them, which would have been altogether unattainable in a lower latitude—we feel that his claim to have extended his voyage into these remote waters must fairly be conceded.

[1] Diodor., 5. 21.

[2] Polyb. ap. Strabon., 2. 4. 2 ; φησὶ δ' οὖν ὁ Πολύβιος ἄπιστον καὶ αὐτὸ τοῦτο, πῶς ἰδιώτῃ ἀνθρώπῳ καὶ πένητι τὰ τοσαῦτα διαστήματα πλωτὰ καὶ πορευτὰ γένοιτο. In a passage in the section which precedes this Pytheas is represented in the ordinary texts as saying that he had traversed the whole of Britain on foot; but the reading here is too corrupt to allow of our resting any conclusion upon it.

[3] *v. supra*, p. 18.   [4] Strabo, 4. 5. 5.   [5] *ibid.*

Concerning the route which Pytheas followed in his journey
northward we have no evidence; in fact, owing to
the fragmentary form in which all the information
we possess about him has reached us, it is easier
to say throughout the whole course of his expedition what
places he visited, than in what order, or from what direction, he
visited them.   One point, however, cannot be left wholly unnoticed in this connexion, namely the question whether Pytheas
penetrated into the Baltic sea.   The principal ground for the
view that he did so is found in a perplexing passage, in which
Polybius makes him assert that he had followed the coast of
Europe from Gades as far as the Tanais[1].   Some additional
support for it is thought to be afforded by the names of the
German and other tribes which he mentions as being found on
the mainland in these parts, and also by his account of the lands
where amber is found, which is thought to refer to the coast of
Germany in the neighbourhood of Danzig, where that material is
abundant.   The Tanais, according to this supposition, is interpreted to mean the Vistula, which enters the sea in those parts,
or perhaps the Dwina in Courland, another amber-producing
country.   It is much more likely, however, as Müllenhoff has
suggested, that the Tanais is here introduced as the traditional
boundary between Europe and Asia, and that Pytheas conceived
that in the course of his voyage he had advanced much farther
towards the east than he really had done, and consequently
"slewed round" (so to speak) his map of these parts, so as to
bring the coast of the North sea into the same meridian with the
Palus Maeotis[2].   Hence, 'as far as the Tanais' would be intended
to signify ' as far east as the meridian of the Tanais.'   The amber
country which he visited is much more likely to have been Friesland on the German Ocean.

Pytheas does not appear to have advanced further towards the
north than the extremity of Britain.   He nowhere
claims to have done so, and his account of the
regions beyond this point appears to be given at

Did Pytheas enter the Baltic?

The Northern Sea.

[1] Polyb. ap. Strabon. 2. 4. 1 ; ταῦτα μὲν τὰ τοῦ Πυθέου, καὶ διότι ἐπανελθὼν
ἐνθένδε πᾶσαν ἐπέλθοι τὴν παρωκεανῖτιν τῆς Εὐρώπης ἀπὸ Γαδείρων ἕως Τανάιδος.
[2] Müllenhoff, op. cit., I. pp. 389, 390.

second hand; indeed many of the difficulties which arise in connexion with this part of his narrative disappear, if we suppose that
he is interpreting the reports of others. He was acquainted with
the remarkable inrush of the sea, and the consequent rise of the
water at springtides, which takes place in the Pentland Firth[1]; but
the existence of this he would learn from the mainland, because
that strait passes between the north of Scotland and the Orkneys.
He received information also concerning an island called Thule,
and it was through him that this name, which
was destined to become famous in the works
of Roman authors, was reported to the dwellers
about the Mediterranean. He states that it was
the northernmost of the British islands[2], and six days' voyage north
of Britain, and in the neighbourhood of the frozen ocean[3]. From
these notices it would seem most probable that the island here
intended was Mainland, the chief of the Shetland islands. The
interval between it and Britain, no doubt, is greatly overestimated,
but the same is the case with all Pytheas' computations by sea.
Some authorities have supposed that Iceland is meant, and others
Lapland; but these conjectures seem to carry us too far afield.
Another point of great interest connected with the subject of
Thule is his statement that it lay under the Arctic
circle, or, as he or his reporter Strabo expressed it,
" where the Arctic circle coincides with the summer
tropic[4]." That this conclusion was based, not on measurements
or personal observation, but on the reports of the Celts of North
Britain, seems to be proved by a passage in Geminus the astronomer (*circ.* 80 B.C.), who quotes Pytheas as saying, that the
barbarians pointed out to him the sleeping-place of
the sun; and also that in those regions the nights
were excessively short, extending in some parts

Thule (pro-
bably Main-
land in the
Shetlands).

The Arctic
Circle.

"Sleeping-
place of the
Sun."

---

[1] Pliny, 2. 217; Octogenis cubitis supra Britanniam intumescere aestus
Pytheas Massiliensis auctor est. Cp. Müllenhoff, p. 366.

[2] Strabo, 2. 5. 8; ὁ μὲν οὖν Μασσαλιώτης Πυθέας τὰ περὶ Θούλην τὴν
βορειοτάτην τῶν Βρεττανίδων ὕστατα λέγει.

[3] *ibid.*, I. 4. 2; ἥν φησι Πυθέας ἀπὸ μὲν τῆς Βρεττανικῆς ἓξ ἡμερῶν πλοῦν
ἀπέχειν πρὸς ἄρκτον, ἐγγὺς δ' εἶναι τῆς πεπηγυίας θαλάττης.

[4] Strabo, 2. 5. 8; παρ' οἷς ὁ αὐτός ἐστι τῷ ἀρκτικῷ ὁ θερινὸς τροπικὸς
κύκλος. For the explanation of this *v. infra*, p. 179.

only to two hours, in others to three, so that within a brief interval
after its setting the sun rose again[1]. By the "sleeping-place of
the sun" was meant the point at which the sun's rays begin
altogether to disappear from view—that is, the Arctic circle, at
which during one day in the year the sun does not appear above
the horizon. This, of course, would not apply to Shetland, which
lies some distance to the south of the Arctic circle, but on such a
question the report of "barbarians" could hardly be expected to
be accurate. It is not surprising that by later and uncritical
writers these accounts were made the subject of much perverse
exaggeration, so that it was said that in the north of Europe there
was unbroken daylight for six months in the year, and perpetual
darkness during the remainder[2].

The question how far Pytheas determined certain parallels of

Pytheas'
Parallels of
Latitude.

latitude in the course of his northern expedition is
beset by numerous difficulties. We gather from
statements in Strabo that Pytheas made such calculations—though how, or on what evidence he did so is not mentioned—at four different points in the neighbourhood of Britain[3];
and that these were introduced on his authority by Hipparchus
into his tables. The first of them gave the length of the longest
day as 16 hours, the second as 17 hours, the third as 18 hours, the
fourth as 19 hours. Nothing is recorded as to the places at which
these observations or computations were made, but they would
represent approximately lat. 48°, or Ushant; lat. 54°, or Flamborough Head; lat. 58°, or Tarbet Ness in Rossshire, and lat.

---

[1] Geminus, *Elementa Astronomiae*, 5. 22. There is a difficulty here,
because Geminus introduces the shortness of the hours of night as the explanation of the expression "sleeping-place of the sun," which in that case
would mean "the place where the sun retired for his short repose." But
Cosmas Indicopleustes (6th cent. A.D.), reporting the same statement of
Pytheas, says that the barbarians explained the term "sleeping-place" as
referring to the darkness being continuous through the twenty-four hours
(Cosm. Ind., in Montfaucon, *Collectio nova patrum*, vol. 2. p. 149).

[2] Pliny, 2. 186.

[3] 2. 1. 18; 2. 5. 42; cp. Berger, *Die geographischen Fragmente des Hipparch*, pp. 66, 67, where those of the computations, which are not actually
said by Strabo to have been made by Pytheas, are proved to be due
to him.

61°, the northernmost of the Shetlands[1].   But here we are met by
the difficulty—how did Pytheas arrive at these results ?   If they
were derived in each case from personal observation of the longest
day, his voyage must have extended over something like five
years—a supposition which is extremely improbable.   If, on the
other hand, they were obtained from reports furnished by the
natives (which seems much more likely), such estimates would be
very untrustworthy, considering how vague the ideas of such
persons could not fail to be concerning the divisions of time.   It
is, no doubt, in favour of Pytheas' statements that they were
adopted by Hipparchus, because it shews that the great astronomer
had confidence in them ; and in order to facilitate our acceptance of
them it has been suggested, that only certain elementary observations are to be attributed to Pytheas, while the deductions from
them—among which the statements about the length of the
longest days in summer, and the greatest height to which the sun
rose above the horizon in winter, are to be included—should be
credited to Hipparchus.   " It was sufficient for Hipparchus," it is
said, "if Pytheas declared that in a certain place and on a certain
day he had observed the sun at midday to be at a certain elevation
above the horizon.   From these data Hipparchus could discover
the elevation of the sun at that spot at the winter solstice, and
could thence determine the latitude of the place[2].   This view of
the parts to be assigned to the earlier and the later astronomer
respectively would deliver us from the necessity of attributing to
Pytheas a greater amount of astronomical knowledge than he
probably possessed, and would also get rid of the difficulty
involved in the extreme length of time supposed to be occupied
by the expedition, if the observations which Strabo mentions were
made by him.   Such a hypothesis deserves respectful attention,
but it cannot be said to receive any support from the authorities
which we possess.   On the whole, when we take into account the
doubts which hang around the evidence for these observations,
and the small means of checking it which now exist, it seems safer

---

[1] See Sir Clements Markham's paper on Pytheas in the *Geographical Journal*, vol. 1, (1893) p. 518.

[2] Berger, *Geschichte der Erdkunde*, Pt. 3, p. 15.

not to lay any great stress on them in determining the question of the extent of Pytheas' voyage.

One more point in Pytheas' account of these northern countries remains to be noticed which certainly is not the least remarkable. This is his description of the Arctic regions, "in which," he said, "neither land, nor sea, nor air any longer existed separately, but there was, so to speak, a mixture of all three, resembling the *pulmo marinus*, in which the land and the sea and all things floated, and this was as it were the element which held together the universe, while it could not be traversed either by foot or sail. He had himself seen that which resembled the *pulmo marinus*, the rest he reported from hearsay[1]." It is certainly not surprising that a description such as this should have aroused scepticism in the minds of the ancients, nor that it should have been a standing puzzle to exercise the ingenuity of modern interpreters. It reads like an account on Pytheas' part of stories communicated to him by the natives concerning the weird unearthly sights—especially the effects of mist and light—which at all times have caused the regions towards the Pole to be a land of marvel, and concerning the strange calms and counter-currents, which often impede navigation in those waters, and among the Romans obtained for them the name of 'the sluggish sea[2]' (*Mare pigrum*). This account he seems to have invested in Platonic language; indeed there is a marked correspondence in certain points between this passage and the description of the world of spirits in the tenth Book of Plato's *Republic*, where a brilliant light is spoken of as 'the bond that holds together the universe'; and the word by which this is expressed (δεσμός, σύνδεσμος) is the same which Pytheas employs[3]. Much additional perplexity, however, is introduced into the question by

Wonders of the Arctic Regions.

[1] Strabo, 2. 4. 1.

[2] See Tacitus, *Agric.*, 10 ; Mare pigrum et grave remigantibus perhibent ne ventis quidem perinde attolli. Also, for the superstitious fancies suggested by the sunlight of the North, *Germ.* 45 ; Extremus cadentis jam solis fulgor in ortum edurat adeo clarus, ut sidera hebetet ; sonum insuper emergentis audiri formaeque decorem et radios capitis adspici persuasio adicit.

[3] Plat. *Rep.*, 10. p. 616 B; see Berger, *Geschichte der Erdkunde*, Pt. 3, p. 23.

the comparison of the combination of the elements to the *pulmo marinus*, or jelly-fish ; and this, as might be expected, has been interpreted in a great variety of ways. It is hard to think—though this is usually *Comparison to the Pulmo Marinus.* assumed—that it is the material substance, or pulpy mass, formed by these creatures on the surface of the water, to which the general aspect of the northern world is here likened ; for the comparison is, to say the least, inapposite. We should also remark that the expression 'that which resembled' (τὸ ἐοικός), which Pytheas uses, applies just as well to a feature of the scene, as to a material object. It may perhaps be worthy of consideration, in view of the great difficulty which the passage involves, whether the point of comparison in the *pulmo marinus* which is here intended is, not its gelatinous substance, but its phosphorescent appearance. These Medusae are found in the northern ocean[1], and their vast swarms are known to be accompanied by marvellous effects of luminous brilliancy[2]. If the phenomenon which the natives reported, and which Pytheas himself saw, was a peculiar glare of light upon the surface of the sea, it would be suitable enough to remark on the resemblance which this presented to the jelly-fish.

Finally, before retracing his course to Massilia, Pytheas visited the district from which amber was obtained. His acquaintance with this we discover by a comparison *The Amber Coast.* of several passages in Pliny, the statements contained in which are undoubtedly derived from his work, either directly, or through the medium of Timaeus the historian, who borrowed largely from it. These are introduced, after the manner of Pliny, without any attempt at criticism, but we seem to gather from them with a fair approach to certainty, that the land which is indicated is the coast of Friesland and the adjacent islands

---

[1] See Elton, *Origins*, p. 70 note 1.

[2] It has now been discovered by naturalists that the jelly-fish are not themselves phosphorescent. They swarm, however, at the same time and under the same conditions with various marine animals which are luminiferous, and it seems to be from this cause that phosphorescence is attributed to them. In any case—and this is the important point for our argument—the popular idea has generally been that they possess this quality.

between the mouths of the Rhine and the Elbe, and perhaps also
Schleswig, further to the north, with its fringe of islands. Thus
in one passage he remarks that opposite Britain,
Testimony of Pliny and Diodorus. dispersed over the German sea, were the Glaesiae
islands, which the later Greeks called the Electrides,
because amber (*electrum*) was produced there[1]. And again he
reports, that a day's sail from an estuary of the ocean, called
Mentonomon, on which the tribe of Guttones dwelt, was the
island of Abalus ; and to it in the spring-time the waves carried
the amber, which was the scum of sea-water solidified : the
natives used it in place of fire-wood, and sold it to their
neighbours the Teutoni[2]. Elsewhere he mentions an island
called Baunonia, on the coast of the North Sea, "over against
Scythia," in which amber was found[3] ; and Diodorus in the
same connexion speaks of an island named Basilia, "in that
part of Scythia which is beyond Gaul," from which amber was
brought to the mainland, and thence exported to the Mediterranean[4]. As regards the islands called Glaesiae
The Word 'glaesum.' it should be remarked that the word *glaesum*—
which, according to Pliny and Tacitus, was the
native name for amber[5]—notwithstanding that the latter of these
two writers attributes its origin to the Aestii on the shores of the
Baltic, was probably learnt by the Romans from the inhabitants
of this North Sea coast, for it represents the Anglo-Saxon word
for amber, ' glær,' and was given to that material because of its
brightness, being etymologically the same with the English verb
' to glare[6].' At the present day, though the Baltic coasts furnish
a much larger supply of amber than the islands of the North Sea,
there is still a considerable export of that article from the west
coast of Schleswig.

---

[1] Pliny, 4. 103.   [2] *ibid.* 37. 35.   [3] *ibid.* 4. 94.
[4] Diodor. 5. 23. 1, 5 ; cp. Pliny, 37. 36.
[5] Pliny, 37. 42 ; certum est gigni in insulis septentrionalis oceani et ab
Germanis appellari glaesum. Tac. *Germ.* 45 ; sucinum, quod ipsi glaesum
vocant.
[6] Müllenhoff, *op. cit.*, i. p. 482 ; Skeat, *Etym. Dict.*, s. v. ' glare.'

CHAPTER IX.

MATHEMATICAL GEOGRAPHY.

Slow Development of Mathematical Geography—Impulse given to it by
Aristotle, by Subsequent Expeditions, and by the Museum of Alexandria
—Spherical Form of the Earth—Aristotle's Arguments for it—Argument
from Objects seen on the Sea Horizon—Strabo's Statement of it—Measure-
ment of the Earth—Method employed before Eratosthenes—Method of
Eratosthenes—Criticism of it—Eratosthenes' Measurement of the Habit-
able World—Its Breadth—Its Length—Parallels of Latitude—First
Parallel of Eratosthenes—Other Parallels—The Climata of Hipparchus
circ. 140 B.C.—Meridians of Longitude—Theory of Zones—Aristotle's
View—Virgil's Description—Eratosthenes' Map of the World—Shape of
the Inhabited World—His Sphragides or 'Seals'—His Geographical
Treatise—Its Contents—Its Chief Errors.

THE remarkable development in the study of mathematical
geography which took place during the third
century before Christ was due to the concurrent influence of several causes. For a considerable time
after speculation first began to be awakened on
this subject the views which were entertained about it continued
to be very unscientific, and even where one school of thinkers
made advances in the direction of the truth, their opinions were
rejected or ignored by other schools, and still more by the preju-
dices of the vulgar. Questions relating to such topics as the
form of the earth, the division of its surface into zones, and the
existence of an ocean encompassing the habitable world, had been
started, but either had received no satisfactory answer or had
been determined on grounds which would not bear the test of
argument. In the course of time astronomical observers, like
Eudoxus of Cnidos (*circ.* 365 B.C.), contributed the data for
establishing more satisfactory conclusions, and others in the

Slow Deve-
lopment of
Mathematical
Geography.

course of speculation succeeded in anticipating, though they could not demonstrate, some of the truths which modern science has established. Thus Heracleides Ponticus, the associate of Plato, taught the rotation of the earth on its axis, though still regarding it as the centre of the universe[1]. But it was reserved

Impulse given to it by Aristotle,

for the master-mind of Aristotle to place these subjects in their true light according to the knowledge that was then available, and by the application of a strictly scientific method to establish the principles in accordance with which the investigation should be pursued. Yet for the discussion of many of the points in question the information which Aristotle possessed was insufficient. Had his *Meteorologica*, the work in which most of his opinions on mathematical and physical geography are contained, been composed after, instead of before, Alexander's Eastern expedition, the case might have been different; but at the time when he wrote, the knowledge that was available concerning the surface of the earth and the features which it presented was too restricted to admit of adequate conclusions being deduced from it. By means of that

by Subsequent Expeditions,

expedition and of the observations of the men of science who accompanied it, and by the discoveries of Pytheas in the north and west of Europe, and the increasing acquaintance with the Indian Ocean and the neighbouring coasts which arose through the explorations set on foot by the Ptolemies, the enquirers who followed him were in a position to advance more boldly, and to determine numerous principles which were of the highest importance both for the theoretical conception of the globe and for the practical purposes

and by the Museum of Alexandria.

of map-making. Finally, the establishment of the Museum at Alexandria provided a central point towards which all these researches might converge, and a great genius who could avail himself of them in the person of Eratosthenes of Cyrene, who occupied the post of librarian of that institution for the space of more than forty years (240—196 B.C.).

The question of the sphericity of the earth is the one which

---

[1] Cornewall Lewis, *Astronomy of the Ancients*, p. 171.

first demands our attention, because on it almost every point
connected with mathematical geography depends.
The Pythagoreans were the earliest teachers who   Spherical Form of the Earth.
maintained this doctrine, but, as far as we can
ascertain, they did so, not by means of any formal proof, but
on the ground of the fitness of things, because the circle is the
most perfect figure.   This view met with no acceptance from the
philosophers of the Ionian school, nor was it adopted by Hecataeus, or even by Herodotus[1].   It is probable enough that
Eudoxus furnished mathematical proof of it, for he was well
qualified to do so by the knowledge of astronomy which he possessed, but on this point we have no evidence.   The first writer
in whose works definite arguments on the subject are found is
Aristotle.   His mode of proof is twofold.   First he   Aristotle's Arguments for it.
deduces it from the law of gravitation, or, as he
expresses it, the tendency of all things towards the
centre.   By the action of this, when the earth was in the course
of formation, and the component elements were coming together
equally from every quarter, the mass thus formed by accretion
was so constituted that its entire circumference must be equi-
distant from its centre.   Secondly, he infers it from what is seen
to take place in lunar eclipses ; for, when the earth is interposed between the sun and the moon, the spherical form of the
obscured part of the moon's surface shews that the body which
causes the obscuration is also spherical[2].   It appears strange
that the proof which to us is the most familiar, be-   Argument from Objects
cause it appeals directly to the eye and to ordinary   seen on the Sea Horizon.
experience, viz. the sight of distant objects gradu-
ally revealing themselves above the horizon :—

> 'the first beam glittering on a sail,
> That brings our friends up from the under world '—

should not have been employed until a late period by the ancients.
We can hardly think it did not occur to them ; and by a converse
line of argument Archimedes (250 B.C.), who regarded the sphericity of the earth as sufficiently proved, deduced from that doctrine

[1] v. supra, pp. 60, 72, 78.
[2] Aristot. De Caelo, 2. 14. 8, 9, 13.

the inference that the surface of the sea must be convex—a conclusion which would naturally involve the gradual revelation of
objects approaching upon it[1].   He does not however notice this;
still less does he use the fact as an argument to support the view
that the earth is circular.   Strabo is the first author
who so employs it, and by him it is clearly stated.

Strabo's Statement of it.

"It is evident," he says, "that, when persons on shipboard are unable to see at a distance lights which are on a level
with the eye, the cause of this is the curvature of the sea; for, if
those lights are raised to a higher level, they become visible, even
though the distance be increased; and in like manner, if the
beholder attains a greater elevation, he sees what was previously
hidden...... Again, when men are approaching the land from the
sea, the parts near the shore-line come more and more in view,
and objects which at first appeared low attain a greater elevation[2]."   Thus the evidences which were adduced to prove the
spherical form of the earth varied somewhat at different periods,
but the doctrine itself was accepted without question from the
time of Aristotle onward, and even before his age, by all scientific
men.   The same thing is true of other points, in which the
principles of scientific geography depended more or less on astronomical observations, such as the division of the globe into two
hemispheres by the equator, and the position of the lesser circles,
called the tropics, which are parallel to it.   In every case, however,
the earth was regarded as forming the centre of the universe.

The idea of measuring the circumference of the earth seems
to have presented itself to the minds of the Greek
philosophers at a comparatively early time.   When
Aristophanes, in the *Clouds*, represents the disciple
of Socrates in his thinking-shop as saying that the object of
geometry was the measurement of the whole earth[3], he implies

Measurement of the Earth.

---

[1] Archimed., *De iis quae in humido vehuntur*, lib. I, probl. 2. ; Παντὸς
ὕδατος ἡσυχάζοντος ὥστε ἀκίνητον μένειν ἡ ἐπιφάνεια σφαιροειδὴς ἔσται ἔχουσα
τὸ αὐτὸ τῇ γῇ κέντρον (*Opera*, vol. 2, p. 357, ed. Heiberg).

[2] Strabo, I. I. 20.

[3] Aristoph., *Nub.* 202—4 :
    ΜΑΘ. γεωμετρία.   ΣΤ. τοῦτ᾽ οὖν τί ἐστι χρήσιμον ;
    ΜΑΘ. γῆν ἀναμετρεῖσθαι.   ΣΤ. πότερα τὴν κληρουχικήν ;
    ΜΑΘ. οὔκ, ἀλλὰ τὴν σύμπασαν.

that the solution of some such problem was contemplated by the meteorologists of that time, whose doctrines he desired to impute to Socrates. A similar attempt seems to be attributed to Archytas (*circ.* 400 B.C.) by Horace, when he speaks of him as 'the measurer of land and sea'[1]. At a later period Aristotle mentions the conclusion arrived at by certain mathematicians, whom he does not name, to the effect that its circumference amounted to 400,000 stadia, or 40,000 geographical miles; and in this he acquiesces, though without putting it forward as the result of his own calculations[2]. The system of measurement which we find to have been employed before the time of Eratosthenes was this:

Two places on the earth's surface having been selected, which were believed to be situated on the same meridian, and the distance between which *(Method employed before Eratosthenes.)* had already been estimated, the points in the heavens which were vertical at those places respectively were next determined, and the arc of the circumference of the heavens which intervened between them was measured. The proportion which this arc bore to the entire circumference of the heavens was then calculated, and from the result the proportion which the distance between the corresponding places on the terrestrial sphere bore to the entire sphere was inferred. The interval between those places having been already calculated, it was possible, by multiplying the distance by the number of times that this arc was contained in the entire terrestrial sphere, to measure the circumference of the earth. The places chosen for the application of this method were Syene in Upper Egypt and Lysimachia on the Hellespont, which were supposed to be on the same meridian, and to be distant 20,000 stadia from one another. The points which corresponded to them in the celestial sphere were Cancer to Syene and Draco to Lysimachia, and the arc that intervened between them was found to be one-fifteenth of the entire circle of the heavens. Hence it was concluded that the circumference of

---

[1] Hor., *Od.* 1. 28. 1, 2 :

> Te maris et terrae numeroque carentis arenae
> Mensorem.

[2] Aristot., *De Caelo*, 2. 14. 16.

the earth amounted to 300,000 stadia, or 30,000 miles[1]. The roughly approximate character of the data for this calculation, in respect both of the points determined in the heavens, and of the estimate of distances on the earth's surface, a portion of which had to be calculated by sea from the reports of navigators, necessarily involved considerable inaccuracy in the result. It is not improbable that this observation is to be attributed to Aristotle's pupil, Dicaearchus—whose importance for geography is shewn by his being enumerated among the greatest masters of that science by Strabo at the commencement of his work[2]—but it is certainly later than the time of Aristotle, since the city of Lysimachia was not founded until 309 B.C.

The method of investigation which Eratosthenes pursued, though less simple than this, was one which guaranteed more accurate results. The gnomon which he used as the instrument for his observations was an upright staff set in the midst of a *scaphe* or bowl, which was so arranged as to correspond to the celestial hemisphere, only inverted, and was marked with lines like a dial. By means of this he discovered that, at Alexandria at the summer solstice, the shadow of the gnomon at midday measured one-fiftieth part of the meridian—*i.e.* of a great circle of the heavens, as measured on the *scaphe*. He assumes at starting the following points—(1) that all the sun's rays fall to the earth parallel to one another ; (2) that when one straight line falls on two parallel straight lines, the alternate angles are equal; (3) that, if arcs of different circles subtend equal angles at the centre, they bear the same proportion to the whole circumference of the circles of which they are parts ; so that, if one of them, for instance, is a tenth part of its circle, the same will be the case with the others. He also takes it as proved that Syene and Alexandria are on the same meridian, and that the distance between them is 5,000 stadia. He then proceeds to argue as follows. In Syene (*B*), which was regarded by the ancients as lying under the tropic, at the summer solstice a ray of the sun (*A B*) when on the meridian, falling on the point of the gnomon, would coincide

Method of Eratosthenes.

---

[1] Berger, *Geschichte der Erdkunde*, Pt. 2, pp. 45, 46.
[2] *Ibid.*, Pt. 3, pp. vii. and 44 ; Strabo, 1. 1. 1.

with the axis of the gnomon, so as to cast no shadow, and, if produced, would strike the earth's centre (E). In Alex-

Northern Ray   Southern Ray

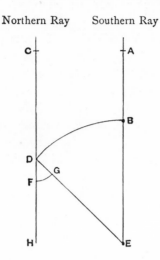

andria at the same time a ray of the sun (CD), falling on the point of the gnomon (D), would form an angle with the axis of the gnomon (DG).   Now, if the axis of the gnomon at Alexandria (DG) is produced to the centre of the earth (E), the line thus drawn (DGE) would intersect the lines formed by these two rays (CDH, ABE), and form alternate angles with them ; one of these angles (BED) being at the centre of the earth (E), the other (EDH) at the point where the northernmost of the two rays meets the point of the gnomon at Alexandria (D).   But, since alternate angles are equal, and the arcs of a circle which subtend equal angles bear the same proportion to the circles of which they are segments, the arc of the celestial sphere marked by the shadow of the gnomon on the *scaphe* at Alexandria (FG) must correspond to the arc of the great circle of the earth which lies between Syene and Alexandria (BD).   Consequently, since it has been already shewn that the shadow of the gnomon at Alexandria measures one-fiftieth part of the great circle of the heavens, the arc between Syene and Alexandria must be one-fiftieth of the great circle of the earth ; and as the distance between Syene and Alexandria is 5,000 stadia, the great circle of the earth must be 250,000 stadia, or 25,000 geographical miles[1].

This calculation involved two minor errors. One of these arose from the belief that the earth was a perfect

Criticism of it.

sphere, instead of being flattened at the poles—a mistake which was unavoidable according to the knowledge of that time. The other was caused by Syene being regarded as lying directly under the tropic, whereas in reality it was 37 miles to the northward of it. This slight inaccuracy was caused by the imperfection of the methods of observation then employed, for the position of the tropic was calculated partly from the sun being seen from the bottom of a well at the summer solstice, and therefore being considered vertical, and partly from the gnomon casting no shadow at that time[2]. A more considerable error proceeded from the distance between Syene and Alexandria being overestimated, for the number of stadia assumed for this by Eratosthenes is in excess by more than one-fifth. Still, after all deductions have been made, the general accuracy of the result is very striking; for whereas the real circumference of the earth at the equator is 25,000 English miles, Eratosthenes estimates the great circle of the meridian at 25,000 geographical miles, which is about one-seventh part in excess. By the ancients it was regarded as an extraordinary achievement of science, and immense importance was attached to it[3].

Eratosthenes also endeavoured to estimate the dimensions of the habitable world. For this attempt the increased

Eratosthenes' Measurement of the Habitable World.

acquaintance with the surface of the globe which had arisen since the time of Aristotle afforded especial facilities, and it had already been essayed

---

[1] This account of Eratosthenes' measurement is given by Cleomedes, *De Motu Circulari Corporum Caelestium*, 1. 10, pp. 95—101, ed. Ziegler.

[2] Strabo, 17. 1. 48; ἐν δὲ τῇ Συήνῃ καὶ τὸ φρέαρ ἐστὶ τὸ διασημαῖνον τὰς θερινὰς τροπάς, διότι τῷ τροπικῷ κύκλῳ ὑπόκεινται οἱ τόποι οὗτοι· ἀπὸ γὰρ τῶν ἡμετέρων τόπων, λέγω δὲ τῶν Ἑλλαδικῶν, προϊοῦσιν ἐπὶ τὴν μεσημβρίαν ἐνταῦθα πρῶτον ὁ ἥλιος κατὰ κορυφὴν ἡμῖν γίνεται καὶ ποιεῖ τοὺς γνώμονας ἀσκίους κατὰ μεσημβρίαν· ἀνάγκη δὲ κατὰ κορυφὴν ἡμῖν γινομένου καὶ εἰς τὰ φρέατα βάλλειν μέχρι τοῦ ὕδατος τὰς αὐγάς, κἂν βαθύτατα ᾖ· κατὰ κάθετον γὰρ ἡμεῖς τε ἔσταμεν καὶ τὰ ὀρύγματα τῶν φρεάτων κατεσκεύασται.

[3] Bunbury, *Hist. of Anc. Geogr.*, 1. pp. 621—625.

by Dicaearchus.   Following Pytheas as his authority, Eratosthenes
fixed the northern limit at the parallel of Thule,
which he regarded as coinciding with the Arctic   Its Breadth.
circle.   In the opposite direction—since the idea which once prevailed that the region between the tropics was uninhabitable had
been dispelled by the knowledge that Syene was on the tropic of
Cancer, and that Meroë and other inhabited places lay far beyond
that line—he determined the limit at the furthest spot towards the
south in which at that period men were known to exist, the land
of the Sembritae (Sennaar).   In the same parallel with this he
rightly placed the Cinnamon region (Somaliland), and also, by a
happy conjecture, Taprobane (Ceylon) to the southward of India.
The interval between these two limits, and with it the breadth of
the inhabited world, he estimated, according to the rough calculations which were available in that age—following a meridian line
drawn from Meroë to the mouth of the Borysthenes, and from
thence to the parallel of Thule—at 38,000 stadia.
In computing the length of the same area from   Its Length.
west to east, he was able to avail himself of the calculations which
had been made, first by the companions of Alexander, and afterwards by Megasthenes and Patrocles, of the extent of the newly
discovered portions of the continent of Asia.   These however
were partly due to conjecture; and since much of the remaining
distance had to be measured by sea, it was necessary here again
to trust to the vague estimates of sailors, which owing to the
delays and uncertainties of navigation were usually in excess of
the reality.   The parallel which he selected for this measurement
followed the line of the Mediterranean, and afterwards that of the
great central mountain-chain of Asia, the Taurus and the
Himalaya.   Starting from a point in the Atlantic to the westward
of the Pillars of Hercules which would be on the same meridian
as the Armorican promontory in Gaul—for he regarded this as
lying further to the west than the Sacrum Promontorium in
Spain (Cape St Vincent)—he calculated the distances by sea as
far as the gulf of Issus, and thence by land to the furthest extremity of India.   The total thus obtained amounted to 77,800
stadia, an estimate which exceeds the reality by about one-third[1].

[1] Strabo, 1. 4. 2, 5.

Accordingly, the length of the inhabited world by his calculation was slightly more than double its breadth. This entire area, together with the inconsiderable tracts towards the extreme north and south which lay beyond its limits, he regarded as surrounded by the ocean; and in confirmation of this view he adduced the phenomenon of the tides, the movement of which was the same, on whatever part of the coast of the outer sea they had been observed[1].

In the course of this examination of the attempts on the part of the Greeks to measure the circumference of the earth and the length and breadth of the habitable world, we have to some extent anticipated the subject of the earliest determination of parallels and meridians, which has gradually developed into our present system of lines of latitude and longitude. Owing to the limited knowledge of the time, and the small number of places whose position had been ascertained by scientific observation, it was natural that the same data should be employed for both sets of enquiries; and consequently we find that the first parallel was drawn from the Sacrum Promontorium and the Pillars of Hercules to the extremity of India, and the first meridian from Meroë to the mouth of the Borysthenes. The former of these two lines in its course from one end of the Mediterranean to the other was regarded as crossing the Straits of Messina, and passing the southern extremity of the Peloponnese and the island of Rhodes, until it reached the gulf of Issus[2]. The latitude of Rhodes had been determined by Eratosthenes himself by means of the gnomon, and it would seem that that of the Straits of Gibraltar also must have been observed—though by whom we know not—for in reality these two places are almost on the same parallel. The only point at which we discover a considerable error of measurement is the Straits of Messina, which are placed as far south as Malta. At this we can hardly be

Parallels of Latitude.

First Parallel of Eratosthenes.

[1] Strabo, ι. ι. 8; τοῖς τε πάθεσι τοῦ ὠκεανοῦ τοῖς περὶ τὰς ἀμπώτεις καὶ τὰς πλημμυρίδας ὁμολογεῖ τοῦτο μᾶλλον· πάντη γοῦν ὁ αὐτὸς τρόπος τῶν τε μεταβολῶν ὑπάρχει καὶ τῶν αὐξήσεων καὶ μειώσεων, ἢ οὐ πολὺ παραλλάττων, ὡς ἂν ἐπὶ ἑνὸς πελάγους τῆς κινήσεως ἀποδιδομένης καὶ ἀπὸ μιᾶς αἰτίας.

[2] *Ibid.* 2. 1. 1.

surprised, when we consider that here the reports of voyagers were the only source of information; and, as regards the rest of the computation, what strikes us most is its approximate accuracy. In a lesser degree the same remark applies to the continuation of the same parallel through the Asiatic continent, for the two first points through which it was drawn—Thapsacus on the Euphrates and the Pylae Caspiae—are nearly in the same latitude with the gulf of Issus, and the third—the foot of the Paropamisus range—is at no extravagant distance to the southward of it; while the remainder of the line is deflected towards the south-east, since it was supposed to follow the course of the Himalaya as far as the Eastern Ocean.   Eratosthenes, also, as we have seen, placed the Arctic circle in Thule; and towards the south he drew another parallel through Meroë.   The latitude **Other Parallels.** of this place had been determined by a Greek called Philon, who had travelled in Aethiopia, and had calculated the number of days before the summer solstice when the sun became vertical there, and had also observed the shadow of the gnomon[1].   Other places, the latitudes of which were known at this time, were Syene, which was on the tropic, Alexandria, which had been measured by Eratosthenes, and Massilia by Pytheas: but as the gnomon, which was the sole instrument available for this purpose, was not in common use, the number of observations was very limited.   Other measurements, indeed, were taken by noticing the length of the longest days and nights at certain points—which according to Strabo was done for the parallel through Gades and Rhodes[2]; but since this must have been accomplished as a rule by residents in those places, because an explorer would not necessarily be on the spot on the longest day, they could not have been numerous.

A marked development of the theory of parallels of latitude, especially from the point of view of scientific carto- **The Climata of Hipparchus** graphy, was made by the astronomer Hipparchus *circ.* 140 B.C. in his system of *climata*, or belts of latitude.   He took for his starting-point Eratosthenes' calculation of 250,000

---

[1] Strabo, 2. 1. 20.

[2] 2. 5. 14 ; συμφωνεῖν γὰρ καὶ τὰ ὡροσκοπεῖα καὶ τοὺς ἀνέμους φασὶ τοὺς ἑκατέρωσε φοροὺς καὶ τὰ μήκη τῶν μεγίστων ἡμερῶν τε καὶ νυκτῶν.

stadia for the circumference of the earth—or rather 252,000, that modification having been adopted with a view to greater convenience in division—and this he subdivided into 360 degrees of 700 stadia each. Then, taking the meridian line through Meroë and the mouth of the Borysthenes, he divided the fourth part of this circle which intervened between the equator and the pole, into sections of 700 stadia each, and drew parallels corresponding to them. The spaces on the earth's surface which intervened between these parallels, and each of which was equal to a degree of latitude, he called *climata*—a term which was afterwards applied to the temperature of those areas, and thus assumed the sense in which 'climate' is used at the present day. He also described the changes in the position of the objects in the celestial sphere which corresponded to each of these degrees, proceeding northwards from the equator[1]. This scheme, it will be perceived, was purely mathematical, and was determined independently of the position of places on the earth's surface; but after drawing out this table of parallels, Hipparchus proceeded to mark upon it those places, the latitude of which had been determined by astronomical observations—that is, by reckoning the number of the hours of the longest day. A plan such as this, however, though it might be theoretically perfect, required, in order to apply it in practice, a larger amount of information than that age could furnish. Nothing less than the combined action of a number of scientific associations at various stations, whose members might observe the movements of the heavenly bodies, and after comparing them might note the results on Hipparchus' tables, together with an organised system of collecting information from travellers, merchants and others, whose employments led them into distant lands, could have made a map constructed on such principles anything more than an arrangement of lines diversified with scattered names. These conditions, it need hardly be said, were not forthcoming, and the excessiveness of the claim which the scheme of Hipparchus involved stood in the way of even its partial realisation. It may have served to point out to men of science at a later period the true method to be followed, but for the time it discouraged the study of

[1] Strabo, 2. 5. 34.

mathematical geography, and restricted it to a narrow circle of students[1].

The attempt to determine meridians of longitude was attended with far greater difficulties than any which stood in the way of measurements of latitude. In default of the magnetic needle, there was no instrument in this case which could afford help, as the gnomon did for parallels; and moreover, since the ancients divided the day and the night into twelve hours each, irrespectively of the difference of the two at different times of the year, the length of the hours varied, except at the equinoxes, so that comparisons of the time of day at different places could not fail to be inexact. Consequently, the estimate in every instance was made to depend entirely on the calculations of unscientific observers. In treating of Herodotus, we have noticed how that writer feels his way towards a meridian line, when he describes the situation of Pteria by its position relatively to Sinope, which lay due north of it; and also when, in tracing the correspondence between the mouths of the Nile and the Ister, which he supposed to be opposite to one another, he draws a line between them through Cilicia Tracheia and Sinope[2]. This line was the best that was available for the Greeks for the purpose of observing a meridian, because their traders reached both ends of it in the course of their communication with Egypt on the one hand and their colonies to the north of the Euxine on the other. In consequence of this, and also, after the foundation of Alexandria, of the facilities which existed for pursuing the same line to the southward along the Nile valley, this direction was followed by the meridian which, as we have seen, was chosen for the earliest measurement of the earth's circumference, and was subsequently adopted by Eratosthenes. The points through which the last-named geographer drew it were, to the southward of Alexandria, Syene and Meroë, and to the northward, Rhodes,

Meridians of Longitude.

---

[1] The detailed account of the different *climata* of the inhabited world, which Strabo has given in 2. 5. 35 foll., is irreconcilable with his statement of Hipparchus' views in § 34, and must be regarded in the main as emanating from Strabo himself, and not from Hipparchus. See Berger, *Die geographischen Fragmente des Hipparch*, pp. 41, 42.

[2] *supra*, pp. 79, 80.

the Troad, Byzantium, and the mouth of the Borysthenes[1].   The accompanying diagram will shew how greatly the latter portion of

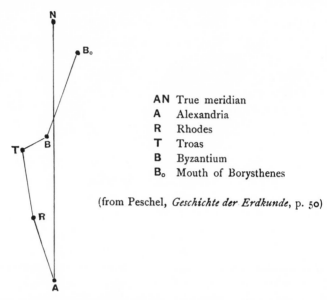

AN True meridian
A   Alexandria
R   Rhodes
T   Troas
B   Byzantium
B₀ Mouth of Borysthenes

(from Peschel, *Geschichte der Erdkunde*, p. 50)

this line deviates from the true meridian.   The same criticism will apply to another meridian which Eratosthenes drew further to the west, viz. that through Carthage, the Straits of Messina, and Rome[2]; for Rome, which is intermediate in longitude between the other two, is more than two degrees to the east of Carthage, and more than three degrees to the west of the Straits.   Hipparchus pointed out that the true method of determining longitudes was by the comparative observation of eclipses[3], but we have no evidence to shew that any such investigations were instituted by him.   Indeed, in this matter, even more than in the determination of the *climata* to which certain places were to be assigned, the requisite facilities were not forthcoming.

[1] Strabo, 2. 5. 7.

[2] *Ibid.*, 2. 1. 40.

[3] *Ibid.*, 1. 1. 12 ; εὖ δὲ καὶ Ἵππαρχος ἐν τοῖς πρὸς Ἐρατοσθένη διδάσκει, ὅτι παντί, καὶ ἰδιώτῃ καὶ τῷ φιλομαθοῦντι, τῆς γεωγραφικῆς ἱστορίας προσηκούσης ἀδύνατον λαβεῖν ἄνευ τῆς τῶν οὐρανίων καὶ τῆς τῶν ἐκλειπτικῶν τηρήσεων ἐπικρίσεως.

The division of the earth into zones, or belts of temperature, which was first promulgated by Parmenides[1], was based on a similar division which had already been drawn out for the celestial sphere.   The scheme of this philosopher included a torrid zone, which was uninhabitable on account of the heat, two frigid zones, which were uninhabitable on account of the cold, and two intermediate zones, which were of moderate temperature, and fitted for the habitation of man. The limits, however, which were to be assigned to these belts were for some time variously estimated, but the habitable area was gradually extended both towards the north and the south, in proportion as the knowledge of the remoter tribes that were found in both those directions increased.   Aristotle is the first writer in whom we find an attempt to determine these limits on scientific principles.

Theory of Zones.

Aristotle's View.

He defined the temperate zone as the belt which lay between the tropic and the arctic circle—a statement, the accuracy of which must depend on the meaning he attached to the latter of these terms.   The earlier sense which the expression 'arctic circle' bore among the Greeks, was that of a circle in the northern heavens marking the limit in that direction of the stars which never set.   From this point of view, every latitude had a different arctic circle; and this accounts for the name 'arctic,' because in the latitude of Greece, where it was first used, the Great Bear just sweeps the sea but does not set—'arctos oceani metuentes aequore tingi.'   According to the modern view, on the other hand, the arctic circle is fixed at the point on the earth's surface where during one day of the year the sun does not rise above the horizon.   It is difficult to determine which of these two senses is the one which Aristotle intended.   From his own brief statement of his opinions, as far as it is intelligible, and also from Strabo's account of them, we should suppose that he uses the term in the modern and scientific sense; but the criticisms which are passed upon him by Posidonius and Strabo imply that he treated the arctic circle as varying with the latitude of the place of observation[2].   At a later period, at all events, the

[1] *v. supra*, p. 60.
[2] Ar. *Meteorol.*, 2. 5. 10; Strabo, 2. 2. 2.

more accurate theory was regarded as established; and the practical application of it was facilitated by the discovery, which had
not yet come to the knowledge of the Greeks in Aristotle's time,
that Syene was on the tropic, and by Pytheas' report that the
arctic circle passed through Thule.   Aristotle also maintained
that both the temperate zones were habitable, but did not enter
into the question whether the south temperate zone was actually
inhabited[1].   The view which prevailed among the ancients with
regard to the whole subject is sketched in outline

Virgil's Description. by Virgil in a familiar passage of the *Georgics*, the
leading points in which are borrowed from the
Hermes, an astronomical poem by Eratosthenes.   In this it will
be seen that the terrestrial zones are represented as corresponding
to celestial phenomena; and also that both the temperate zones,
but they only, are regarded as habitable.   " Five zones there are
which gird the heaven," the poet says, " whereof one ever glows
with the blazing sun and ever is parched .with fire ; and round it
to right and left sweep the two outermost, stiff with blue ice and
lowering with storms ; while two between these and the central
zone are granted by the bounty of the gods to suffering
mortals, and between them a path has been drawn, along
which the procession of the signs of the zodiac might turn in
slanting course[2]."

We learn from Strabo that Eratosthenes' primary object in

Eratosthenes' Map of the World. the study of geography was to reform the map
of the world[3].   It cannot be doubted that before
his time a great advance had been made in the
construction of maps since the days of Anaximander, but we
have little means of knowing in what this progress consisted,
though it is certain that Dicaearchus contributed largely to it.   In
the course of the present chapter we have seen how Eratosthenes
determined the dimensions of the globe, the extent of the inhabited world, and the positions of the chief parallel and the
chief meridian which intersected it.   He proceeded to inscribe

---

[1] Ar. *Meteorol.*, 2. 5. 11, 16.
[2] Virg. *Georg.*, 1. 233—9. The passage in the *Hermes* of Eratosthenes is
given in Conington's note *ad loc.*
[3] Strabo, 2. 1. 2.

the inhabited world in a parallelogram the sides of which just
touched its extremities, and then drew across it eight parallels
of latitude and seven meridians of longitude, including the two
just mentioned, at irregular distances from one another, these
distances being determined by the situation of the chief points
whose position had been ascertained either by scientific observations or by the reports of travellers. The spots through which
the parallels were drawn were, beginning from the south, the
Cinnamon Region, Meroë, Syene, Alexandria, Rhodes, the Troad,
the mouth of the Borysthenes, and Thule ; while those that were
crossed by the meridians were the Pillars of Hercules, Carthage,
Alexandria, Thapsacus on the Euphrates, the Caspian Gates, the
mouth of the Indus, and that of the Ganges. He   Shape of the
treated the inhabited world as an island, and made Inhabited
it in shape an irregular oblong, the extremities of   World.
which tapered off to a point both to east and west, the lines of
coast converging on the one side towards the land of the Coniaci
at the furthest extremity of India, on the other towards the
Sacrum Promontorium in Spain.   His authorities for this outline
were—towards the south-west probably the *Periplus* of Hanno,
towards the south-east the voyage of Nearchus, towards the
north-east the writings of Patrocles, and towards the north-west
Pytheas. Ignoring the prevailing division into three continents,
he divided this area into a northern and a southern portion, the
limit between which was formed by the Mediterranean Sea and
the Taurus mountains, *i.e.* the range which intersected the whole
of Asia. For purposes of description he intro-
duced a further subdivision of this into *sphragides*   His Sphrag-
or ' seals[1] '—a term, which reminds us somewhat of   ides or ' Seals.'
the *actae* of Herodotus, and is not less enigmatical than that
expression.   It was intended to designate sections of the earth's
surface ; but even the principle by which these were determined
is not clear, since they do not seem to have corresponded throughout either to geometrical partitions or to territories marked by
natural boundaries.   Our means of judging of this point, however, are very limited, since Strabo's account of them, on which
we have to depend, is confined to a part of the continent of Asia.

[1] Strabo, 2. 1. 22 foll.

In this, the first *sphragis* is formed by India, the second by Ariana, that is, the Iran plateau with the districts in its neighbourhood, the third by the country between the mountains of Media and the Euphrates, and the fourth by the region to the westward of that last named as far as the Mediterranean. At this limit our information ceases.

The treatise in which the geographical researches of Eratosthenes were embodied was divided into three books.

His Geographical Treatise. Its Contents.

The first of these contained a sketch of the progress of the study of the subject from the earliest times to his own age. The second treated of mathematical and physical geography, including, in addition to the topics which we have already noticed, discussions on the formation of the earth, and the changes which had taken place on its surface. The third was divided into two parts, the first of which embraced the preliminary data for the projection of his map, while the other was devoted to descriptive geography at large. In the last-named portion he appears not to have confined himself to a delineation of the features of the ground and the outline of the coasts, but to have accompanied them by notices of the natural productions of the various countries and the races who inhabited them : at the same time the narrow limits within which this wide subject was confined preclude the possibility of his having treated it in much detail. Still, even a summary of the geographical knowledge of the third century before Christ, containing as it did a large amount of fresh material gathered from various quarters, must have been an extraordinary advance on any previously existing source of information. As might be expected from the state of knowledge which

Its Chief Errors.

prevailed at that period, the regions about which Eratosthenes was chiefly in error were those which lay in the extreme north and the extreme south of the world. Of the conformation of northern Europe he was altogether ignorant ; and about the central area of that continent north of the Danube he had little to communicate. As regards the corresponding part of Asia, he held fast by the erroneous view that the Caspian communicated with the Northern Ocean, and believed that the Jaxartes flowed into that sea. Nor had he any conception of the southward

projection either of India or of Africa.   The country, in respect of
which his information is most strikingly in advance of that possessed
by previous writers, is Arabia.   This is accounted for by the existence on either side of that land of the two great monarchies of
Egypt and Syria, the latter of which had its seat at Babylon or
Seleucia ; for, by means of the commerce which these promoted,
a number of trade-routes were developed in various parts of the
interior of the intervening territory.   So unique was the opportunity thus afforded for obtaining intelligence about a land which
has at all times been difficult to penetrate, that even Strabo,
though writing in the Augustan age, was largely dependent on
Eratosthenes for his account of Arabia.

CHAPTER X.

PHYSICAL AND HISTORICAL GEOGRAPHY.

Physical Features of Greece—Impression produced by them on Aristotle—
Physical Geographers—Agatharchides—His Account of the Aethiopian
Gold-mines—Similar Description in the Book of Job—Eudoxus of Cyzicus
—Artemidorus—Posidonius—His Travels—His Varied Interests—Error
about the Circumference of the Earth—Tides—Observations of Aristotle,
of Pytheas, and of Posidonius—Winds—Aristotle's Scheme—Timosthenes'
Scheme—Popular Scheme—'Temple of the Winds' at Athens—Period-
ical Winds—Rivers—Their Sources, Underground Courses, Power of
Erosion, Deposit of Alluvium, Tidal Waves—Earthquakes and Volcanic
Action—Views of Anaximenes, Anaxagoras, and Aristotle—Earthquakes
relieved by Volcanoes—Observations of Posidonius—Flora—Theophras-
tus' *History of Plants*—The *Descriptio Montis Pelii*—Fauna—Anthropo-
logical Notices—Agatharchides on the Ichthyophagi and Aethiopians—
Posidonius on the Iberians and Gauls—Historical Geography as found in
Aristotle—His Restricted Views—Ephorus the Forerunner of Polybius—
Geographical Section of his History—His Advanced Criticisms—Polybius
circ. 210-128 B.C.—How affected by the Circumstances of his Age—His
Travels in Western Europe—His Opinion of the Importance of Travel—
Interest in Physical Geography—His Application of Geography to History
—Descriptions of Countries—Cisalpine Gaul—Media—Descriptions of
Cities—Sinope—Agrigentum—New Carthage—General Remarks.

IN the first chapter of the present work it has been observed
that Greece was in many ways a suggestive country
to its inhabitants on the subject of physical geography. Its remarkable isthmuses, such as that of
Corinth, which was familiar to every Greek, and those of the
peninsulas of Athos and Pallene in Chalcidice, and the still more
peculiar belt of sand by which the island of Leucadia was joined
to the neighbouring continent; the narrow inlets, which penetrated
at many points into the land, and the strange currents which were
produced within them by the influx and efflux of the sea; the
numerous islands, which were either grouped in clusters or
scattered over the surface of the water :—these, and many other
features by which its area was diversified, furnished as it were an

*Physical
Features of
Greece.*

epitome of the subject, from the observation of which it was easy to advance towards the larger problems which presented themselves in other portions of the globe. The effect of these influences on the mind of Aristotle is ~~~Impression produced by~~~ especially traceable. The destruction of the cities ~~~them on Aristotle.~~~ of Helice and Bura on the coast of Achaia by an earthquake and a simultaneous rising of the sea—an event which became as famous in the ancient world as the earthquake at Lisbon has been in modern times—took place during his boyhood, and seems to have greatly impressed his imagination, for he refers to it more than once in his *Meteorologica*[1]. At Chalcis in Euboea, where he resided at one period of his life, he interested himself in the peculiar currents of the Euripus[2]; and from this circumstance arose the quaint legend, which is found in several ancient writers, that he died from vexation at being unable to discover the explanation of their movement[3]. Other instances of the impression made by similar objects on the mind of the philosopher will be presently mentioned. For the study of physical as well as mathematical geography, however, Aristotle lived several generations too early, so that in many cases his enquiries resulted in error owing to the want of sufficient data. It was not until the latter half of the second century before Christ that this part of the subject was cultivated in earnest, but from that time until the Augustan age it was predominant over every other branch. Before we begin to consider it in detail, it may be well to give some account of the leading explorers and men of science who contributed to its development.

The first among these who calls for our notice is Agatharchides of Cnidos (*circ.* 170—100 B.C.), a learned and voluminous writer, who, in addition to various ~~~Physical Geographers.~~~ historical treatises, composed a work on the Erythraean Sea. Considerable portions of this have been preserved by Photius, and from these we learn that a number of

---

[1] *Meteorol.*, 1. 6. 8; 2. 8. 43. Aristotle was born in 384 B.C., and the destruction of Helice and Bura took place in 373 B.C.

[2] *Ibid.*, 2. 8. 9.

[3] Procop., *Bell. Goth.*, 4. 6, pp. 485, 486, ed. Bonn. ; Dionys. Byz., *Anaplus Bosp. Thrac.*, in Müller's *Geogr. Gr. Min.*, vol. 2, p. 16.

passages in Diodorus, which refer to that region, are derived
from the same source.   As Agatharchides passed
Agathar-
chides. the latter part of his life at Alexandria, where he was
tutor to the young king, Ptolemy Soter II (Lathyrus),
he enjoyed ample opportunities of obtaining information about
the coast of the Red Sea and the Indian Ocean, and the interior
of the neighbouring countries of Aethiopia and Arabia.   It was
through his book that the fame of the wealth and prosperity of
the Sabaeans in the south-west corner of Arabia—the modern
Yemen—was popularly known, so that the name of Arabia Felix
became attached to that country.   Among other subjects, he paid
especial attention to the mode of life of the tribes in those
regions; but the most interesting part of his narrative relates to
the mode of working the Aethiopian gold-mines near the Egyptian
coast of the Red Sea, which he has described in much detail,
and the hardships suffered by the slave population who were
employed in them.   These, he tells us, in some cases were
prisoners taken in war, in others condemned criminals, or persons
who had been made the victims of calumny; and not infrequently
their whole families were consigned to the same terrible fate.

" Those who are thus condemned to penal servitude, being
very numerous, and all in fetters, are kept con-
His Account
of the Aethio-
pian Gold-
mines. stantly at work both by day and night without any
repose, and are jealously guarded to prevent their
escape; for they are watched by companies of
barbarian soldiers who speak a language different from theirs, to
prevent their winning any of them over by friendly intercourse or
appeals to their humanity...... Unkempt, untended as they are,
without even a rag to hide their shame, the awful misery of these
sufferers is a spectacle to move the hardest heart.   None of them,
whether sick or maimed or aged, not even weak women, meet
with compassion or respite; all are forced by blows to work
without intermission, until they expire under this hard treatment.
So overpowering is their affliction, that they are ever anticipating
worse evils in the future, and welcome death as a blessed change
from life."

The following is the description of the method of working in
the mines and of the preparation of the ore :

"The hardest of the auriferous strata they expose to a hot fire, and so loosen its texture, before they proceed to work upon it; but the kind of rock which is less firm, and yields to a comparatively slight force, they break up with quarrying implements, and on this task tens of thousands of these unfortunates are employed.   Now the general superintendence of the mines is entrusted to the artificer who tests the stone, and he directs the workmen; and the strongest in limb of those who are doomed to this hard lot break away the glittering marble with iron hammers—and that by main force in default of skill—and excavate subterranean passages, not indeed in straight lines, but following the cleavage of the gleaming rock.   These workmen, as they pass their time in darkness owing to the turnings in these galleries, wear lamps attached to their foreheads; and while they manage in various ways to follow the sinuosities of the rocks, cast down on the floor the fragments which they have detached. On this they are unceasingly occupied under the lash of an exacting taskmaster.   Then the children who are under age penetrate through the galleries into the chambers hollowed in the rock, and having laboriously thrown up the fallen pieces, convey them into the open to a place set apart for the purpose outside the pit's mouth.   There the prisoners who are more than thirty years old, receiving in their turn their fixed proportion of the quarried stone, pound it in stone mortars with iron pestles, till the fragments are reduced to the size of bean-pods.   These pieces are next passed on to the women and old men, who cast them into a number of handmills placed in a row, where they stand, two or three to each handle, and grind them, breaking up quite small the portions assigned to them, as men grind meal......
Finally the stone thus pulverised is put into the hands of skilled workmen, who complete the process.   This is done by rubbing it along the surface of a wide board placed on a slight incline, and at the same time pouring water over it; in this way the earthy particles are decomposed by the moisture, and trickle down the sloping board, while those which contain the gold keep their place owing to their weight.   This is repeated several times. First they rub it lightly with their hands, and afterwards they remove the thin earthy matter by means of fine sponges which

they apply lightly to it, until the gold dust is left completely pure. Again, when this has been collected, other artificers place it in earthenware jars accòrding to a fixed weight and measure, adding in proportion to the quantity lumps of lead and salt, with a small amount of tin, and husks of barley; and having covered all this in with a closely fitting lid, and smeared it over carefully with clay, they bake it in a furnace for five consecutive days and nights. At the expiration of that time, when it has been left to cool, they find no trace of the other ingredients in the vessels, but obtain the gold pure, and but slightly diminished by waste[1]."

The description of mining operations which is found in one part of the above passage corresponds in so many of its details to the following account of the same thing in the Book of Job, that the question arises, whether the same place may not be referred to in both of them.

Similar Description in the Book of Job.

> " Surely there is a mine for silver,
> And a place for gold which they refine.
> Iron is taken out of the earth,
> And brass is molten out of the stone.
> Man setteth an end to darkness,
> And searcheth out to the furthest bound
> The stones of thick darkness and of the shadow of death.
> He breaketh open a shaft away from where men sojourn;
> They are forgotten of the foot that passeth by;
> They hang afar from men, they swing to and fro.
> As for the earth, out of it cometh bread:
> And underneath it is turned up as it were by fire.
> The stones thereof are the place of sapphires,
> And it hath dust of gold.
> That path no bird of prey knoweth,
> Neither hath the falcon's eye seen it:
> The proud beasts have not trodden it,
> Nor hath the fierce lion passed thereby.
> He putteth forth his hand upon the flinty rock;
> He overturneth the mountains by the roots.
> He cutteth out channels among the rocks;
> And his eye seeth every precious thing.
> He bindeth the streams that they trickle not;
> And the thing that is hid bringeth he forth to light[2]."

[1] Diodor., 3. 12—14.   [2] Job xxviii. 1—11.

In these remarkable verses the shafts and underground passages in the mines, and the depth and remoteness of the scene of
the working, are referred to in a manner which closely corresponds
to the narrative of Agatharchides. It is true that the Aethiopian
mines are not the only ones from which the description in Job
may have been derived. Mr Kenrick in his *Phoenicia* long ago
pointed out the resemblance (which indeed is equally striking)
between this passage and the accounts of the mines in southern
Spain which are found in Diodorus, Strabo, and Pliny; and he
very reasonably suggested that information on this subject might
have reached the author of the Book of Job from a Phoenician
source[1]. But when we find that the knowledge of mining operations was obtainable from a country as near to Palestine or Arabia
as Aethiopia was, we are hardly disposed to go so far afield
as the western extremity of the Mediterranean to search for it.
To this we may add, that the extreme antiquity of the working of
the Aethiopian mines by the rulers of Egypt, which Diodorus
himself mentions, would suit the view that they were referred to
by the author of the Book of Job, since an early date is usually
assigned to the composition of that poem.

Nearly contemporary with Agatharchides was Eudoxus of
Cyzicus, an intelligent enquirer, whose story was
so strange, that from Strabo's time onwards it has   Eudoxus of
often been treated with scepticism. It happened   Cyzicus.
that, while he was in Alexandria, to which place he had been
sent on a mission from his native city, an Indian was brought
thither, who was the sole survivor from the crew of a vessel which
had been wrecked on the Red Sea coast. This stranger, as soon
as he had been taught sufficient Greek to make himself understood, described the circumstances of his voyage, and offered, if
the king, Ptolemy Euergetes II (Physcon), would fit out a vessel,
to conduct it to India. His proposal was accepted, and Eudoxus
was allowed to take part in the expedition; but when the
adventurers returned laden with wealth, their expectations of
gain were disappointed, for the whole of their valuable cargo was
appropriated by the king. Nothing daunted, however, by this
unfair treatment, in the succeeding reign Eudoxus engaged in

---

[1] Kenrick's *Phoenicia*, pp. 264, 265.

another enterprise under royal patronage in the same direction, which was again successful; but on his return voyage he was driven by stress of weather for some distance down the coast of Africa. There he met with a trophy, which he brought back with him to Alexandria, in the form of the ornamented prow of a ship, which was said by the natives to have come from the westward; and when he was assured by the traders to whom he displayed it, that from its appearance it must have belonged to one of a class of vessels that were despatched from Gades, he concluded that this particular ship had sailed round the south of Africa, and thus he was prompted to attempt the same feat of circumnavigation. Accordingly he organised an expedition on his own account, and after visiting Dicaearchia (Puteoli) and Massilia, and obtaining assistance from those cities, he reached Gades, and from thence proceeded southward along the African coast. The difficulties, however, which he encountered, seem to have been greater than he anticipated, and he was ultimately obliged to return to Europe; but there can be little doubt that, as he was inspired from the first with the spirit of research, he must have contributed largely to the stock of knowledge of his time. Somewhat later in date than these two was Artemidorus of Ephesus (*circ.* 100 B.C.), whose work on geography was highly prized in ancient times, and is frequently referred to by Strabo. He also was an extensive traveller, and his account of the shores of the Mediterranean and the Euxine, and of the customs of their inhabitants, to which he devoted special attention, was largely derived from personal observation.

Artemidorus.

But a far more important authority on geography than any of these was Posidonius (135—50 B.C.), who deserves the title of the most intelligent traveller in antiquity. He was a striking representative of that encyclopædic knowledge which was characteristic of the Hellenistic age. The list of subjects on which he composed treatises comprises philosophy, mathematics, physics, grammar and history; and though probably the only work in which he dealt with geography as a separate study was one on *The Ocean*, he was regarded as an eminent authority on that science. In philosophy he was a leader of the Stoic school, and he lectured on that subject in

Posidonius.

Rhodes, where Cicero was among his pupils; and both with that
statesman and with Pompey he was on terms of
intimacy. His travels included, not only the more His Travels.
accessible countries in the neighbourhood of the Mediterranean,
but the interior of Spain, Gaul, and Britain, in which lands he
became acquainted with the most remote tribes, and carefully
studied their mode of life. It may give some
idea of the variety of his interests and of the His Varied
Interests.
minuteness of his observation, if we enumerate a
few of the points which he is known to have investigated. He
carefully studied the phenomena of the tides at Gades, where he
remained thirty days[1]. He visited the Spanish mines—not only
those in the south of the country, but also those in the north-
western district, the modern Galicia—and described their galleries
and system of drainage[2]. In the same region he noticed the
existence of red rock-salt, and remarked that it turns white
when pounded[3]—a statement, which seems improbable at first
sight, but is perfectly true, because the colour in this case is
prismatic, and consequently disappears when the crystalline
formation is destroyed. He states that the depth of the sea in
the neighbourhood of Sardinia was greater than that of any other
sea that had been sounded[4]; and modern observations have
shewn that this part of the Mediterranean is excessively deep.
In Gaul his attention was attracted by the appearance of the
Plaine de la Crau between Arles and Marseilles, the entire area
of which, extending for many square miles, is covered with round
rolled stones; and he speculated on the origin of these[5]. To
him also we owe the accounts which are found in ancient writers
of the division of the Celtic hierarchy into the three orders of
Bards, Prophets, and Druids, and of their respective functions,
the truth of which is recognised by scholars at the present day[6].
Posidonius, however, was the originator of a serious error in
mathematical geography, which permanently affected the calculations of those who came after the Circum-
him. This related to the circumference of the Error about
ference of the
Earth.

[1] Strabo, 3. 1. 5.　　　　[2] Ibid., 3. 2. 9.
[3] Ibid., 3. 3. 7.　　　　[4] Ibid., 1. 3. 9.
[5] Ibid., 4. 1. 7.　　　　[6] Ibid., 4. 4. 4; Diodor., 5. 31.

earth, which, as we have seen, had already been determined by
Eratosthenes. In this conclusion of his predecessor Posidonius
was indisposed to acquiesce, and he endeavoured to solve
the problem by means of observations of the position of the
star Canopus at Alexandria and at Rhodes; but, owing to the
inaccuracy both of these measurements and of the computation
of the distance between the two places, he greatly underestimated
the circuit of the globe, reducing it from 250,000 stadia, as
computed by Eratosthenes, to 180,000[1]. Unfortunately, in consequence of the great weight that was attached to his authority,
this estimate was adopted by his successors, and was even accepted by Ptolemy.

The history of the discovery by the Greeks of the movement
of the tides is peculiarly interesting, because the
knowledge of this phenomenon was only gradually
obtainable by them, since the Mediterranean is, except in a slight
degree, and in certain limited areas, such as the head of the
Adriatic, a tideless sea. Herodotus notices the ebb and flow of
the water in the Maliac gulf[2], and also in the Red Sea[3]; and he
uses the same terms in which these are described, when speaking
of the extraordinary reflux and flux of the waves, which caused
the destruction of a portion of the Persian force under the
command of Artabazus which was besieging Potidaea[4]. The
shifting currents of the Euripus, which served as a starting-point
for speculations on this subject, are noticed by all three of the
Greek tragedians; Aeschylus describing them as the "tides of
Aulis surging to and fro[5]," and Sophocles as the "groaning
strait[6]," while Euripides speaks of the " eddies of the whirling
Euripus[7]." Aristotle, as we have seen, observed
its movements, and he remarks generally on the
tendency of the sea to sway to and fro, when a

Tides.

Observations
of Aristotle,

---

[1] Strabo, 2. 2. 2.

[2] Herod., 7. 198; ἤιε ἐς τὴν Μηλίδα παρὰ κόλπον θαλάσσης, ἐν τῷ ἄμπωτίς
τε καὶ ῥηχίη ἀνὰ πᾶσαν ἡμέρην γίνεται.   [3] Ibid., 2. 11.

[4] Ibid., 8. 129.   [5] Aesch., Ag., 191; παλιρρόχθοις ἐν Αὐλίδος τόποις.

[6] Soph., Ant., 1145; στονόεντα πορθμόν.

[7] Eurip., Iph. Taur., 6, 7;

<blockquote>
ἀμφὶ δίναις, ἃς θάμ' Εὔριπος πυκναῖς
αὔραις ἑλίσσων κυανέαν ἅλα στρέφει.
</blockquote>

large body of water is forced into a narrow space, and hemmed in
there by the coasts which environ it[1].   The tides of the ocean,
however, he seems to have referred rather to the influence of
winds than to any more certain cause[2].   Shortly after his time
additional information on the subject was furnished by Nearchus
with regard to the Indian Ocean, and by Pytheas   of Pytheas,
concerning the Atlantic.   The latter of these two
voyagers, being a man of science and an enthusiastic enquirer,
made careful observations on the regular recurrence of the tides,
with the view of determining the causes which produced them,
and established the correspondence between their diurnal recurrence and the movement of the moon[3].   It was reserved for
Posidonius, however, to draw attention to the influences which are exercised by the sun and moon   and of
                                                    Posidonius.
conjointly in producing the monthly variations in
the tides.   By him it was pointed out that at the new moon,
when the two luminaries are in conjunction, and also at the full
moon, the tides are highest, or, as we say, the spring tides are
produced; whereas at the first and last quarters they are lowest,
that is, there are neap tides[4].

In speaking of the geography of the Homeric age we noticed
that at that period only four winds—Boreas, Eurus,   Winds.
Notus and Zephyrus—were recognised by the Greeks,
and that these correspond to the four cardinal points[5].   At the
same time this division, owing to its simplicity, unavoidably introduced some confusion, because winds of different characters
were in some instances represented by the same name; this was
notably the case with Zephyrus, which designated both the violent
north-west wind which blew from Thrace, and the soft gale from
the west, which was the zephyr of the poets.   In the course of
time, as might be expected, more accurate distinctions were made,
and a more elaborate nomenclature was adopted; and these observations were arranged on scientific principles and reduced to a

---

[1] Ar., *Meteorol.*, 2. 1. 11.
[2] See Berger, *Geschichte der Erdkunde*, Pt. 2. p. 114.
[3] *v. supra*, p. 155.
[4] Strabo, 3. 5. 8; cp. Pliny, 2. 212.
[5] *v. supra*, pp. 40, 41.

scheme by Aristotle[1].   He retained the existing names for those

that blew from the cardinal points, with the exception of Eurus, which properly signified the Scirocco
or south-east wind; in the place of this he adopted
for the east wind the name Apeliotes, which was already in use in
that sense.   He then raised the number of the winds from four to
eight, and, after assuming the points of north and south as known,
with Boreas and Notus as the winds corresponding to them, determined the quarters from which the remainder blew by the variations
of sunrise and sunset.   Thus the east wind, Apeliotes, blew from
the equinoctial rising, and the west wind, Zephyrus, from the
equinoctial setting; the north-east wind, Caecias, blew from the
summer rising, and opposite to it the south-west, Libs, from the
winter setting; the south-east wind, Eurus, from the winter rising,
and opposite to it the north-west, Argestes or Sciron, from the
summer setting.   To these, with a view to more minute subdivision, he added four more winds, raising the entire number to
twelve: thus between Boreas and Argestes he inserted a wind
called Thrascias; between Boreas and Caecias one called Meses;
between Eurus and Notus, Phoenicias; and between Notus and
Libs a wind which he does not name, but which was afterwards
called Libonotus or Leuconotus.   The quarters from which these
winds blew, however, were not exactly defined, as was the case
with the others.   For geographical, and probably also for nautical
purposes, this elaborate scheme was retained in use, for we find it
mentioned by Timosthenes, who was admiral of the fleet of
Ptolemy Philadelphus, and wrote a treatise *On Harbours*, which

is frequently quoted by Strabo.   This writer made
a further advance by naming the distant portions of
the world which corresponded to the quarters from
which these various winds blew.   Thus he made the Bactrians to
correspond to Apeliotes, the Indians to Eurus, the Red Sea to
Phoenicias, and so on all round the points of the compass[2].

But for ordinary purposes the eight-fold division
was the one permanently retained in use.   This we
might infer from the rare occurrence of the names

[1] *Meteorol.*, 2. 6.

[2] Agathemerus, *Geograph.*, 2. 6, 7.

of the four additional winds, but we have clear proof of it in the sculptured figures which are still to be seen on the ancient monument which throws the greatest light on this subject—the Horologium of Antonius Cyrrhestes, or, as it is popularly called, the 'Temple of the Winds,' at Athens. This is a low octagonal tower, on each of the eight walls of which there is a bas-relief, representing the wind 'Temple of the Winds' at Athens. that blew from the direction towards which it faces, and these correspond to the eight winds which Aristotle first enumerates. An additional element of interest is supplied by the dress and accompaniments of these figures, by which the character attributed by the Greeks to the winds which they represent is described. Boreas, for instance, is depicted as a bearded man of stern aspect, thickly clad and wearing strong buskins, and he blows a conch shell as a sign of his tempestuous character. Caecias, another cold and inclement wind, carries a shield, the lower part of which is full of hailstones. Notus, the most rainy wind, holds an inverted urn, the whole contents of which he is pouring out upon the earth. Zephyrus, on the other hand, who is the harbinger of spring, appears as a graceful youth, almost unclothed, with the fold of his robe filled with flowers. In addition to these winds, which determined, or were determined by, the quarters of the heavens, Aristotle notices the periodical winds that prevail in the Aegean—the Ornithiae or Bird-winds (so called Periodical Winds. because they brought the birds of passage), which blew in the springtime from the north, and the Etesian winds also from the same direction[1]. Owing to his remembrance of the latter of these, Megasthenes, in his account of India and its rainy season, applies the name of Etesian winds to the south-west monsoon[2].

In every country the rivers are the chief element of movement, and for this reason they resemble a living agency more than any other natural feature. The changes Rivers. which they are continually producing on the face of the earth are everywhere apparent, and human life has at all times been largely dependent upon them, whether as an aid to the cultivation of the soil, or as a means of transit from place to place, or as furnishing

[1] Ar., *Meteorol.*, 2. 5. 7, 9.
[2] Strabo, 15. 1. 13.

one of the first necessaries of existence, and thus determining the localities fitted for the abode of man. In consequence of this they have attracted attention in all ages, and among the Greeks, as soon as speculation on the phenomena of nature arose, we meet with interesting observations both on the general characteristics of rivers and on their more marked peculiarities. Aristotle first

Their Sources,

pointed out that almost all large rivers take their rise in great mountain ranges—a statement which he illustrates by instances taken from all the three continents; and he compares the elevated portions of the globe to a vast sponge, which retains the water that falls in rain, and after a while sends it forth again from numerous sources[1]. Another

Underground Courses,

feature by which he was attracted was the disappearance of rivers, and their pursuing a subterraneous course, of which he gives the following account. "That there are such chasms and openings in the ground is clear from the rivers that are engulfed. Now this happens in many parts of the earth, as, for instance, in Peloponnesus, where there are several instances in the neighbourhood of Arcadia. The reason is that, whereas that is a mountain district, it has no channels leading from the depressions of the ground to the sea. For when an area is filled and has no outflow, it finds for itself a passage vertically, by the force of the water that presses from above[2]." The places in Arcadia here referred to are the valleys which contain the lakes of Pheneus and Stymphalus, and the phenomena of both of these are accurately described by Eratosthenes, who says that the river of Pheneus finds its way into a passage, or "strainer," as he calls it, and that when this is closed the valley becomes a lake; but when it opens the waters sink, and the river Ladon, with which it communicates underground, is flooded. The same thing happens to the lake of Stymphalus, the stream from which forms the river Erasinus in the Argive territory[3]. A further

Power of Erosion,

point, to which Polybius draws attention in his description of the site of Psophis in the Peloponnese, is the action of a river in hollowing out a

[1] Ar., *Meteorol.*, I. 13. 11—22.
[2] *Ibid.*, I. 13. 27, 28.
[3] Eratosth. ap. Strabon., 8. 8. 4.

ravine by insensible degrees[1]. Again, the formation of alluvium
about the mouths of rivers, which we have noticed
as being brought prominently before the minds of   Deposit of
the Greeks from an early period by their observation   Alluvium,
of the Delta in Egypt, led to further speculations; and first
Aristotle, and afterwards Polybius, affirmed that owing to this
cause the Palus Maeotis was rapidly filling up, so that vessels of
less draught than those previously in use were required to navigate it[2]. Polybius adds that, on a smaller scale, the same thing
was taking place in the Black Sea. Finally, Posidonius remarked on the inrush of the tide into the   Tidal Waves.
estuaries and the lower courses of rivers, a phenomenon which he
had noticed at the mouth of the Thames during his visit to Britain[3].

The frequent occurrence of earthquake shocks, to which
throughout its history Greece has been much exposed, naturally attracted the attention of the   Earthquakes
                                                     and Volcanic
Greeks, and caused them to speculate on the   Action.
changes which might have been produced on the face of the earth
by such convulsions. As early as the time of Aeschylus we find
that the idea prevailed that Sicily had been separated from Italy
by such an agency, and that the name of Rhegium, or "The
Rent," was derived from this circumstance[4]. Herodotus expresses
a similar opinion with regard to the disruption of Olympus and
Ossa, and the formation of the vale of Tempe[5]. Among the
earlier philosophers we meet with two theories that were put
forward to account for these movements. The first
of these, which is attributed to Anaximenes, referred   Views of
                                                         Anaximenes,
them to fractures of the crust of the earth, which

---

[1] Polyb., 4. 70. 7; ποιεῖ δὲ καὶ τὸ παράπαν ὀχυρὰν καὶ δυσπρόσοδον τὴν
πόλιν διὰ τὸ μέγεθος τοῦ κοιλώματος, ὃ κατὰ βραχὺ τῷ χρόνῳ κατείργασται,
φερόμενος ἐξ ὑπερδεξίων τόπων.

[2] Ar., Meteorol., 1. 14. 29; Polyb., 4. 40. 3—10.

[3] Priscianus Lydus, Solutiones ad Chosroem, p. 72, ed. Bywater.

[4] Aeschyl. ap. Strabon. 6. 1. 6; ὠνομάσθη δὲ 'Ρήγιον, εἶθ', ὥς φησιν
Αἰσχύλος, διὰ τὸ συμβὰν πάθος τῇ χώρᾳ ταύτῃ· ἀπορραγῆναι γὰρ ἀπὸ τῆς ἠπείρου
τὴν Σικελίαν ὑπὸ σεισμῶν ἄλλοι τε κἀκεῖνος εἰρήκεν·

ἀφ' οἷ δὴ 'Ρήγιον κικλήσκεται.

[5] Herod., 7. 129; ἔστι γὰρ σεισμοῦ ἔργον, ὡς ἐμοὶ ἐφαίνετο εἶναι, ἡ διάστασις
τῶν οὐρέων.

were produced by its passing through a process of drying, after having previously been saturated with moisture[1]. The other was
Anaxagoras, that of Anaxagoras, who believed that they were caused by the fiery element of the aether, which had penetrated into the interior of the earth, and was struggling to escape thence[2]. It will be seen that the view of Anaximenes excluded the idea of any connexion between earthquakes and volcanic agency, whereas that of Anaxagoras naturally suggested
and Aristotle. it. In the hands of Aristotle this connexion became the leading feature in the discussion of the question. According to him both of them were due to the action of winds, which were confined beneath the surface of the earth, and were endeavouring to find a vent. These winds—perhaps at the present day we should rather describe them as gases—were developed by the heat of the earth acting on the moisture which penetrates into it. The element of fire which appears in volcanic action was due to the vapours becoming rarified and so igniting[3]. This theory subsequently met with general acceptance: we find it adopted by Ovid in his description of the upheaval of the promontory of Methana near Troezen in the Argolic peninsula, which happened about the year 282 B.C.—in which passage he compares the process to what happens in the inflation of a bladder:—

> Near Troezen stands a hill, exposed in air
> To winter winds, of leafy shadows bare :
> This once was level ground ; but (strange to tell)
> Th' included vapours that in caverns dwell,
> Lab'ring with colic pangs, and close confined,
> In vain sought issue for the rumbling wind:
> Yet still they heaved for vent, and, heaving still,
> Enlarged the concave, and shot up the hill;
> As breath extends a bladder, or the skins
> Of goats are blown t' inclose the hoarded winds:
> The mountain yet retains a mountain's face,
> And gathered rubbish heals the hollow space[4].

[1] Ar. *Meteorol.*, 2. 7. 6.
[2] *Ibid.*, 2. 7. 2.
[3] Ar. *Meteorol.*, 2. 8.
[4] Ov. *Met.*, 15. 296—306 (translation by Dryden and others).

Pliny also gives his adherence to the same view[1]. By more careful observation of these occurrences it was further
established that the volcanoes served as a vent, by
means of which the frequency and violence of the
earthquake movements were lessened. Thus Strabo, when speaking
of a succession of shocks by which the island of Euboea was
affected, remarks that they ceased when an eruption took place in
the Lelantian plain between Chalcis and Eretria[2]. And again, he
explains the cessation in South Italy of any such convulsions as
that which was supposed to have originated the Straits of Messina,
by the formation in that neighbourhood of cones of eruption like
those of the Lipari islands[3]. After Aristotle, the man of science
who contributed most to the study of this subject
was Posidonius. He described in considerable
detail, and in terms which closely correspond to
the records of modern observers of similar occurrences, the elevation of a new volcanic islet among the Lipari islands, which took
place during his lifetime. Strabo thus reports his narrative :—
" Posidonius says that within his memory, one day about the
summer solstice, just at dawn, the sea was seen to rise to an extraordinary height between the islands of Hiera and Euonymus, and
continued to increase steadily for a certain time, until suddenly it
ceased. Those who ventured to sail near to the spot were appalled
by the sight of the dead fish that were carried by the current, and
by the heat and stench, and so took to flight; but one of the
vessels, which approached nearer than the others, lost part of its
crew, while the rest hardly escaped to Lipara, and from time to
time were attacked by delirium like epileptic patients, though at
intervals they recovered their senses. Several days afterwards the
surface of the sea was seen to be covered with mud, and at many
points jets of flame, with exhalations and smoke, burst forth, and
the scum subsequently hardened and assumed the appearance of
mill-stone[4]." He is also quoted by Strabo in connexion with the

Earthquakes relieved by Volcanoes.

Observations of Posidonius.

---

[1] Pliny, 2. 192; ventos in causa esse non dubium reor...condito scilicet in
venas et cava ejus occulta flatu. neque aliud est in terra tremor quam in nube
tonitruum, nec hiatus aliud quam cum fulmen erumpit incluso spiritu luctante
et ad libertatem exire nitente.

[2] Strabo, 1. 3. 16.   [3] 6. 1. 6.   [4] 6. 2. 11.

eruptions of Etna[1], and as mentioning an earthquake which happened in Phoenicia[2]. In fact, there can be little doubt that when we meet with descriptions of phenomena of this kind elsewhere in the writings of the latter geographer—and they are very numerous—they are in the great majority of cases to be referred to Posidonius as their original authority[3]. Perhaps the most notable instance is the account of the eruption of Thera (Santorin), which occurred in the year 197 B.C., on which occasion, we are told, flames rose from the water for four days between Thera and the neighbouring Therasia, so that the whole sea boiled and blazed, and little by little an island was ejected, being lifted as it were by mechanical force, and composed of fire-stones, extending over an area of twelve stadia in circumference[4]. It is interesting to observe in this connexion, as an evidence of the influence which these aspects of nature exercised on the mind of Posidonius, that he could not persuade himself that the island of Atlantis, which is described in Plato's *Timaeus*, was wholly fictitious, because it was said to have disappeared in the sea in consequence of an earthquake[5].

The flora and fauna of different countries were also recognised as subjects which merited careful observation, and their geographical distribution attracted especial attention. In the *History of Plants* of Theophrastus, who was a pupil of Aristotle, we meet with constant references to the habitat of the different trees and shrubs that are mentioned, together with remarks on the climates which were most suitable for their development, and the differences produced in them through this cause. Thus, in one place the trees that were found in Macedonia are enumerated, the mountain growths being distinguished from those of the lowlands, and some of these are compared with the corresponding vegetation in Crete[6]; in another an account is given of the trees and plants which were found growing in the Copaic lake or in its

Flora.

Theophrastus' *History of Plants*.

---

[1] Strabo, 6. 2. 3.   [2] 1. 3. 16.
[3] See Dubois, *Examen de la Géographie de Strabon*, p. 325.
[4] Strabo, 1. 3. 16.
[5] Strabo, 2. 3. 6; cp. Plato, *Tim.*, p. 25 c.
[6] Theoph., *Hist. Plant.*, 3. 3.

neighbourhood[1]. Speaking of the fondness of the box-tree for a cold climate, Theophrastus says that it grew on the Thessalian Olympus, though it did not attain a great size there, but that it was most abundant on Cytorus in Bithynia, while the finest specimens were found in Corsica[2]. He also remarks on the Corsican pine-forests, both because of their extent and of the size of the trees, in which respects he says they were unrivalled in Europe[3]. Another interesting botanical notice is found in an account of Mount Pelion, which forms part of a *Description of Greece*, written in the latter half of the third century before Christ, which has been attributed, though erroneously, to Dicaearchus[4]. The greater part of this is occupied with an enumeration of the trees and plants that grew on that mountain, which was famous for its vegetation, as we might infer from its Homeric epithet 'quivering with foliage' (εἰνοσίφυλλον). We learn from it that, while there was a great variety of different kinds, especially of fruit trees, the most abundant trees were the beech, the silver fir, two sorts of maple, the cypress and the juniper[5]. Again, as regards the fauna of different countries, Agatharchides furnishes descriptions of a variety of strange animals that were found in Aethiopia—the rhinoceros, the camelopard, different kinds of baboons, the hyena and others[6]; while in Megasthenes we meet with curious notices of the Indian apes and the method employed in catching them. This author writes:—

The Descriptio Montis Pelii.

Fauna.

"In the forest which I have mentioned the historians of Alexander speak of an extraordinary multitude of long-tailed apes of great size. On one occasion the Macedonians, seeing a number of these drawn up in line on some bare hill-tops (for these animals have a strong element of human intelligence, not inferior to the elephant), took them for an army, and charged them as if they were enemies; but desisted, when they learnt the

---

[1] Theoph., *Hist. Plant.*, 4. 10.   [2] 3. 15. 5.
[3] 5. 8. 1, 2.
[4] See C. Müller's Prolegg. to his *Geogr. Gr. Minores*, pp. lii., liii.
[5] *Geogr. Gr. Minores*, vol. 1. pp. 106—8.
[6] Agatharch., *De Mari Erythraeo*, §§ 71—77, in Müller, *op. cit.*, 1. pp. 158—162.

truth from Taxiles, who at that time was in the king's company. There are two methods of catching these apes. As they are quick in imitation, and also easily make their escape into the trees, their pursuers, when they see one sitting on a tree, place water in a bowl within sight of it, and with this they dabble their own eyes; afterwards they set a bowl full of birdlime instead of water, and going away watch from a little distance off. Then the ape descends from the tree, and when it has smeared its eyes with the birdlime, and can no longer use them because they are tight shut, they rush upon it and capture it alive. This is one method, and the other is the following. The men first clothe themselves with sacks, in the style of trousers, and when they quit the spot, leave behind other sacks of a thick material, smeared within with birdlime; when the apes get inside these, they are easily captured[1]."

Nor do modern books on Natural History furnish anything more quaint than Posidonius' account of the appearance of the Barbary apes, which he saw in a forest by the sea-shore, when sailing along the African coast on his way from Gades to Italy[2]; or a more exciting story than Polybius' narrative of the capture of the swordfish in the Straits of Messina, where they were hemmed in within a narrow space, when pursuing the shoals of tunnies. This last proceeding is reported as follows by Strabo :—

"Polybius goes on to describe the capture of the sword-fish, which takes place in the neighbourhood of Scyllaeum. A man is posted on the look-out, to give a general signal to the occupants, two in number, of each of a multitude of small two-oared skiffs. One of these rows, while the other takes his stand in the bows with his harpoon, when the look-out man has signalled that the sword-fish are in sight, for as they swim they show one-third of their bodies above water. Now when the skiff comes close to one of them, the fisherman launches his harpoon, and then draws it out again from the fish's body, leaving the head of the weapon behind; for this is barbed, and is purposely affixed loosely to the shaft, and has a long cord attached to it. With this they play the wounded fish till it is tired of struggling and trying to escape;

[1] Megasthenes ap. Strabon., 15. 1. 29.
[2] Posidon., ap. Strabon., 17. 3. 4.

then they haul it to land, or, if it is not of great size, take it up into the skiff. Even if the harpoon falls into the sea, it is not lost being put together of oak and pine-wood, in order that, when the oaken part would sink owing to its weight, the remainder may float and be easily picked up. Sometimes it even happens that the rower is wounded through the planks of the skiff; so long is the sword with which these fish are armed, and so great their strength, which renders their capture not less dangerous than a boar-hunt[1]."

Finally, the observation of the characteristics and manner of life of different tribes of the human race, or what we now call the study of anthropology, was first systematised at Alexandria, and was gradually developed until it reached the important position which it holds in Strabo's *Geography*. The work of Agatharchides on the Erythraean Sea contains numerous notices of this character. He describes in great detail the habits of the Ichthyophagi on the coast of Arabia, who resembled those whom Nearchus met with farther to the east beyond the Persian gulf. They are represented as being unacquainted with distinctions of right and wrong, and as existing in the lowest state of barbarism, their only food being the fish that were cast up on the shore, while on account of the absence of water they drank only every fifth day, when they migrated in a body to places in the interior of the country where there were springs. Their dwellings were either caves in the rocks, or huts constructed out of the backbones of fishes and covered with sea-weed[2]. The waterless condition of this part of southern Arabia— the Hadramaut—at the present day, and the fish diet of its inhabitants and their camels, are testified to by recent travellers[3]. Agatharchides remarks on the shortness of life of these people, owing to their want of exertion and employment, notwithstanding their freedom from diseases[4]. The Aethiopian tribes of which

(marginal notes: Anthropological Notices. ... Agatharchides on the Ichthyophagi)

---

[1] Polyb., ap. Strabon., 1. 2. 16.

[2] Agatharch., in Müller, *op. cit.*, §§ 31—46.

[3] See Mr Theodore Bent's account in the *Geographical Journal* for 1894, pp. 317, 318.

[4] Agatharch., § 39.

the same writer has given an account, are for the most part distinguished by him according to the names of the
objects from which they obtained the means of sub-
sistence—as Struthophagi or Ostrich-eaters, Acrido-
phagi or Locust-eaters, Elephantophagi or those who killed
elephants and lived on their flesh, and Rhizophagi or Root-eaters,
who dwelt on the banks of the Astaboras (Atbara), and supported
themselves on the roots of reeds which grew in the neighbouring
marshes[1]. What he tells us also about the Troglodytes, who dwelt
on the coast of the Red Sea, and especially concerning their custom
of putting to death the aged and diseased, and their rites of burial,
is very curious[2]. In like manner Posidonius in the
course of his extensive travels kept an accurate
record of the habits of the remote peoples through
whose country he passed, and to this Strabo is largely indebted
in his description of those regions. We are thus furnished with
interesting information about the condition of the inhabitants of
Spain and Gaul at that time, who, though rude, represent a much
higher type than those whom we meet with in Agatharchides.
In the account which he gives of the mountaineers of northern
Spain—the Gallaeci, Astures, and Cantabri, who correspond in
position to the modern districts of Galicia, the Asturias, and part
of the Basque provinces, and may be regarded as the truest
representatives of the Iberian race—we find descriptions of their
food and meals, their lively dances, the dark-coloured cloaks
worn by the men and the gay garments and elaborate head-
dresses of the women, their observance of the *couvade*, their use
of barter instead of money as a means of exchange, their custom
of inheritance in the female line, and the punishments which they
inflicted on criminals—for those who were condemned to death,

Marginal notes: and Aethiopians.

Posidonius
on the Iberi-
ans

---

[1] Agatharch., §§ 50 foll. With regard to the Locust-eaters we may compare
what Mr Bent tells us about the tribes in that neighbourhood at the present day.
'They are, like the ἀκριδοφάγοι whom Agatharchides places on their coast,
large consumers of locusts when in season; they catch them only when they
have reached the flying stage, and roast them in the ashes. We saw clouds of
locusts in this district, devouring all the scanty herbage and literally filling the
air.' *A Visit to the Northern Soudan,* in *The Geographical Journal,* vol. VIII.
(1896), p. 338.

[2] §§ 61—63.

he tells us, were flung headlong over precipices[1]. The natives
of Gaul are similarly portrayed : we hear of their
simplicity of character, their teachable spirit, their   **and Gauls.**
fondness for display, and their impetuous courage ; we are told
that they wore wide trousers and tunics with sleeves, and that the
arms which they carried were proportionate in size to their great
stature ; and their mode of government and the conduct of their
assemblies, and also the barbarous customs which prevailed
amongst them, such as human sacrifices and carrying off the
heads of the enemies whom they slew in battle, are carefully
described[2].

Let us now turn to Historical Geography. This branch of the
subject, when considered in its wider application—
that is, as the study of the influence of strongly   **Historical
Geography**
marked natural features, and especially of the
boundaries of countries, on the history of nations and of the
world at large—did not attract much attention before the time of
the Roman conquest of Greece ; indeed, this could hardly have
been otherwise, because the limited area to which Greek politics
were confined precluded any such extended outlook as an investigation of this kind presupposes. In Aristotle, no
doubt, we meet with general reflexions on this   **as found in
Aristotle.**
question, which are characterised by his usual penetration, though we feel that he is looking from a Greek point of
view. Such are his observations in the *Politics* on the influence
of climate on national character. " The inhabitants of the colder
countries of Europe," he remarks, " are brave, but deficient in
thought and technical skill ; and, as a consequence of this, they
remain free longer than others, but are wanting in political organisation, and unable to rule their neighbours. The peoples of
Asia, on the contrary, are thoughtful and skilful, but without
spirit, whence their permanent condition is one of subjection and
slavery. But the Hellenic race," he adds, " as it is intermediate
between them in geographical position, so also combines their
qualities ; it is at once spirited and thoughtful, and so continues

[1] Strabo, 3. 3. 7 ; 3. 4. 16—18.
[2] *Ibid.* 4. 4. 2—5.

to be free and to have the best government, and would be capable
of ruling the world if it had a common political organisation[1]."
In another part of the same work he notices that, while the sea is
an element favourable to democracy owing to the sense of freedom which it engenders[2], steep places, which might serve as
strongholds to command the town that lay below and the surrounding district, tend to foster oligarchy or monarchy[3].   But

His Restrict-
ed Views.

Aristotle's conception of the best form of state,
based as it was entirely on Hellenic models, precluded the application of geography to a wider field
of history.   This was almost impossible for a writer who maintained that the city-state should be of such a size that the citizens
might know one another, because without personal acquaintance
proper persons could not be elected as magistrates[4]; and also
that the country of which this city was to be the capital should be
as far as possible self-sufficing in its products, and easily taken in
by the eye[5].   The same remark applies to the other writers of the
period of Greek independence.   With one exception, Polybius is
the first Greek author who rightly estimated the importance of
geography in the study of history, and he wrote under the influence of Roman ideas.

The exception here referred to is Ephorus.   This writer, who

Ephorus the
Forerunner of
Polybius.

lived in the first half of the fourth century B.C., and
therefore two hundred years earlier than Polybius,
may in several respects be regarded as his fore-
runner.   This is true of his mode of treating history, as Polybius
himself remarked; for while this writer in the Introduction to his
work claims for himself that he was the first historian who had
taken a synoptic view of history[6], he elsewhere admits that
Ephorus, though he alone, had already conceived a comprehensive
treatise on that subject[7].   This was a universal history in thirty
books, extending from the mythical period to the time of Philip

---

[1] Ar. *Pol.*, 7. 7. 2.   [2] *Ibid.*, 7. 6. 7, 8.

  Ibid., 7. 11. 5.   [4] *Ibid.*, 7. 4. 13.

[5] *Ibid.*, 7. 5. 1, 3.

[6] Polyb., 1. 4. 3, 4.

[7] *Ibid.*, 5. 33. 2; Ἔφορον, τὸν πρῶτον καὶ μόνον ἐπιβεβλημένον τὰ καθόλου
γράφειν.

of Macedon, which included in its scope the barbarian nations as
well as the Greeks.　Another point in which he anticipated
Polybius was in devoting a separate section of

Geographical
Section of his
History.

his work to geography—a method of arrangement
which Strabo notices as being common to both of
them[1]; and in consequence of the prominence which they gave
to that subject, the same writer enumerates them, notwithstanding
that history was their primary object, among the leading geographers[2].　In the case of Ephorus this section was the fourth and
fifth books of his 'Histories,' the former of which was devoted to
Europe, the latter to Asia and Africa[3].　If we may judge from
some of the passages which Strabo has quoted from
him, the praise which he received was well deserved.

His Advanced
Criticisms.

He strikes the keynote of the geography of Greece,
when he says that the determining element in it is the sea[4].　Nothing could be truer than his remark concerning Boeotia, that
its inhabitants possessed an extremely advantageous position in
Greece from their commanding three seas—on the one side the
Corinthian and Crisaean gulfs, which opened towards Italy,
Sicily, and Libya; on the other the bays of the Euboic sea, both
north and south of the Euripus, which looked towards Macedonia
and the Hellespont, and also towards Cyprus and Egypt—and
moreover, that Euboea, after it was joined by a bridge to the
mainland, almost formed part of that country: but that these gifts
of nature had been wasted on them, because they undervalued
the civilising influences of education[5].　Again, in the case of
Aegina he notices how the thinness of the soil caused the inhabitants to take to the sea, and by this means to become a successful
commercial people[6].　Comments such as these prove that the

---

[1] Strabo, 8. 1. 1; οἱ δ' ἐν τῇ κοινῇ τῆς ἱστορίας γραφῇ χωρὶς ἀποδείξαντες τὴν
τῶν ἠπείρων τοπογραφίαν, καθάπερ Ἔφορός τε ἐποίησε καὶ Πολύβιος.

[2] 1. 1. 1.

[3] See C. Müller's *Fragmenta Hist. Gr.*, vol. i. p. lx.

[4] Strabo, 8. 1. 3; ἡγεμονικόν τι τὴν θάλατταν κρίνων πρὸς τὰς τοπογραφίας.

[5] *Ibid.*, 9. 2. 2.

[6] *Ibid.*, 8. 6. 16; Ἔφορος δ' ἐν Αἰγίνῃ ἄργυρον πρῶτον κοπῆναί φησιν ὑπὸ
Φείδωνος· ἐμπόριον γὰρ γενέσθαι, διὰ τὴν λυπρότητα τῆς χώρας τῶν ἀνθρώπων
θαλαττουργούντων ἐμπορικῶς.

writer regarded geography with a philosophical mind, and read almost like the criticisms of a later and more advanced age.

Polybius, however, is the author in whom geography first ob-

Polybius
circ. 210—128
B.C.

tained full recognition as the handmaid of history. The reason of this is to be found partly in the character of the age in which he lived, and partly in the circumstances of his own life. The period which he represents is that in which the history of Greece was first merged in universal history. Before that time, and especially during the era

**How affected
by the Circum-
stances of his
Age.**

which preceded the rise of Macedonian influence, the interests of Greece had been self-centered, and it was the function of her historians to record the struggles, whether external or internal, of her

several states, and to draw from them the lessons which they suggested. The actors on this stage were animated by fresh vigour and intense energy, and for this reason, as well as on account of the genius and originality of the writer, the work of Thucydides is immeasurably superior to that of Polybius; but at. the same time the events which Polybius describes exercised a wider influence on the ages that followed, since the spirit of Hellenic thought had then begun to permeate the world at large, and the current of its history was being blended with a wider stream. The occurrences, also, which took place during the lifetime of "the historian of the Decline and Fall of Ancient Greece," as Polybius has been aptly called[1], were such as it has been the lot of but few persons to observe. Born at Megalopolis in Arcadia, when the Achaean League was still powerful, he witnessed the subjugation of Greece by the Romans, and through the intimacies which he contracted with leading politicians at Rome during his long residence as a hostage in that city, he was able to obtain some concessions from the conquerors in behalf of his countrymen. He was present at the destruction of Carthage, and thus beheld the final overthrow of the most powerful enemy of the Roman state. At an earlier period he had watched the downfall of the Macedonian monarchy, and the practical, though not formal conquest of that of Syria by the same power. In the

---

[1] Freeman, *History of Federal Government,* 1. p. 227.

midst of events such as these, entailing as they did far-reaching consequences, it was impossible for an acute observer to hold fast by a restricted view of the course of history.   And the extent of the area which was affected by these conquests could not fail to suggest an intelligent study of the countries which were the scene of this extraordinary revolution.

For the work of illustrating history by means of geography Polybius was well prepared by his extensive travels. The principal scene of these was Western Europe and the neighbouring parts of Africa.   In one pas- His Travels in Western Europe. sage of his History he speaks of having undertaken dangerous and laborious journeys in Libya, Spain, and Gaul, and along the shores of the ocean that bordered them; and his object in doing so, he says, was that he might remove the ignorance of those lands, which up to that time had prevailed among his country-men[1].   He was, in fact, the first writer who availed himself of the knowledge obtained through the conquests of the Romans in the West.   Elsewhere he mentions that he had followed Hanni-bal's route across the Alps.   "I speak with confidence on these points," he says, " because I have questioned persons actually engaged on the facts, and have inspected the country, and gone over the Alpine pass myself, in order to inform myself of the truth and see with my own eyes[2]."   We learn also from Pliny, (though, strange to say, on his authority alone) that he was com-missioned by Scipio during the third Punic War to command an exploring expedition along the west coast of Africa, and various details of his observations in those parts are recorded[3].   The results of those journeys are apparent, both in the descriptions of countries and places which serve to illustrate his History, and in the extracts from his geographical treatise, now lost, which have been preserved for us by Strabo.   His knowledge of the Iberian peninsula is especially noticeable, and we find not only that he was acquainted with the rivers in that country which flow

---

[1] Polyb. 3. 59. 7, 8.

[2] *Ibid.*, 3. 48. 12.

[3] Pliny, *H. N.*, 5. 9, 10; Scipione Aemiliano res in Africa gerente Polybius annalium conditor ab eo accepta classe scrutandi illius orbis gratia circumvectus prodidit etc.

into the Atlantic—the Baetis, the Anas, and the Tagus, but that
he attempts to estimate the length of the last-named stream from
its source to its mouth, assigning to it a course of 8000 stadia[1].
His account of the silver mines in the neighbourhood of New
Carthage, also, is evidently derived from personal enquiry, for he
mentions the number of slaves employed there, and the amount of
revenue derived from them, and describes in detail the process by
which the ore was prepared for smelting[2].   The Alps, again, he has
graphically depicted, and he mentions the four passes which were
known at that time to lead through them, viz. that which skirts the
Ligurian sea, that which passes through the land of the Taurini
(the Mont Genèvre), that through the territory of the Salassi (the
Little St. Bernard), and that by way of Rhaetia (the Brenner)[3].

His Opinion
of the Import-
ance of Travel.
The advantage which he had himself received from
these journeys impressed him so forcibly, that he
came to regard travel as an essential part of the
equipment of the historian and geographer; insomuch that he
finds fault with Timaeus as a historical writer, because he ignored
altogether this source of evidence—"for," says Polybius, "the
eyes are more accurate witnesses than the ears[4]."   One result of
the experience of travelling in his case was the interest which he

Interest in
Physical Geo-
graphy.
was led to take in physical geography, a notable
instance of which is found in his account of the
volcanic island of Hiera (Vulcano) in the Lipari
group, the condition of the craters of which he describes, and the
way in which it is affected by the winds which blow from different
quarters[5].   He also remarks concerning the stream of the Timavus,
which rises about a mile from the sea at the head of the Adriatic,
that its sources with one exception are brackish, so that the
natives call the spot the fountain-head and mother of the sea[6].
The accuracy of his observation has in this case been strikingly
confirmed by modern research; for, whereas he alone of the
ancient writers who have described that river mentions this peculiarity, it is noticed also by Cluver, the greatest modern authority
on the geography of Italy, who says that at high tides all the

---

[1] Strabo, 2. 4. 4.
[2] Ibid., 3. 2. 10.
[3] Ibid., 4. 6. 12.
[4] Polyb., 12. 27. 1—3.
[5] Strabo, 6. 2. 10.
[6] Ibid., 5. 1. 8.

springs except one turn brackish, 'doubtless from some subterranean communication with the sea.'

Let us now examine the ways in which Polybius employs his geographical knowledge for the elucidation of his   His Applicahistorical narrative.   We have already seen that he   tion of Geography to History. followed the example of Ephorus in setting apart a distinct portion of his work—it was the thirty-fourth book of his History—for the treatment of geography, and he has given us his reasons for doing so.   These were, first, that he desired to avoid frequently interrupting his historical narrative by digressions on the subject of geography; and secondly, that he wished by this means to secure the thorough and systematic treatment of geography itself[1].   This arrangement, however, does not prevent him from describing the geography of separate countries and the topography of places in the body of his   Descriptions of Countries. work, whenever it is convenient.   The object which he had in view in doing this, he tells us, was to place the scene and the circumstances of a historical event clearly before the minds of his readers, and thereby to render the event itself more real to them, for "what men want to know is, not so much the fact that a thing took place, as the way in which it happened"; and also to explain occurrences which would otherwise be perplexing, notably in the case of strategical operations, which are constantly determined by the nature of the ground[2].   Hence, as an introduction to the Gallic war of 225 B.C., Polybius gives us an elaborate description of the shape, the boundaries, and the products of Cisalpine Gaul, of its position   Cisalpine Gaul. relatively to the rest of Italy, of the course of the Padus which intersected it, and of the situation of the tribes by whom it was inhabited[3].   Similarly, in connexion with the campaign of Antiochus the Great against Molon, the   Media. revolted satrap of Media, in 220 B.C., he furnishes a singularly clear and intelligent account of that country in respect of its central position in Asia, the elevation of its surface, the mountains that border or divide it, the passes which it commands, and the relation which it bears to the surrounding

[1] Polyb., 3. 57. 4, 5.   [2] Ibid., 5. 21. 4—7.
[3] Ibid., 2. 14—17.

regions[1]. His descriptions of cities are numerous and graphic.
When they are brief, as is sometimes the case, the
Descriptions
of Cities.
salient points at least are mentioned which determine the character of the site. Such, for instance,
is his account of Sinope, the striking position of which on the
southern coast of the Euxine has been noticed in an earlier
chapter[2] :—

"Sinope lies on the right-hand shore of the Pontus as one
sails to Phasis, and is built upon a peninsula jutting
out into the sea: it is on the neck of this peninsula,
connecting it with Asia, which is not more than two stades wide,
that the city is so placed as to entirely close it up from sea to
sea; the rest of the peninsula stretches out into the open sea,—a
piece of flat land from which the town is easily accessible, but
surrounded by a steep coast offering very bad harbourage, and
having exceedingly few spots admitting of disembarcation[3]."

Somewhat fuller than this is his description of Agrigentum,
the accuracy of which will be recognised by everyone who has
visited that place :—

"The city of Agrigentum is not only superior to most cities
in the particulars I have mentioned, but above all
Agrigentum.
in beauty and elaborate ornamentation. It stands
within eighteen stades of the sea, so that it participates in every
advantage from that quarter ; while its circuit of fortification is
particularly strong both by nature and art. For its wall is placed
on a rock, steep and precipitous, on one side naturally, on the
other made so artificially. And it is enclosed by rivers: for along
the south side runs the river of the same name as the town, and
along the west and south-west side the river called Hypsas. The
citadel overlooks the city exactly at the north-east, girt on the
outside by an impassable ravine, and on the inside with only one
approach from the town. On the top of it is a temple of Athene
and of Zeus Atabyrius, as at Rhodes: for as Agrigentum was
founded by the Rhodians, it is natural that this deity should have
the same appellation as at Rhodes. The city is sumptuously

---

[1] Polyb., 5. 44.   [2] v. supra, p. 47.
[3] Ibid., 4. 56. 5, 6 (Shuckburgh's translation, from which also the other
passages here quoted are taken).

adorned in other respects also with temples and colonnades. The temple of Zeus Olympius is still unfinished, but in its plan and dimensions it seems to be inferior to no temple whatever in all Greece[1]."

Again, when a city has been the scene of events of the first importance, its site and the ground in its neighbourhood are delineated with the fullest detail. This is the case with New Carthage in Spain :—

"It stands about half-way down the coast of Iberia in a gulf which faces south-west, running about twenty stades inland, and about ten stades broad at its entrance. New Carthage. The whole gulf is made a harbour by the fact that an island lies at its mouth, and thus makes the entrance channels on each side of it exceedingly narrow. It breaks the force of the waves also, and the whole gulf has thus smooth water, except when south-west winds setting down the two channels raise a surf: with all other winds it is perfectly calm, from being so nearly landlocked. In the recess of the gulf a mountain juts out in the form of a chersonese, and it is on this mountain that the city stands, surrounded by the sea on the east and south, and on the west by a lagoon extending so far northward that the remaining space to the sea on the other side, to connect it with the continent, is not more than two stades. The city itself has a deep depression in its centre, presenting on its south side a level approach from the sea; while the rest of it is hemmed in by hills, two of them mountainous and rough, three others much lower, but rocky and difficult of ascent; the largest of which lies on the east of the town running out into the sea, on which stands a temple of Asclepius. Exactly opposite this lies the western mountain in a closely corresponding position, on which a palace had been erected at great cost, which it is said was built by Hasdrubal, when he was aiming at establishing royal power. The remaining three lesser elevations bound it on the north, of which the westernmost is called the hill of Hephaestus, the next to it that of Aletes,—who is believed to have attained divine honours from having been the discoverer of the silver mines,— and the third is called the hill of Cronus. The lagoon has been

[1] Polyb., 9. 27.

connected with the adjoining sea artificially for the sake of the maritime folk; and over the channel thus cut between it and the sea a bridge has been built, for beasts of burden and carts to bring in provisions from the country[1]."

Nor does Polybius fail to notice the influence which the conformation of countries exercised on the course of history on a larger scale. Thus we feel that he duly appreciated the importance of the Isthmus of Corinth to Greece, when in comparing that country to Italy he lays stress on the fact, unimportant though it may seem at first sight, that the limb in which the whole organism terminates has not been severed from the body in the one case, as it has been in the other—or, as he himself expresses it, that the passage from Northern Greece to the Peloponnese is made by land, that from Italy to Sicily by water[2]. Very interesting, too, is the contrast which he draws between the passage of the Straits of Gibraltar and that of the Hellespont in respect of their importance to the ancient world :—

General Remarks.

"The position of Abydos and Sestos, and the advantages of the situation of those towns it would, I think, be waste of time for me to state in great detail, because the singularity of those sites has made them familiar to all persons of intelligence. Still I imagine that it will be not otherwise than useful to remind my readers briefly of the facts, by way of attracting their attention. A man would best realise the advantage of these cities, not by regarding their sites by themselves, but by comparing and contrasting them with those about to be mentioned. For just as it is impossible to sail from the ocean—or as some call it the Atlantic—into our sea, except by passing through the Pillars of Heracles, so it is impossible to sail from our sea into the Propontis and the Pontus except through the channel separating Sestos and Abydos. But as though Fortune had designed these two straits to counterbalance each other, the passage between the Pillars of Heracles is many times as broad as that of the Hellespont—the former being sixty, the latter two stades[3]; the reason

---

[1] Polyb., 10. 10.   [2] Polyb., 1. 42. 1, 2.

[3] The distance here is strangely underestimated; the real width of the Hellespont in its narrowest part is 7 stades.

being, as far as one may conjecture, the great superiority in size of the external Ocean to our sea: while the channel at Abydos is more convenient than that at the Pillars of Heracles. For the former being lined on both sides by human habitations is of the nature of a gate admitting mutual intercourse, sometimes being bridged over by those who determine to cross on foot, and at all times admitting a passage by sea. But the channel at the Pillars of Heracles is seldom used, and by very few persons, owing to the lack of intercourse between the tribes inhabiting those remote parts of Libya and Europe, and owing to the scantiness of our knowledge of the external Ocean[1]."

The combination of realism with reflective observation, which we thus meet with in Polybius' treatment of geography in connexion with history, makes us feel that we have entered on a new and peculiarly useful application of the subject; and this, as we shall presently see, was afterwards carried out on a larger scale by Strabo, whose views were greatly influenced by those of his predecessor.

[1] Polyb., 16. 29.

CHAPTER XI.

GEOGRAPHY AS PROMOTED BY THE ROMAN CONQUESTS.

Exploration of Unknown Lands by the Greeks and by the Romans—Opportunity afforded by the Mithridatic War—Campaigns of Lucullus in Armenia and Mesopotamia—Pompey in Iberia and Albania—Narrative of Theophanes—His Description of the Caucasus, of the Cyrus and Araxes, and of the Tribes—The Iberi—The Albani—The Tribes bordering on the Euxine—Expedition of Balbus against the Garamantes, of Petronius in Aethiopia—The 'Atlantic Islands' (Madeira)—Fortunatae Insulae (The Canaries)—Progressive Conquest of Spain by the Romans—Southern and Eastern Provinces—Lusitania—Central Districts—Tribes of the North-West—Formation of the Roman Province in Gaul—Caesar's Conquest of Gaul—His Ethnographical and Geographical Notices—Transference to Towns of Names of Tribes—Caesar's Description of the Country of the Veneti—His Expeditions into Britain—His Information about it—Acquaintance of the Romans with Germany—Campaigns of Drusus and of Tiberius—Conquest of Rhaetia, Vindelicia, and Noricum—Of Pannonia—Importance to Geography of the Roman Roads—Careful Measurement of Distances—The Wall-map of Agrippa—Itineraries derived from it.

WE have now reached the period when the progress of geographical knowledge was mainly due to the advance

Exploration of Unknown Lands by the Greeks

of the Roman arms. Hitherto we have seen that its development was caused almost entirely by the enterprise and enquiring spirit of the Greeks, and by the spread of their commerce, which brought them into communication with distant peoples. At an early stage in their history the wide diffusion of their colonies along the shores of the Mediterranean and the Euxine brought in a vast fund of information with regard to the countries in the neighbourhood of those seas; together with intimations, in many cases vague and inexact, concerning the races inhabiting the lands which lay behind them. After a while the extension of the Persian empire in the direction of the Aegean, and the wars with the Greeks in which that power was involved, opened out to view a wide tract of Western Asia; and the same thing took place, though on a smaller scale, in Africa owing to the increasing intercourse of the Greeks with Egypt. Regions still more remote were also gradually revealed by the agency of adventurous explorers, such as Hanno the Carthaginian, who visited the west coast of Africa, and Pytheas, who penetrated into the northern seas. Then followed the expedition of Alexander, which marked an era in the extension of the subject, both on account of the immense area which was then for the first time brought within the field of knowledge, and because the cities which were founded by that conqueror in various parts of his newly acquired dominions served as centres for obtaining additional information. In this way the knowledge which prevailed in antiquity of the Ganges valley, and of the customs and institutions of its inhabitants, was once for all obtained by Megasthenes, and more accurate intelligence concerning the neighbourhood of the Red Sea and the shores of the Indian Ocean was brought to Alexandria under the Ptolemies. But when, after the fall of Carthage in 146 B.C., and the capture of Corinth by Mummius in the same year, *and by the Romans.* the preponderance of power passed from the east to the west, and the Romans found that they were able to attempt the conquest of distant countries, the campaigns in which their armies were engaged led them from time to time into regions as yet but little known, and thus contributed fresh materials for constructing the map of the world. The most considerable expansion of geographical knowledge at this time was in the direction of western Europe, as might be expected from the limited acquaintance which the Greeks had previously possessed with that part of the globe; but in the other continents also a considerable area of country was now for the first time explored.

On the side of Asia the third Mithridatic war furnished the chief opportunity of acquiring information about lands as yet imperfectly known. Mithridates, king *Opportunity afforded by the Mithridatic War.* of Pontus, who had amassed enormous treasures, and possessed a large and well-disciplined army, had extended his dominions in Asia Minor over part of Cappadocia, and over Armenia Minor, the district which lay to the westward of the Euphrates; and advancing toward the north had subjugated not only Colchis, but the Tauric Chersonese, and to some extent the country beyond, which lay between the Tyras (Dneister) and the Tanais (Don). His position was further strengthened by his alliance with Tigranes, the powerful king of Armenia, to whom he had given his daughter Cleopatra in marriage. Already on two former occasions he had engaged in war with the Romans, with whose allies in Asia Minor he was continually interfering; but the cause of this final struggle with them was the bequest of Nicomedes III, king of Bithynia, who on his death in 74 B.C. left his dominions by will to the Roman people. This arrangement, and the subsequent reduction of Bithynia to the form of a Roman province, was resisted by Mithridates, and upon this, war broke out afresh between the two powers, and on a great scale. On the two first of the campaigns which followed we have no need to dwell, because they were carried on in well-known districts of Asia Minor; the interest of the war from a geographical point of view commences after the defeat of Mithridates at Cabeira by Lucullus, who was in command of the Romans, in 72 B.C., when

Campaigns of Lucullus in Armenia

that monarch was forced to abandon his kingdom, and to take refuge with Tigranes in Armenia. That country, accordingly, which had remained almost unvisited since the days when it was traversed by Xenophon and the Ten Thousand, became for a time the seat of war; and though the writers from whom our knowledge of the events which took place there is derived, Appian and Plutarch, pay little attention to the topography, we cannot doubt that the ancients at that time obtained a clearer idea of many of its remarkable features[1]. This was the first occasion on which the Romans had passed through the Anti-Taurus and entered the wild uplands in which the sources of the Tigris and Euphrates are found, and there they had some experience of the severity of the climate, from which Xenophon and his soldiers previously suffered. Then, too, for the first time,

and Mesopotamia.

they crossed the Taurus, where it separates that land from Mesopotamia, and descended towards the lower courses of the two great rivers, which were destined at a later period to be the scene of numerous encounters between them and the Parthians. Lucullus advanced through the province of Sophene, which occupies the wide bend

[1] For a description of these *vide supra*, p. 113.

formed by the stream of the Euphrates just where it leaves
Armenia, and within which the western branch of the Tigris
rises; and from thence he marched on Tigranocerta, the newly
founded capital of Tigranes, which he captured. The site of that
city has been much disputed, and perhaps the shortness of the
period during which it flourished, and the consequent absence of
such means of identification as coins, may render it impossible to
determine it with certainty, but the position which best corresponds
with the statements of Strabo and Tacitus, the most weighty
authorities on the subject, and which also suits the accounts of
Lucullus' campaign, is that of a village called Tel Ermen, a little
distance to the south-west of Mardin, at which considerable remains
of antiquity are found[1]. The river Arsanias, on the banks of
which Lucullus defeated the combined forces of Mithridates and
Tigranes, is almost certainly the Murad, or eastern branch of the
Euphrates, which Xenophon also crossed[2]. After this Lucullus
subdued the important fortress of Nisibis in Mesopotamia; but
here his successes ended in consequence of the insubordination
which prevailed among his troops, and he was superseded in his
command, Pompey being appointed in his stead.

The campaigns which followed under the leadership of that
general were productive of far more important results to geography, for in the course of them accurate
information was obtained concerning the lands that
lay between the Black Sea and the Caspian. For some time after

Pompey in Iberia and Albania.

his arrival Pompey was engaged in expelling Mithridates from
Asia Minor, where he had recovered a large part of his dominions
during the absence of Lucullus in Mesopotamia; and after he had
accomplished this he advanced into Armenia, where Tigranes
submitted to him without a struggle. He was thus at liberty to
follow Mithridates, who had retired, first into Colchis, and afterwards by a difficult route along the shore of the Euxine, until he
reached Panticapaeum (Kertch) on the European side of the
Cimmerian Bosporus, which place he hoped to make a starting-
point for further resistance. In the course of his pursuit Pompey

[1] Sachau, *Ueber die Lage von Tigranokerta;* Berlin, 1881.
[2] See Pliny, *H. N.,* 6. 128; and cp. the author's *Turkish Armenia,* pp.
244, 298.

found it necessary to subdue the tribes that lay to the northward of Armenia—the Iberi, who occupied the highlands to the south-ward of the Caucasus, about the upper waters of the Cyrus (Kur), and the Albani, who dwelt about the lower course of that river, extending as far as the coast of the Caspian Sea. These nations and the lands which they inhabited were equally unknown, and during this expedition Pompey crossed the Cyrus, and advanced within three days' march of the Caspian. Plutarch tells us that he was prevented from reaching its waters by the multitude of deadly serpents which swarmed in those parts[1]—an evident exaggeration, but one which was based on fact, for the poisonous snakes of the plain of Mogan, as that district is called at the present day, have attracted the attention of modern travellers.

For an account of these countries we are indebted to Theo-phanes of Mytilene, who was an intimate friend of Pompey and his companion on this campaign, of which he wrote a history. The singularly full and graphic description of them which is found in Strabo was derived in the main from him, and this writer refers to him in several passages as the most important authority on the subject[2]. He speaks of the Caucasus—which chain resembles the Pyrenees in the uniformity of its direction and its unbroken line of heights—as forming a wall across the isthmus which intervenes between the two seas, and he notices the pass that leads through it from "the nomad peoples towards the north," which is evidently the Dariel pass of modern times[3]. He also describes its luxuriant vegetation, a feature which is especially remarkable in its south-western valleys and slopes. Again, the Suram range, as the mountains are called which form the watershed of the country, from which the streams flow to east and west, is characterised by him as a number of transverse chains, which run off from the Caucasus towards the south, and join those of Armenia and Colchis[4]. The course of the river Cyrus is also carefully traced, and an interesting account is given of the formation of the delta at its

Narrative of Theophanes.

His Descrip-tion of the Caucasus,

of the Cyrus and Araxes,

---

[1] Plut., *Pomp.*, 36.
[2] *e.g.*, Strabo, 11. 2. 14; 11. 5. 1; 13. 2. 3.
[3] Strabo, 11. 3. 5.　　　　　[4] *Ibid.*, 11. 2. 15.

mouth; in addition to which we are informed that the Araxes, which flowed from the mountains of Armenia, reached the sea in its neighbourhood, but did not join its stream, as it does at the present day[1]. The variations which are found in ancient authors with regard to this last point afford a curious subject of speculation. The statement of Theophanes is repeated by Mela[2], whereas Pliny[3], though with some reserve, and Appian[4] affirm that those rivers met before entering the sea. Plutarch, again[5], mentions both views without pronouncing between them, while Ptolemy[6] says that the Araxes discharged its waters, partly into the Caspian Sea, and partly into the Cyrus. The last of these notices has been employed as a means of reconciling the others, and the conclusion has not unreasonably been drawn, that the change in the course of the Araxes, which caused it to communicate with the Cyrus, commenced early in the Christian era, and that for a considerable time that river continued to flow both through its old and its new channel.

Theophanes' account of the customs and manner of life of the tribes that inhabited this area of country is also highly valuable. Of these the Iberi were the most *and of the Tribes.* civilised, for they possessed towns and markets, and had tiled roofs to their houses and some pretence to architecture in their dwellings. The population was divided into four classes, of which the first was the royal caste, *The Iberi.* which furnished the leaders both at home and in war; the second

---

[1] Strabo, 11. 3. 2; 11. 4. 2; in the latter of these passages, after the mouth of the Cyrus has been described, it is said, πλησίον δὲ καὶ ὁ Ἀράξης ἐμβάλλει.

[2] 3. 40, 41.

[3] *H. N.*, 6. 26; Araxes...ut plures existimavere, a Cyro defertur in Caspium mare.

[4] *Mithr.*, 103; τὸν Κύρνον ποταμόν, ὃς δώδεκα στόμασι πλωτοῖς ἐς τὴν Κασπίαν θάλασσαν ἐρεύγεται, πολλῶν εἰς αὐτὸν ἐμβαλόντων ποταμῶν, καὶ μεγίστου πάντων Ἀράξου.

[5] *Pomp.*, 34; τὸν Κύρνον ποταμόν, ὃς ἐκ τῶν Ἰβηρικῶν ὁρῶν ἀνιστάμενος καὶ δεχόμενος κατιόντα τὸν Ἀράξην ἀπ᾽ Ἀρμενίας, ἐξίησι δώδεκα στόμασιν εἰς τὸ Κάσπιον. Οἱ δὲ οὔ φασι τούτῳ συμφέρεσθαι τὸν Ἀράξην, ἀλλὰ καθ᾽ ἑαυτόν, ἐγγὺς δὲ ποιεῖσθαι τὴν ἐκβολὴν ἐς ταὐτὸ πέλαγος.

[6] 5. 13. 6; [ὁ Ἀράξης] τῇ μὲν εἰς τὴν Ὑρκανίαν [θάλασσαν] ἐκβάλλει, τῇ δὲ συμβάλλει τῷ Κύρῳ ποταμῷ.

the priests, who acted as arbitrators, when disputes arose with the neighbouring tribes; while the third comprehended the soldiers and the cultivators of the soil, and the fourth the mass of the common people, who were employed in menial tasks, and were regarded as slaves of the king. Their domestic organisation was patriarchal, the property of each family being possessed in common, and administered by the eldest member of the family[1]. The

The Albani.

condition of the Albani, on the other hand, was much more primitive. We learn that they did not use money for purposes of traffic, but made their exchanges in kind, and that they were unacquainted for the most part with weights and measures. The custom of human sacrifices also prevailed amongst them, and like the Gauls and the Lusitani, they were wont on these occasions to divine from the bodies of the victims. Their occupations were mainly pastoral, and where they cultivated the soil the implements they used were of the rudest description; but, notwithstanding this, the crops which they obtained were exceedingly rich in consequence of the fertility of the soil—a description which applies at the present day to the corresponding district of Shirvan, which lies between the Kur, the Caspian Sea, and the eastern part of the Caucasus. Though naturally a peaceful race, they were able to put a large military force into the field, so that they opposed Pompey with an army of

The Tribes bordering on the Euxine.

sixty thousand infantry and twelve thousand cavalry[2]. The tribes which bordered on the coast of the Euxine to the northward of the Phasis were very numerous, and as many as seventy of them were said to frequent the Greek colony of Dioscurias (Sukhum Kaleh), which lay in their neighbourhood, as a trading centre[3]. We learn also that they spoke different dialects, and this was no doubt the result of the conformation of the ground in those·parts, which is broken up into a number of separate valleys by the spurs of the Caucasus. The name of one of them, which appears in Greek as Heniochi, can be recognised in the modern form Hainuch. Some of them led a piratical life, attacking the merchant ships in the Black Sea, or making descents on various parts of the coast, for which

[1] Strabo, II. 3. 1, 6.
[2] *Ibid.*, II. 4.   [3] *Ibid.*, II. 2. 16.

purpose they employed vessels of a primitive character, capable of containing from twenty-five to thirty men apiece[1]. Of these Tacitus has furnished us with a detailed description in an account which he gives of a rising in Pontus during the reign of Vitellius. "The barbarians," he says, "insolently scoured the sea in hastily constructed vessels of their own called 'camarae,' built with narrow sides and broad bottoms, and joined together without fastenings of brass or iron. Whenever the water is rough, they raise the bulwarks with additional planks according to the increasing height of the waves, till the vessel is covered in like a house. Thus they roll about amid the billows, and, as they have a prow at both extremities alike and a convertible arrangement of oars, they may be paddled in one direction or another indifferently and without risk[2]."

In Africa the advance of geographical knowledge was the work of a later period, and was on a more restricted scale. Virgil, in a passage of the sixth *Aeneid* where he is celebrating the glories of Augustus, represents Anchises as prophesying that he should extend his dominion beyond the Garamantes[3]. We have already heard of this people in connexion with Herodotus, who places one of the Oases in their territory, and we have seen that they occupied the district of the interior of Africa south of Tripoli, which is now called Fezzan[4]. The expedition to which Virgil refers was that of Cornelius Balbus in the year 20 B.C., and the mention of it by the poet implies that it was regarded as a remarkable achievement. Balbus, who was governor of the Roman province of Africa, advanced into the country of these independent tribes, and was so far successful in reducing them to temporary subjection that he received the honour of a triumph. Few details of his movements have come down to us, but we know that he captured their chief town, Garama[5], the site of which with

Expedition of Balbus against the Garamantes,

---

[1] Strabo, 11. 2. 12.   [2] Tac. *Hist.*, 3. 47.
[3] *Aen.* 6. 795;

         super et Garamantas et Indos
      Proferet imperium.

[4] *v. supra*, p. 96; Herod., 4. 183.
[5] Pliny, *H. N.*, 5. 36.

considerable ruins still bears the name of Germa, and is about 70 miles distant from Mourzouk, the modern capital of Fezzan. Almost contemporary with this campaign was the expedition of C. Petronius into Aethiopia. In 22 B.C. Candace the queen of that country—taking advantage of the withdrawal from Egypt of a part of the Roman forces, which were being employed in the invasion of Arabia which Aelius Gallus had undertaken by the order of Augustus— had attacked and captured the city of Syene and the neighbouring island of Elephantine, which formed the frontier station of the Romans in that quarter. Petronius, however, who was in command in Egypt, not only recovered these places, but invaded Aethiopia, and defeated the army of Candace. After this he made himself master of three important towns, Pselchis, Premnis, and Candace's royal city, Napata, which are mentioned as having been taken in the order here given[1]. Of these, Pselchis, which is called Pselket in the hieroglyphics, and lay between the first and second cataract, is undoubtedly the modern Dakkeh, which place is situated a little distance to the south of Korosko, where the great westward bend of the river in the direction of Dongola commences. Again, the site of Napata, with the remains of temples and pyramids in its neighbourhood, has been discovered at a place called Merawi, near the conspicuous height of Jebel Barkal, just below the fourth cataract. The points thus fixed enable us approximately to determine that of Premnis also. Strabo, from whom our knowledge of the campaign is derived, tells us that in passing from Pselchis to that town Petronius' line of march lay across the desert; and by this he can hardly fail to mean that he followed the modern caravan route from Korosko to Abu Hamed, which forms the chord of the arc here made by the Nile. It is natural therefore to conjecture that Premnis lay at no very great distance from Abu Hamed, because in passing from Pselchis to Napata by this route Petronius would rejoin the river near that place, from which Napata is distant about a hundred miles lower down the stream[2].

of Petronius in Aethiopia.

---

[1] Strabo, 17. 1. 54.

[2] See Bunbury, _Hist. of Anc. Geogr._, 2. pp. 168, 183, 184.

In this connexion we may notice a discovery that forcibly impressed the men of that time, the mention of which occurs in the course of Sertorius' career in Spain. In the year 81 B.C. that adventurous com- The 'Atlantic Islands' (Madeira). mander, when he found himself unable to make head against the forces which Sulla had sent to oppose him in that country, happened to meet near the mouth of the Baetis with some seamen who had recently visited the 'Atlantic Islands.' These they described as being two in number, separated by a very narrow channel, and lying in the open sea at a distance of ten thousand stadia (1,000 geographical miles) from the African coast. The climate of the islands they reported to be delightfully temperate, exempt from cold and violent winds and from excessive rain, with a soft and moist air, which not only rendered the soil fertile for cultivation, but produced self-sown fruits in great abundance. The account thus given took such hold on the imagination of Sertorius, that he was seized with a strong desire to betake himself to this spot, where he might "escape from tyranny and unceasing wars, and live in tranquillity"; but he was forced to desist from the project by the unwillingness of the Cilician pirates who formed the crews of his ships to accompany him. As was natural, these islands were identified with the 'Islands of the Blessed,' which had been celebrated from early days in Greek poetry—"where is no snow, nor yet great storm, nor any rain; but alway ocean sendeth forth the breeze of the shrill West to blow cool on men[1]": indeed, we are told that the barbarians themselves believed that in them were to be found the Elysian plains and the Abodes of the Happy, of which Homer had sung[2]. Though the distance from the continent which is attributed to these islands must in any case have been a great exaggeration, yet it seems impossible to regard the Canaries, lying as they do within easy reach of the African coast, as corresponding to them; and the circumstance that they are spoken of as two only, suggests that Madeira and the neighbouring Porto Santo were meant, rather than such groups as the Azores or the Cape Verde islands. The humidity and equable character of the climate of Madeira, also, and the great productiveness of the ground, are in favour of this view.

[1] Hom. *Od.*, 4. 566—8.   [2] Plutarch, *Sertor.*, 8, 9.

At a later period, however, there is no doubt that the
Fortunatae   islands which were known by the name of Fortu-
Insulae   natae Insulae were the Canaries. The informa-
The Canaries). tion which the Romans possessed about these
was derived from the treatise on Africa by Juba king of Mauretania, who had ample facilities for learning the truth about
them. This prince was carried to Rome as a captive during
his childhood, in 46 B.C., and having been educated there,
became a man of distinguished learning. In his youth he was
a friend of Augustus, who first restored him to his father's
kingdom of Numidia, and afterwards transferred him to the
sovereignty of Mauretania. His statements with regard to these
islands are preserved in Pliny's *Natural History*[1], and the names
that he assigns to them, which are mostly of Latin origin, are of
service in identifying them. Thus Canaria retains its appellation
unchanged as Grand Canary, while Nivaria or Ninguaria, which,
he says, was so called from its perpetual snows, is evidently Tene-
rife, with its celebrated Peak, 12,182 feet in height; and he also
remarks on the clouds by which it is so frequently shrouded. A
third, Ombrios, which is described as having a lake in the midst of
its mountains, seems to correspond to Palma, the central crater of
which is called Caldera or " the Cauldron," and is surrounded by
many lofty summits.

The advance of the Roman arms in Spain may be passed over
Progressive   with a brief notice, because it belongs for the most
Conquest of   part to an earlier period than that of which we are
Spain by the   now speaking, and its effects in opening out the
Romans.   interior of that peninsula have already been ad-
verted to in our remarks on Polybius and Posidonius, the first
writers who communicated to the world the information obtained
by this means. When the Carthaginians were finally expelled
from Spain at the conclusion of the Second Punic war, the
territory which they had occupied was erected into a Roman
Southern   province in 206 B.C. The part thus acquired, how-
and Eastern   ever, was not more than one half of the country; it
Provinces.   comprised the southern districts between the Sierra
Morena and the sea, and those towards the east, which are

[1] *H. N.*, 6. 203—5.

bounded on one side by the Mediterranean, and on the other by the inland chain that runs parallel to it and forms the watershed between the rivers that flow into that sea and those which reach the Atlantic: this area would correspond to the modern provinces of Andalucia, Murcia, Valencia, and Catalonia. It was only by slow degrees that the rest of the peninsula was subjugated, for the successive mountain ranges which intersect it form so many natural lines of defence, and oppose great difficulties in the way of an invading force, while the hardy tribes of the interior, accustomed as they were to guerilla warfare, were skilled in distracting the attention of their opponents and harassing them in their advance. Strabo has rightly remarked that this characteristic of the natives rendered the task of subduing them much more arduous and protracted than anything which the Romans experienced in Gaul[1]. Such was, in particular, the policy of Viriathus in Lusitania, who kept the Romans at bay for eight years (148—140 B.C.). After his treacherous assassination, however, that country was sub- Lusitania. dued by D. Junius Brutus, and that general for the first time led an army beyond the Durius (Douro) as far as the Minius (Minho). But the turning-point in the advance of the Romans was the capture by blockade and the subsequent destruction of Numantia by Scipio Africanus in 133 B.C. That city was situated near the sources of the Douro in the heart Central Districts. of the peninsula, and by its fall the Roman dominion was established throughout central Spain; from that time onwards the only tribes that continued to defy the conquerors were the Astures and Cantabri, Tribes of the North-West. who inhabited the mountains of the north-west, corresponding in position to the modern districts of the Asturias and part of the Basque provinces. These were finally subdued in 19 B.C., after a war which continued several years, and was conducted at first by Augustus in person, and afterwards by Agrippa. The passes which led from the interior to the extreme north-west

---

[1] Strabo, 4. 4. 2, where it is said of the Gauls, ἀθρόοι καὶ κατὰ πλῆθος ἐμπίπτοντες ἀθρόοι κατελύοντο, and of the Spaniards, οἱ δ' ἐταμίευον καὶ κατεκερμάτιζον τοὺς ἀγῶνας, ἄλλοτε ἄλλοι καὶ κατ' ἄλλα μέρη λῃστρικῶς πολεμοῦντες.

angle, through which the route still lies into Galicia, were secured by the foundation of the colonies of Asturica Augusta (Astorga) and Lucus Augusti (Lugo), the fine Roman walls of which still testify to their ancient strength.

The neighbouring country of Gaul was the most important field of geographical discovery that was opened out

Formation of the Roman Province in Gaul.

during the century which immediately preceded the Christian era. Long after the power of Rome had made itself felt in Syria and Egypt the Alps continued to form an effectual barrier to the advance of the great republic in that direction, and it was not until the defeat of the Salyes, who occupied the district between Marseilles and Nice, by the consul M. Fulvius Flaccus in 125 B.C., and their subjugation by C. Sextius Calvinus two years later, that the Romans secured a permanent footing there. The latter of these two officers established a military post at the place which had before been the stronghold of the tribe, and this afterwards became famous as Aquae Sextiae (Aix). Again, the Vocontii, whose territory lay between the Durance and the Isère, were conquered by Flaccus, and shortly afterwards the Allobroges, who inhabited the mountainous regions of Dauphiné between the Isère and the Rhone, were reduced to a state of dependence, so that the Roman dominion in this part was extended from the shores of the Mediterranean to the lake of Geneva. On the further side of the Rhone a footing was also obtained by the establishment of a colony at Narbo (Narbonne); and the capture of Tolosa (Toulouse), the capital of the tribe of Tectosages, in 106 B.C., advanced their territory as far as the Garonne. The lands which were thus brought under the Roman sway were formally organised under the name of 'The Province,' a title which became so permanently associated with this domain, that it has been perpetuated in the modern Provence. In this way the influence of Rome was confirmed and its civilisation propagated through the southern part of Gaul, but from that date the limits of its sovereignty remained unchanged until the time of Caesar.

That leader accepted the command in Gaul with the definite intention of conquering the whole of the country,

Caesar's Conquest of Gaul.

and this purpose he accomplished with great completeness in the course of nine years (58—50 B.C.).

His successive campaigns carried him and his lieutenants even into the remotest districts, and the knowledge which he thus obtained both of their natural features and of their inhabitants enabled him to accumulate a large store of facts, by which his history is throughout elucidated. He notices at starting the three great nations which occupied Gaul—the Aquitani in the south, the Celts or Gauls in the centre, and the Belgae in the north—together His Ethnographical and Geographical Notices. with the rivers which separated them one from another, the Garumna (Garonne) in the one case, and the Sequana (Seine) and Matrona (Marne) in the other. He shews himself well acquainted with the principal mountain chains—the Jura and the Mons Vosegus (Vosges) towards the east, and the Mons Cebenna (Cevennes) in the south—and with the Silva Arduenna, or forest district of the Ardennes, which spread over a wide tract in Belgica. His accuracy extends to geographical details, when there is any need to introduce them: thus he remarks that the stream of the Vacalus (Waal) is a branch of the Rhine which flows into the Meuse[1], and he observes that Lutetia (Paris) is situated on an island in the Seine[2]. He obtained exact details respecting the subdivisions of the tribes with which from time to time he came into conflict, and of these he has drawn up lists in various parts of his work. Their position can in a large number of instances be verified owing to the permanence of their names, which came to be attached, either to the districts in which they dwelt, or, as often happened, to the chief town of the district. The latter process, in the course of which the previous appellation of the city was superseded, has given birth to the names of many important places in France. Thus the tribe of Transference to Towns of Names of Tribes. Lexovii, whose city was called Noviomagus, is recognised in the modern Lisieux, and the Senones have given their name to Sens in place of that of Agedincum; Mediolanum, the capital of the Eburovices, is now Evreux, and Avaricum of the Bituriges is Bourges. A marked instance of the interest which Caesar took in the remote tribes, and of his carefulness in recording the geographical features of the lands which they

[1] *Bell. Gall.*, 4. 10.   [2] *Ibid.*, 7. 57.

occupied, is furnished by his account of the Veneti in Armorica, who inhabited the sea-coast north of the mouth of the Loire. Against these he first sent his lieutenant, P. Crassus, in 57 B.C., and in the following year he entered their territory himself, and after assembling a fleet of sufficient size to enable him to cope with their vessels, finally reduced them to submission.

Caesar's Description of the Country of the Veneti.

In his narrative of the campaign he delineates the peculiarities of the coast of the Morbihan, as this district of France is now called—the creeks and inlets of the sea, which interfered with communication by land, and the position of the towns on the extremities of jutting tongues of land, which caused them to be hard of access to an invader, because at high tide the approach from the land-side was cut off, and at low water it was a difficult matter for ships to approach them in consequence of the shoals. He then proceeds to describe the vessels used by these hardy navigators, who were accustomed to make voyages to Britain—their oaken timbers, their almost flat keels, which allowed of their grounding without difficulty, their height in the bows, and their leathern sails. Against these the Romans had the one advantage of using oars, which their opponents were without; and thus, when they had disabled their rigging by means of hooks attached to long poles, they were able to board their vessels, after which the superior courage of the Roman soldiers prevailed. When victory declared itself on the side of the invaders, the people at large submitted, but Caesar thought fit that they should be put to death or sold into slavery[1]. In this way a race was exterminated who were distinguished for commercial enterprise, as we have already remarked when speaking of the tin trade with Britain[2].

Caesar's two expeditions into Britain were important as mark-

His Expeditions into Britain.

ing the first occasion on which the Romans set foot in that island, but they do not seem to have made any considerable addition to what was already known through Posidonius concerning it[3]. Both those writers

[1] *B. G.*, 3. 8, 9, 12—16.   [2] *v. supra*, p. 36.
[3] Posidonius' account is embodied in Strabo's description of Britain, 4. 5.
1—3.

were acquainted only with the south-eastern portion and the adjoining districts of the interior. Caesar's starting-point was the Portus Itius, a harbour of the Morini, whose territory lay in that part of Gaul which adjoins the Straits of Dover. Among the many competing sites which claim to be identified with that place the two that deserve especial consideration are Wissant, a village on the coast to the east of Cape Gris Nez, and Boulogne; but both this question and that of the point on the coast of Britain at which he landed are so debateable, that it is not possible to speak with great confidence on the subject. The first of these expeditions was little more than a reconnaissance, for Caesar on that occasion hardly penetrated at all into the country; in the second, with a view to which he prepared a large fleet and a force of five legions and two thousand cavalry, he advanced into the interior as far as the Thames, which river he crossed at a point about eighty miles from the sea, somewhere perhaps between Kingston and Brentford. He did not, however, proceed much further than this, for in no long time Cassivelaunus, the chief of the Trinobantes, who commanded the British forces, made submission to him, and Caesar was willing to quit the island on terms favourable to the natives. In consequence of this it is not surprising if his knowledge of the country was limited. He rightly describes it as triangular in shape; with the island of Hibernia, which he   His Informa-
estimates at half the size of Britain, on its western   tion about it.
side. He is also the first writer who notices the Isle of Man; for it seems to be this, and not Anglesea, that he means by Mona, for he speaks of it as lying half-way between the two larger islands. In Pliny the Isle of Man is called Monapia[1]. As regards the inhabitants he remarks that the most civilised were those that dwelt in the south-eastern parts, who were settlers of Belgian race, having migrated from the mainland, and both in their dwellings and their manner of life resembled those in Gaul. The tribes of the interior he characterises as barbarous in their customs and as leading the life of herds-men[2].

[1] H. N, 4. 103.   [2] B. G., 5. 12 –14.

Caesar also was the first Roman commander who led an
army across the Rhine, though he penetrated but
a little way into Germany.   The information which
he obtained about that country was mainly derived
from his allies the Ubii, and from the prisoners
whom he captured when fighting against Ariovistus; and in
this way he has accurately recorded the names of a number of
the tribes.   He also describes the Hercynian Forest, the mention
of which he says that he had found occurring in the writings
of Eratosthenes and other Greeks; and he attributes to it a
width of nine days' journey, and a length of sixty, reaching from
the confines of the Helvetii along the course of the Danube as
far as Dacia, where it turned towards the north[1].   There is no
notice, however, in his work of the great rivers of northern
Germany, and it was not until long afterwards that his countrymen obtained an accurate knowledge of that
land.   The next Roman general who crossed the
Rhine was Drusus, the stepson of Augustus, who
in the course of three campaigns traversed a great part of its
western districts.   In the year 12 B.C. he started from the Island
of the Batavi, as the country between the mouths of the Rhine
and the Meuse was called, and overran the territory of the
Usipetes and Sigambri, which lay higher up on the right bank
of the stream.   The following year witnessed his advance to
the Visurgis (Weser), and as far as the land of the Chatti who
lived about its head-waters, where he established a garrison:
and finally his third campaign carried him from this point, which
formed his base of operations, through the territory of the
Cherusci, and after crossing the Visurgis he reached at last
the banks of the Albis (Elbe).   But the achievement on which
the fame of Drusus subsequently rested, since it greatly impressed the imaginations of his countrymen, was his navigation
of the Northern Ocean in a Roman fleet, a thing which had
never before been attempted.   This took place during the latter
part of his first campaign.   Under his directions a canal, which
bore the name of the Fossa Drusiana, was constructed from the
Rhine to the Lake Flevus, a large piece of water, which then

*Acquaint-
ance of the
Romans with
Germany.*

*Campaigns
of Drusus*

[1] *B. G.*, 6. 24, 25.

occupied a part of the area now covered by the Zuyder Zee, and communicated with the ocean. By means of this he conducted the fleet which he had prepared to the coast of the North Sea, and proceeded along it as far as the mouth of the Amisia (Ems), receiving at this time the submission of the Frisians, who inhabited the neighbouring district. He was repulsed, however, by the Chauci, whose territory lay on the right bank of that river—a disaster which was partly due to the want of experience of the tides in those seas from which the Romans suffered. After the premature death of Drusus, his brother Tiberius, the future emperor, was appointed to his command, and was successful in his operations against the Germans, but did not at that time advance further into their country. At a later period, after his seven years' retirement at Rhodes, when this government was renewed to him by Augustus (A.D. 5), he caused his fleet to sail up the Elbe from its mouth, and himself with his land forces effected a junction with it on the banks of that river. On this occasion the Chauci accepted the supremacy of Rome, while their neighbours towards the interior between the Weser and the Elbe, the Langobardi, whose name now occurs for the first time, were defeated by the invaders. Subsequently to this, the further advance of the Romans in that quarter, and indeed their permanent establishment at any point beyond the Rhine, was precluded by the great defeat of Varus by Arminius, involving the destruction of three legions (A.D. 9)—an event of the first importance in history, because in consequence of it the races of Germany were developed under native, and not Roman, institutions.

and of Tiberius.

The two brothers Tiberius and Drusus were also instrumental in subjugating the countries which lay to the north-eastward of Italy, and commanded the approaches to it from that quarter. The area embraced by these was bounded on the north and east by the Danube, and on the south by the Alps and the line of the river Save, as far as its point of junction with the Danube at Belgrade. It comprised the countries of Rhaetia, Vindelicia, Noricum and Pannonia, which correspond, generally speaking, to the Tyrol,

Conquest of Rhaetia, Vindelicia, and Noricum.

the part of Bavaria which lies to the northward of it, the southern provinces of Austria, and a portion of Hungary. In the year 15 B.C. Drusus marched up the valley of the Adige, and having defeated the forces of the Rhaetians near Tridentum, the modern Trent, advanced into their land by the line of the Brenner pass. Shortly afterwards Tiberius, approaching the country from the opposite quarter, ascended the valley of the Rhine, and having launched a flotilla on the lake of Constance, succeeded in taking the enemy in the rear, and penetrating into the upper valley of the Inn. The campaign thus begun resulted in the complete reduction of the tribes of the eastern Alps, together with the neighbouring districts of Vindelicia and Noricum. The foundation of the colony of Augusta Vinde-licorum (Augsburg) at this time had the effect of securing the Roman conquest, and of guarding the approaches to the mountain chain. These victories of the stepsons of Augustus were celebrated by Horace in two famous odes, which glorify the family of the Neros, and extol the difficulty of the achievement[1]. The Pannonians, however, offered a more effectual resistance to the Roman arms. Their country was of importance to Italy because of the trade-route which from early times had passed through it from Germany to the head of the Adriatic[2]; and the facility of access which its proximity afforded to an invading force was felt to be a source of danger. So much was this the case, that in 6 A.D. there was a panic in Rome, when it was reported in that city that the Pannonians had descended on the province of Istria. Accordingly, after the subjugation of the neighbouring nations which has just been mentioned, first Agrippa, and after his death Tiberius, invaded and ravaged their country; but the effect of

Of Pannonia.

[1] Hor. *Od.*, 4. 4. 17;

> Videre Raeti bella sub Alpibus
> Drusum gerentem Vindelici;

and 4. 14. 14;

> Major Neronum mox grave proelium
> Commisit immanesque Raetos
> Auspiciis pepulit secundis.

[2] *v. supra*, p. 32.

this was only temporary, and it was not until the year 9 A.D., at the expiration of several hard fought campaigns, that they finally submitted to the Romans. The necessity of keeping them in check accounts for the subsequent maintenance of a large force of soldiers in Pannonia, whose rebellion on receiving the news of the death of Augustus and the accession of Tiberius as emperor has been forcibly depicted by Tacitus[1]. The Danube now became throughout its whole length the northern boundary of the Roman empire, since Moesia, which occupied the area that extended from its right bank to the foot of the Haemus mountains in the lower part of its course, had been conquered by Marcus Crassus in 29 B.C., and had been reduced not long after to the form of a Roman province.

In the review which has thus been taken of the advances made by the Roman arms in the regions bordering on the civilised world during the Augustan age and the period immediately preceding it, we see that a considerable addition was made to the knowledge of the face of the globe which already existed.   But both in these countries, and in those which had previously been incorporated in the empire, the accurate treatment of geography was furthered by the practical spirit of the administration of the Romans, which caused them to construct roads as means of communication throughout their subject provinces. The object which they had in view in this system was, no doubt, to facilitate the passage of their armies, and to secure the rapid transmission of intelligence to the provincial centres and to the capital itself, and thereby to concentrate their dominion and guarantee it against dismemberment.   But, at the same time, the careful measurement of distances which was thus introduced, and the clearer acquaintance with the relative position of places and the direction followed by rivers and mountain chains which was obtained, tended to promote exactness in geographical study.   Polybius speaks of the road through southern Gaul from the Spanish frontier to the Rhone as having in his time been paced, and the distances along it marked

Importance to Geography of the Roman Roads.

Careful Measurement of Distances.

---

[1] Tac. *Ann.*, I. 16 foll.

by milestones[1]; and he remarks the same thing of the Egnatian
Way, the length of which he gives according to this computation,
from Apollonia and Epidamnus (Dyrrhachium), its two starting
points on the Adriatic, as far as the river Hebrus in Thrace[2].
During the following century and a half these lines of communication had been so extended and multiplied, that they
formed a network throughout the lands that were subject to
Rome.   Thus in Gaul, subsequently to its conquest by Julius
Caesar, four great roads were constructed in such a way as to
open out the whole country, starting from Lugdunum as their
centre and leading respectively to the Rhine, to the coast of the
British Channel, to the Western Ocean near the mouth of the
Garonne, and southward through the Provincia—a proceeding
by which the prosperity of the country was greatly promoted.

The Wall-map of Agrippa.   Agrippa, under whose auspices this was effected,
was also the author of a geographical record, which
was of the utmost service in promoting that study.
This was the map of the Roman empire and the countries in its
neighbourhood, the plan of which he devised, and the material
for constructing which he collected; and which after his death, as
we learn from Pliny[3], was set up by the orders of Augustus in the
Porticus Octaviae at Rome.   To it was attached a commentary,
giving the dimensions of the different provinces, and the distances which intervened between the most important places.   The
authorities which were principally used in compiling this chart,
were, no doubt, the itineraries, in which the distances along the
great roads were recorded; and from it in turn reduced copies

Itineraries derived from it.   were made for the use of the provincial governors
and the commanders of the forces.   These were
called *Itineraria picta* or *Itineraria adnotata*,
according as they gave a plan of the roads, or a list of the

[1] Polyb., 3. 39. 8; ταῦτα γὰρ νῦν βεβημάτισται, καὶ σεσημείωται κατὰ
σταδίους ὀκτὼ διὰ 'Ρωμαίων ἐπιμελῶς.

[2] Polyb., ap. Strabon., 7. 7. 4; βεβηματισμένη κατὰ μίλιον καὶ κατεστηλω-
μένη μέχρι Κυψέλων καὶ"Εβρου ποταμοῦ.

[3] Pliny, 3. 17; Agrippam quidem in tanta viri diligentia praeterque in hoc
opere cura, cum orbem terrarum urbi spectandum propositurus esset, errasse
quis credat, et cum eo divum Augustum? Is namque complexam eum porticum
ex destinatione et commentariis M. Agrippae a sorore ejus inchoatam peregit.

stations along them, with the number of miles that separated
one station from another. Of the former of these mention is
made at a later period by Vegetius in his treatise *On the Art of
War*, where he is speaking of the importance to a general of
acquaintance with the country through which he is marching, in
order to prevent surprise and to be on his guard against ambush.
The circumspect commanders of former days, he remarks, are
said to have had itineraries of the provinces which were the scene
of their campaigns, not only set down in writing, but also painted;
and he goes on to recommend that these should be sufficiently
detailed to include the short cuts, the by-ways, the mountains and
the rivers[1]. Of this class of documents we are fortunate in
possessing a specimen in the Peutinger Table; while the other
class, or *Itineraria adnotata*, is represented by the Antonine
Itinerary.

[1] Veget., *De Re Militari*, 3. 6.

CHAPTER XII.

STRABO.

Strabo and the Augustan Age—His Geography a Summary of the Knowledge
then existing—Strabo's Life, Teachers, and Places of Residence—Extent
of his Travels—Almost Limited to Asia Minor, Egypt, and Central
Italy—Advantages which he Derived from them—His Philosophical
Opinions—Stoic Tenets—His Political Opinions—Imperial Sympathies—
Strabo's Historical Work—Date of Composition of his *Geography*—Place
where it was written—Readers for whom it was intended—Its Compre-
hensiveness—Subjects Incidentally introduced—Predominance of His-
torical Geography—Influence of a Land on its Inhabitants—Artistic
Treatment of the Subject—Methods of lightening the Narrative—Neglect
of Strabo's Work in Antiquity—Admiration of it in the Middle Ages—
Modern Estimates—Limits of Strabo's Survey, in Europe, Asia, and
Africa—Contents of the *Geography*—The Introduction—Remarks on
Mathematical, Physical, and Historical Geography—Spain, Gaul, and
Britain—Italy and Sicily—Northern and Eastern Europe—Greece—
Veneration for Homer as a Geographical Authority—Northern and Central
Asia—Asia Minor—Southern Asia—Egypt and the Rest of Africa.

IT may be regarded as a piece of extraordinary good fortune

Strabo and the Augustan Age. that the most important work on geography which was produced in antiquity should have coincided in date with the Augustan age. The knowledge of the world which the ancients possessed had then almost reached its furthest limits, while the interest which had been awakened by Greek enquirers in the scientific side of the subject had not yet been neutralised, as it was destined soon to be, by utilitarian views of geographical study. At various preceding periods, as we have seen, the different branches of the enquiry had occupied, each in its turn, the most prominent position. In the latter half of the third century before Christ, mathematical geography reached its culminating point at Alexandria under Eratosthenes. The following century saw the rise of historical geography under Roman influences in the hands of Polybius.

THE WORLD ACCORDING TO STRABO

University Press Cambridge

Edwd. Weller Cambridge

Later still, the scientific explorations of Posidonius caused the study of physical geography to predominate. It remained that some one should arise, who could sum up the work that had been accomplished in these different lines; and such a writer was found in Strabo. His *Geography*, whatever its defects, is our great repertory of information concerning the knowledge of these subjects which the ancients possessed, and the wide range of his interests guaranteed that none of them should be neglected. In estimating its importance from a modern point of view, we have to take into account not merely its intrinsic merits, but also the greatness of the loss which we should have suffered if it had perished. It is the one complete treatise on geography which has survived from antiquity, and, moreover, we are chiefly indebted to it for our acquaintance with the writings of his predecessors. These are so entirely lost, that they are only known through quotations preserved in other authors, and it is in Strabo that the majority of such passages are found.

His Geography a Summary of the Knowledge then existing.

Strabo was a native of Amasia in Pontus, a city which was at one time the residence of the sovereigns of that country, and became a considerable centre of Greek culture. The date of his birth has been much disputed, but it was probably 63 B.C., the year of Cicero's consulate[1]. The events of his life are almost entirely unnoticed by other writers, and in endeavouring to trace them we are forced to have recourse to statements incidentally introduced in his *Geography*. We find that three prominent teachers of that time took part in his education. When quite a youth, he attended at Nysa on the Maeander the lectures in grammar and rhetoric of Aristodemus, the same who gave instruction to the sons of Pompey. Afterwards he proceeded to Rome, where he was the pupil, first of Tyrannion the grammarian, who superintended the education of Cicero's two sons, Marcus and Quintus, and afterwards of the Peripatetic philosopher Xenarchus. As Tyrannion was an authority on geography, it is not improbable

Strabo's Life,

Teachers,

[1] For the evidence which bears on this and similar points relating to Strabo reference may be made to the Introduction to the author's *Selections from Strabo*.

that Strabo imbibed a taste for that subject from him. The
and Places of remainder of his long life—he seems to have been
Residence. 84 years of age at the time of his death, or even
older—was passed for the most part either in Rome or in Asia
Minor. The duration of these sojourns we have no means
of determining; but his mention of buildings of recent erection
in Rome, and of objects newly introduced there, which he had
himself seen, proves that he visited the capital at intervals;
and, on the other hand, he is shewn to have returned to Asia
Minor, both by his allusions to periods of residence in certain of
its cities, and by his exact and observant descriptions of places
in various provinces of that region, which imply that he was
acquainted with them as a grown-up man. We also know from
his own testimony that he dwelt for a long period in Alexandria;
and the date of this can be approximately fixed, for it was then
that he made the expedition through Egypt, which was the most
considerable of his journeys, in the company of his friend and
patron Aelius Gallus, who was prefect of the country, and this
expedition seems to have taken place in 25—24 B.C.

Widely different opinions have been held as to the extent of
Strabo's travels. He claimed for himself that he
Extent of had journeyed in different directions as far as any
his Travels. other writer on geography—that is to say, from
Armenia to the western part of Etruria, and from the Euxine to
the confines of Aethiopia[1]; and this may have been literally true.
But before we concede to a person the title of a great traveller, it
is necessary to estimate the extensiveness of the journeys which
were carried out by him within a certain area, and the scientific
spirit of research in which they were undertaken. In Strabo's
case the conclusion to which we are brought by an examination of
Almost the evidence which his work affords as to the places
Limited to Asia which he visited is that, except in Asia Minor, in
Minor, Egypt,
and Central Egypt, and in Central Italy, he did not deviate far
Italy. from the route which he would naturally take in
passing to and from his home and the great centres of civilisation
in which he resided at different intervals. His journeys into
distant lands were determined by the circumstances of his life,

[1] Strabo, 2. 5. 11.

rather than by any desire on his part to prosecute researches, or
to verify the statements of former writers. In Asia Minor he was
well acquainted with the extreme eastern and western districts of
the country—with Pontus, Cappadocia, and Cilicia, which were
within easy reach of his home at Amasia; and with Western Phrygia,
Lydia, Ionia, and Caria, which he had visited either at the time
of his education at Nysa or on subsequent occasions. Egypt he
had explored at his leisure and thoroughly, as might be expected
from the opportunities offered by his residence at Alexandria, and
from his having ascended the Nile as far as the First Cataract
with Aelius Gallus. In Italy he had become acquainted with the
coast-towns of Etruria as far north as the Bay of Luna, and was
familiar with Latium and the neighbourhood of the Bay of Naples:
he knew also the line of the Appian Way with the ports of Brundisium and Tarentum, and part of the eastern coast of Sicily, of
which he would see something when on his way from Rome to
Alexandria. Of the rest of the world, however, he had very little
knowledge from personal observation. He could hardly have
visited even the coast of Syria, otherwise he would not have failed
to touch at Tyre; yet, in describing the many-storeyed houses
of that city, which, he says, exceeded in height those in Rome, he
quotes from other authorities[1]. In Greece there is no clear proof
that he stopped at any place except Corinth; and the fulness of
detail with which he has delineated that town contrasts strongly
with his notices of the rest of the country[2]. The Adriatic coast
of Italy was also a *terra incognita* to him; and in consequence of
this his account of Ravenna, in particular, is defective, for he
relies on earlier authorities, and omits all notice of the great works
which were carried out there by the orders of Augustus[3]. The
remoter regions of the world, such as Spain or Babylonia, he does
not profess to have visited. Still, though Strabo cannot be spoken
of as a great traveller in the same sense as Posi-
donius, it would be a mistake to suppose that his   Advantages
                                                           which he
journeys were of small importance to him as a   derived from
                                                           them.
writer on geography. In reality he learnt from
them to take a wide view of his subject, to interest himself in a

[1] 16. 2. 23.   [2] 8. 6. 20—23.
[3] 5. 1. 7.

variety of topics and in different peoples, and to get that power of
vividly realising and forcibly representing to others the matters he
treats of, which can only be obtained from ocular inspection, or
at least from familiarity with similar objects. At the same time
his mind was trained in the art of observation; and the result of
this is that he writes, not as a student in his closet, but as one
who was accustomed to notice and to criticise.

A word or two must be added concerning Strabo's philosophical
and political opinions, because these make themselves felt from time to time in the course of his
work. In philosophy, as two of his instructors,
Tyrannion and Xenarchus, were Peripatetic philosophers, it is
somewhat surprising to find that he was himself a Stoic. At what
period of his life he became an adherent of that school we have
no means of ascertaining, but perhaps the change may have been
in part due to his intimacy with the Stoic Athenodorus, who was
first the teacher, and afterwards the adviser, of Augustus. In
consequence of this, his belief in a divinity or in the
gods, as far as he possessed any, was pantheistic,
and with him the primal agency which caused the organisation of
the world was Providence—an impersonal force, which produced
the interconnexion of all the parts, and caused its unity and perfection[1]. Accordingly, when the natural features of a country are
found to be adapted to the needs of its inhabitants, and to contribute
to their development, this is characterised as 'conformity to nature'
(ὁμολογία), and is regarded as the 'work of Providence' (προνοίας
ἔργον)[2]. The views here expressed, and the terms by which they
are represented, are definitely those professed by the Stoics. In
politics Strabo was a hearty advocate of the Roman
government. He was strongly impressed by the
influence of the *pax Romana*—by the safety of life
and property in districts formerly disturbed, the security afforded
to commerce by the extinction of piracy, and the advantages to
civilisation which arose from a central political administration[3].

The same feeling caused him to look favourably on
the concentration of the power in the hands of a
single ruler; indeed he remarks that an empire of

His
Philosophical
Opinions.

Stoic Tenets.

His Political
Opinions.

Imperial
Sympathies.

---

[1] 17. 1. 36.   [2] 4. 1. 14.   [3] 1. 1. 16.

such magnitude could hardly be carried on except under the paternal supervision of one person[1]. So far did these opinions carry him, that he not only regarded the harsh treatment of revolted provinces by the Romans as a form of necessary discipline[2], but he mentions the conquest of his own fatherland, Pontus, by that people with a singular absence of feeling[3].

A considerable part of Strabo's literary life was occupied in writing a work on history, which he called 'Historical Memoirs' ('Ιστορικὰ Ὑπομνήματα). This treatise, which seems to have been a continuation of the history of the world from the point where the History of Polybius ended, 146 B.C., is referred to by name by the author himself in his *Geography* and by Plutarch[4]; and it was extensively used both by Josephus and Arrian. Though it no longer exists, it is highly probable that many of the historical notices, which so frequently occur in the *Geography*, are summaries of portions of it. The last-named work was the product of the later period of Strabo's life, but there is no need to assign it, as many writers have done, to a date as far advanced as from 17 to 23 A.D.—a conclusion from which we would gladly escape, because it involves the necessity of believing that a treatise, which is characterised in a high degree by freshness and vigour, was produced by an old man. If we have rightly fixed 63 B.C. as the year of Strabo's birth, he would have been 80 years of age in 17 A.D. The chief argument in favour of the late date is found in the numerous passages in which events are mentioned which took place in the interval between 17 and 23 A.D.; but the occurrence of these does not necessitate the conclusion that the work at large was composed at that time. It seems more probable, especially when we consider the magnitude of the task, that its execution extended over a long period, and that it was brought up to date by the insertion of subsequent incidents at a later period. This supposition also may serve to some extent to account for the marked inequality of style and treatment which is traceable in various parts of the *Geography*. A more difficult question arises when we attempt to determine the place at

Strabo's Historical Work.

Date of Composition of his Geography.

Place where it was written.

---

[1] 6. 4. 2.　　　[2] 5. 4. 13.　　　[3] 12. 3. 33.
[4] I. I. 23; II. 9. 3; Plutarch, *Lucull.* 28.

which it was written. The alternative here lies between Rome on the one hand, and on the other some provincial residence, such as Strabo's native city Amasia. The arguments in favour of the former of these turn mainly on the intimate acquaintance which the writer shews, until quite the end of his life, with events that were passing at the capital, and with occurrences affecting the Roman empire, which might not be expected to reach the ears of provincials. His knowledge of these is very striking; and, however much allowance we may make for the rapid circulation of news at this time and the consequent facility of obtaining information, it might turn the scale in favour of Rome as the place where the work was composed, or at least completed, were it not for one overpowering argument on the other side. This is derived from the extraordinarily slight recognition which it met with in antiquity, so that it is not even named by so diligent a compiler as Pliny. Considering the merits and importance of the work, this would seem almost impossible if it had been published in a great literary centre such as Rome; whereas the difficulty disappears, if we suppose it to have seen the light in a remote place like Amasia.

Another point which calls for consideration as affecting our estimate of the *Geography*, is the class of readers for whom it was intended. On this subject Strabo's own statements appear to be somewhat misleading. He says at the commencement of his treatise that the object of geographical study is that it should be of service to men in high position—in other words, to the Roman generals and statesmen, to whom were assigned the conquest and administration of provinces[1]; and this view he confirms by other remarks to the same effect. A perusal of his work, however, suggests the idea that these introductory observations are of the nature of an advertisement, intended to attract Roman readers. Its contents are by no means of such a character as specially to suit the needs of imperial officials. His elaborate disquisitions on mythology, his long historical notices, his enumerations of philosophers and literary men produced by different cities, and his descriptions of physical phenomena, seem intended to interest a very different class of

[1] I. I. 18.

persons. The truth of the matter seems to be that Strabo, while
he wished to be read by Romans, expected rather to be read by
Greeks; but he wrote neither for the one nor for the other exclu-
sively, but for cultivated men without reference to their nationality.
His treatise as a whole is congenial both to the practical ideas of
the one people, and to the scientific spirit of the other; and he
says himself that he intends it to be popular, and adapted to 'the
general course of study which is pursued by free-born and cultured
men[1].'

The conspicuous merit of Strabo's work is its comprehensiveness. He aimed at bringing together, and ex-
hibiting in a readable form, all that it was   Its Compre-
                                                    hensiveness.
important to know about the different countries
of the earth and their inhabitants, and in this respect his
Geography was unique in antiquity. All the four branches, into
which, as we have seen in our first chapter, the subject divides—
mathematical, physical, descriptive, and historical geography —
are represented in his pages. In speaking of each district, he
deals with the conformation of the ground, the nature of the
products, the character and condition of the inhabitants, their
history, and similar topics : and in doing this he does not confine
himself within the range of what we call classical antiquity, for
he includes in his review the whole of the ancient world and
its occupants, whether barbarous or civilised. The   Subjects
variety of the subjects which he incidentally intro-   Incidentally
                                                          introduced.
duces greatly enhances the interest of his survey.
Geological peculiarities have an especial attraction for him. Not
only has he furnished us with a large collection of facts relating
to volcanoes and earthquake movements, but he notices other
strange features of the ground, such as the rolled stones of
the Plaine de la Crau (Campi Lapidei) in southern France[2].
Climate also is a topic to which he often refers. He dwells
on the cloudy, sunless atmosphere of Britain[3], and the monsoons
and the rainy season in India[4]; and he remarks that the amount
of snow that falls is greater, and the snow-line is lower, on the
northern side of a range of mountains than on the southern[5].

[1] I. I. 22; cp. 2. 5. I.   [2] 4. I. 7.
[3] 4. 5. 2.   [4] 15. I. 13.   [5] 16. I. 13.

On the subject of trees and plants he contributes a great variety of information; thus he describes the palm-groves and balsam-gardens of Jericho, the papyrus and the Egyptian bean, and the trees which supplied the precious woods that were used for furniture at Rome. He also paid great attention to the mode of life, the habitations and dress, and the traditions of numerous half-civilised peoples; and to the religious beliefs and rites which prevailed in various parts of the world—as, for instance, at the two Comanas in Eastern Asia Minor, and among the Druids in Gaul, and the Brahmans in India. On matters, too, which belong to a higher sphere of intelligence his work furnishes interesting observations; such as works of art, the opinions of philosophic schools, and scientific discoveries, *e.g.* that of the true calendar by the priests of Heliopolis in Egypt.

Among these various departments of geographical study the one which predominates in Strabo's work is un-doubtedly the historical. Not only does he every-where introduce the history of a country side by side with its geography, but he illustrates the one by the other, and endeavours to point out the intimate connexion that existed between the two. In describing the pass of the Climax on the coast of Lycia he refers to the danger to which Alexander's troops were exposed in traversing it[1]. The mention of the lines of Roman roads through eastern Spain recalls Caesar's march along them before the battle of Munda[2]; and so on throughout the entire work. Besides this he is fond of tracing the influence of the features of a land on the character and history of its inhabitants. A notice-able instance of this is his discussion of the manner in which the physical peculiarities of Italy contributed to the development of the power of Rome. In this he dwells on the advantages which that country derived in respect of safety from its peninsular character, which secured it against attack, and in respect of commerce from its excellent harbours; on its varied and temperate climate, and the difference of elevation in different parts, which caused it to enjoy the products both of the moun-tains and the plains; on its plentiful water-supply, and ample

Predomi-nance of Historical Geography.

Influence of a Land on its Inhabitants.

[1] 14. 3. 9.   [2] 3. 4. 9.

provision of the necessaries of life; and finally, on its central position among the great races of the ancient world[1]. Remarks such as these, in which the modifying power exercised by external nature over the history of man is traced, are the most original feature in Strabo's work, and go far to justify the title of 'The Philosophy of Geography,' which has been applied to it. Though similar notices occur from time to time, as we have seen, both in Ephorus and Polybius, yet no ancient writer except Strabo has systematically followed out and generalised on the working of these influences.

Another feature of the *Geography* which distinguishes it from other works on the same subject, besides its many- *Artistic* sidedness, is the artistic spirit in which it was *Treatment of* composed. This becomes most apparent, if we *the Subject.* compare it with the lists of names which are crowded together in the geographical section of Pliny's *Natural History*, or with the dry details which make up the treatise of Ptolemy. In contrast with these, the facts which are brought together in Strabo's well-arranged chapters are skilfully grouped, in a manner which clearly shews that in combining so great a variety of materials the form as well as the matter has been considered. With a view to this, the accumulation of names which appeared to the author to be either superfluous or barbarous in sound is avoided, as for instance in the case of the Arabian tribes, some of which he purposely omits on account of the vulgarity and clumsiness of their pronunciation[2]. A treatise on general geography, he says, is a colossal work, and in this, as in a colossal statue, insignificant minutiæ, which would detract from the general effect, should be neglected[3]. For the same *Methods of* reason Strabo endeavours to lighten the reader's *lightening the* task by enlivening his narrative in various ways. *Narrative.* Ascents of high mountains, such as Etna and Mount Argaeus in Cappadocia, are noticed, together with the observations of those who made them. Sporting experiences are recorded; thus ferreting is mentioned as having been employed in Spain as a remedy for a plague of rabbits[4], and the methods of hunting

---

[1] 6. 4. 1.   [2] 16. 4. 18.
[3] 1. 1. 3.   [4] 3. 2. 6.

and decoying elephants in India are described[1]. No opportunity is missed of introducing a good story, and the proverbs and proverbial expressions that occur are very numerous. Comparisons, again, some of which are remarkably apposite, are used to illustrate geographical features. The Peloponnese is likened in shape to the leaf of a plane-tree[2]; the Oases in the Libyan desert to the spots on a leopard's skin[3]; the Trojan Ida, with its long range and numerous spurs, to a millepede[4]. Many of these, no doubt, were borrowed from other writers, but Strabo's skill is shewn by the way in which he makes use of them. He also enlarges the reader's view by drawing attention to the resemblances which are traceable between districts and features of the ground in different countries. Ravenna and Alexandria are compared in respect of their healthiness, notwithstanding the shallow water in their neighbourhood[5]; the intermittent streams are noticed by which the Lacus Fucinus in Latium and the river Amenanus in Sicily were fed[6]; and the saying is quoted, in which the Acro-corinth and the acropolis of Messene on Mount Ithome were spoken of as the two horns by which the cow (the Peloponnese) might be held[7]. In these and other ways the texture of the work is diversified, and the materials of which it is made up are enriched, and thus the composition at large is raised to a higher level.

The estimates which have been formed of Strabo's work, and the attention which it attracted, have varied greatly at different periods. We have already noticed the neglect from which it suffered in antiquity, as shewn by the absence of any mention of it by the writers of the succeeding age. Athenaeus (about the beginning of the third century) refers to it in two passages, but neither of these has any direct bearing on geography: its geographical importance is first recognised by Marcianus of Heraclea—a writer who cannot be placed earlier than the third century—who mentions Strabo as one of the authorities most to be relied on with respect to distances. With this exception we hardly find any reference

Neglect of Strabo's Work in Antiquity.

[1] 15. 1. 42.   [2] 8. 2. 1.
[3] 2. 5. 33.   [4] 13. 1. 5.
[5] 5. 1. 7.   [6] 5. 3. 13.   [7] 8. 4. 8.

to it till the time of Stephanus of Byzantium, towards the end
of the fifth century, by whom it is frequently cited[1]. **Admiration**
During the middle ages, however, exactly the **of it in the**
opposite of this was the case. To the writers of **Middle Ages.**
that time he was known as *the* geographer, and Eustathius
in particular frequently quotes him by that title. Again,
in modern days a great discrepancy of opinion has existed
with regard to Strabo's merits. Some authorities, among whom
Müllenhoff is the most conspicuous, have treated
him as a dull, unintelligent compiler. Others, who **Modern Estimates.**
refrain from passing so sweeping a condemnation,
regard his *Geography* as little more than a new edition of the
work of Eratosthenes. This view, however, is sufficiently disproved by a comparison of the size of the two treatises, for
whereas Strabo's ran to the length of seventeen books, that of
Eratosthenes was comprised in three, and only a portion of the
last of these was devoted to descriptive geography. Indeed,
however much Strabo may have been indebted to others for his
materials, his independence of judgment is shewn by his carefulness in comparing his authorities and balancing their statements,
and by the trouble which he takes to cast the facts which he
collects in a mould of his own. A more impartial, though at
the same time a laudatory, estimate is furnished by one whose
encyclopædic studies specially qualified him to pass judgment
on such a subject—Alexander von Humboldt. "The gifted
geographer of Amasia," he says, "does not possess the numerical
accuracy of Hipparchus, or the mathematical and geographical
information of Ptolemy; but his work surpassed all other geographical labours of antiquity by the diversity of the subjects, and
the grandeur of the composition[2]."

As the object of Strabo's work was to furnish a survey of the
whole of the habitable world that was known in **Limits of**
his day, the extent of the area which it included **Strabo's**
and the limits within which it was restricted can **Survey,**
be sufficiently inferred from what we have already seen of the
knowledge of the subject which was possessed by the Greeks

---

[1] Bunbury, *Hist. of Anc. Geogr.*, 2, pp. 334, 335.
[2] *Cosmos* (Otte's trans.), vol. 2. p. 555.

under the successors of Alexander, and of the additions which
were made to it by the advance of the Roman
arms.   In western Europe, Spain and Gaul as far
as the coast of the Atlantic, and the south-eastern part of Britain,
were fairly well known; but towards the north the Elbe and the
Danube still marked the limit of accurate geographical knowledge.   Something more might have been added concerning the
lands and seas in that direction from the narrative of Pytheas,
had not Strabo been strongly impressed with the untruthfulness
of that writer ; and a similar mistrust of Herodotus, whom he
regarded as a mere retailer of fiction, caused the same thing to
happen with regard to the countries northward of the Euxine,
from Strabo's account of which the valuable information furnished
by the old historian is excluded.   The lands on
the further side of the Palus Maeotis were also
unexplored, but the chain of the Caucasus and the regions to
the southward of it between the Black Sea and the Caspian
had become known through the narrative of Theophanes.   The
Caspian was still believed to communicate with the Northern
Ocean, and beyond it the Jaxartes remained, as it was in the days
of Alexander, the limit of discovery.   In India the peninsula
of Hindostan continued to be unknown, and the Ganges was
regarded as flowing into the eastern ocean.   The
Cinnamon country and the territory of the Sembritae about the upper Nile were the southernmost points that
Strabo was acquainted with in Africa, and no one had penetrated
into the interior of that continent beyond the land of the Garamantes.   The student of the geography of the Augustan age
requires further to be reminded, that not a little of the information
contained in Strabo's work dates from a period earlier than that
era.   In some instances, as notably in that of Ravenna, which
we have already mentioned, this arises from the author not having
availed himself of the latest sources of evidence ; but to a great
extent it was unavoidable.   In writing of India, for instance, he
was obliged to follow the narrative of persons who wrote some
centuries before his age ; and the same thing was the case in a
lesser degree with regard to various other countries.   Under such
circumstances the writer is not in fault, for he can but make the

in Europe,

Asia,

and Africa.

best of the materials that are available; but his work cannot
fail to suffer from a certain amount of anachronism.

We may now proceed to consider briefly the contents of
Strabo's work.   The two first books are devoted
to an Introduction, in which he states the aim and   Contents of
                                                        the *Geography*.
scope of his treatise and the principles on which
he conceives that it ought to be composed, and draws attention
to the general features which characterise both the
entire area of the world and the several continents.   The Intro-
                                                       duction.
In this part also he sets forth his views on mathematical and physical geography.   His treatment of the former of
these is the least satisfactory portion of his book, for he deals
with it unsystematically in the form of controversy
with Eratosthenes, Hipparchus, and others who had   Remarks on
                                                      Mathematical,
preceded him in that study.   In criticising them,
however, he betrays his own inferiority, so that not infrequently
he either misunderstands their views, or is himself in error.   On
the other hand, his remarks on physical geography
are of great value.   He has brought together a   Physical,
large amount of material to throw light on the changes which
have passed over the face of the earth owing to the retirement
of the sea, and to earthquakes and volcanic eruptions; and he
discusses the causes which have brought these to pass.   The two
main principles which he enunciates as his own are mentioned
with high praise by Sir Charles Lyell, as being anticipations of
the latest conclusions of modern science.   These are (1) the
importance of drawing inferences with regard to the more extensive physical changes from those which take place on a lesser
scale under our own eyes; and (2) the theory of the alternate
elevation and depression of extensive areas[1].   With regard to the
shape of the inhabited world he followed the view of Eratosthenes,
who described it as forming an irregular oblong with tapering
extremities towards the east and west.   This figure Strabo compares to the chlamys, or Greek mantle, which was rectangular in
outline, and usually about twice as long as it was broad, with a
gore, or triangular piece, attached to either extremity[2].   For

[1] Lyell, *Principles of Geology*, vol. I. pp. 24, 25; Strabo, I. 3. 5, 10.
[2] 2. 5. 14.

geographical purposes this oblong area was supposed to be inscribed within a parallelogram, the sides of which were drawn so as to pass through its extreme limits. He also introduces a number of remarks, of great interest from the point of view of historical geography, on the shape of the three continents into which this area was divided, and the superiority of Europe to the other two as a habitation for man. Europe, he remarks, is very varied in its outline, and Africa forms a contrast to it from its uniformity, while Asia in this respect holds an intermediate position between them. The advantage of this multiplicity of form consists in the facilities of communication which it affords to the inhabitants, and from this the historical interest of such countries arises. Europe is also more favourable to the development of character from its temperate climate, its equal distribution into mountains and plains, which supply respectively a warlike and a peaceful element to the population, and its furnishing its occupants with the necessaries of life rather than superfluities and luxuries[1].

and Historical Geography.

The second and third books treat of the western countries of Europe—Spain, Gaul, and Britain. For Spain the principal authorities on whom Strabo relies are Polybius, Artemidorus, and Posidonius, all of whom had visited that country, but Posidonius' information was far the most valuable, on account of his intimate acquaintance with the remote parts of the interior. The same traveller furnished him with the chief materials for his account of Gaul and Britain, but these he was able to supplement from the writings of Cæsar. The geographer's idea of the coast-line of these countries was in several respects faulty, for he regarded the Sacrum Promontorium (Cape St. Vincent), instead of the Magnum Promontorium (Cabo da Roca) near the mouth of the Tagus, as the westernmost point of Spain, and he ignored the deep recess in the coast formed by the Bay of Biscay, and the projection of the Armorican peninsula, so that he conceived of the coast of Gaul in this part as stretching along almost in a continuous line, with that of Britain opposite to it. He also erroneously supposed, like the other geographers of his time, that the direction followed by the Pyrenees was from

Spain, Gaul, and Britain.

[1] 2. 5. 18, 26.

north to south; but in other respects his general idea of the geographical features of these countries was accurate. He was acquainted with the five great rivers of Spain which flow towards the Atlantic—the Baetis (Guadalquivir), the Anas (Guadiana), the Tagus, the Durius (Douro), and the Minius (Minho)—and with the Iberus (Ebro), which reaches the Mediterranean. He knew also the watershed which divides these, and which gradually rises as it advances southward, until it joins the Sierra Nevada; and he was aware that along the northern coast there was a mountain region between the Pyrenees and Cape Finisterre. In Gaul he draws especial attention to the completeness of the river system, in which respect that country has greater advantages than any other in Europe, and to the easy communication which existed between one river-basin and another, and the consequent facilities which were provided for trade routes[1]. Very effective, too, is the contrast here presented by the advanced civilisation of the province of Baetica, which at this time was completely Romanised, and the primitive condition of the tribes in the centre and north of Spain; and the leading features of character of the Iberian race in that land, and of the Celtic tribes in Gaul, are interestingly delineated. We find here also a striking description of the two famous cities of Gades and Massilia, both in respect of their sites and of the condition of their inhabitants. It gives us an impressive idea of the commerce of Gades, when we are told that the greater part of its population was to be found, not in the place itself, but on the sea[2]: and in the account of Massilia we find a sketch of its political constitution, to which Aristotle had devoted a treatise, and a notice of its learning and its schools, which caused it to become a Greek university for southern Gaul[3].

Italy and Sicily are the subject of the fifth and sixth books. Here again Strabo is greatly indebted to Posidonius, though no small part of his material was derived Italy and from his own observation and researches, or from Sicily. Agrippa's wall-map and its accompanying commentary—for this seems to be what is meant by the 'Chorography,' to which he frequently refers. He commences with a true conception of the

[1] 4. 1. 14.   [2] 3. 5. 3.   [3] 4. 1. 5.

Alps, which formed the northern boundary of this area, for he describes them as starting from the same neighbourhood as the Apennines, at Vada Sabatia (Vado) to the westward of Genoa, and extending thence to the head of the Adriatic in a great curve, the concave side of which is turned towards Italy[1]. He traces the lines of the chief Roman roads, with the cities that lay in their neighbourhood; and in consequence this portion of his work is somewhat overcrowded with names—an unavoidable result, since their importance forbade their omission. Owing to the prevalence of volcanic action in this part of Europe, numerous references are here introduced to this class of phenomenon. The islands in the Bay of Naples, and Vesuvius, which, though quiescent at that time, gave evidence in its appearance of its former activity; the Aeolian (Lipari) islands and Etna; and other features, such as the jets of volcanic gas in the lake of the Palici in the interior of Sicily, are described[2]; and many interesting details are communicated, especially about Etna, the formation of the lava beds of which, and the changes in the form of its crater, are noticed[3]. As might be expected from Strabo's lengthened residence in Rome, full details are furnished about Latium and Campania; and his graphic descriptions of Tibur, Praeneste, and the Alban Hills, of the Pomptine marshes, of the Lake Avernus and the Lucrine Lake, and of the artificial harbours of Puteoli, which was at that time the most important city of Italy after Rome, give clear evidence of personal observation. Not less valuable is the account of Naples as a place of literary leisure, and of the traditional Hellenic culture which survived there; elsewhere also he tells us that that city was the only place in South Italy besides Tarentum and Rhegium where Greek was spoken in his age[4]. It was no part of his plan to enter into elaborate details about the famous edifices of Rome, and the only building there which is delineated with any minuteness is the Mausoleum of Augustus, which would seem to have been the sight of the day. But his general remarks on the public works in the capital—the roads, aqueducts and sewers—are excellent; and the same thing may be said of his sketch of the Campus Martius, with the bright

[1] 4. 6. 1; 5. 1. 3.
[2] 6. 2. 9.
[3] 6. 2. 3, 8.
[4] 6. 1. 2.

scene afforded by the races and other sports to which it was devoted, the works of art in its neighbourhood, and the handsome structures which were beginning to encroach upon it[1]. They enable us forcibly to realise the impression made on an intelligent stranger by Rome in the Augustan age.

From Italy, before proceeding to Greece, Strabo retraces his steps northward, and in his seventh book gives an account, as far as his scanty information allows, of the northern and eastern districts of Europe— Germany and the lands between it and the Euxine, the countries to the north of that sea and about the Palus Maeotis, and the region to the south of the Danube, comprising Illyricum, Epirus, Macedonia, and Thrace. In treating of the northern part of this area he availed himself of the intelligence which had been recently obtained through the campaigns of Drusus and Germanicus, and he remarks in an interesting manner on the nearness of the upper waters of the Danube and the Rhine[2]: but, as we have already seen, his knowledge of the north of Europe was unnecessarily limited, owing to his mistrust of Pytheas and Herodotus. All the more striking in consequence of this is the accurate account which he has given of the Tauric Chersonese[3] (Crimea); his acquaintance with this was due in great measure to the narratives which existed of the expeditions of Mithridates in those parts, and of his ultimate occupation of the country. In the latter part of this book there is a sketch of the topography of Actium, Nicopolis, and the entrance of the strait, which was the scene of the famous battle[4]; and also of that of the Thracian Bosporus and the Golden Horn, together with a graphic account of the tunny-fishing which took place there[5]. The concluding chapters, which dealt with Macedonia and Thrace, are unfortunately lost, and our knowledge of their contents is derived from epitomes; this, however, is the only portion of the entire treatise which is wanting.

Strabo's next three books are devoted to Greece; the eighth to the Peloponnese, the ninth to northern Greece, the tenth to the islands, both those to the west, and those to the east of the continent. There is a want of thoroughness

Northern and Eastern Europe.

Greece.

---

[1] 5. 3. 8.   [2] 7. 1. 5.   [3] 7. 4.
[4] 7. 7. 6.   [5] 7. 6. 1, 2.

in this part, which causes it to be the least satisfactory section
of the *Geography*. The chief reason for this is to be found in
Strabo's extravagant veneration for Homer as a
geographical authority. In this he was only following the example of most of his predecessors, especially Hipparchus, Polybius, and Posidonius, to
whom the Homeric poems had become a sort of Sacred Book,
the statements contained in which might not be questioned; and
Eratosthenes, who opposed the view that points in general
geography were to be determined in accordance with the poet's
expressions, became the object of attacks in consequence. In
Strabo's case two other influences tended to increase his bias in
that direction—one his Stoic opinions, for an excessive devotion
to Homer had become one of the tenets of that sect: the other
his connexion with the literary school of Pergamus, which was
now at feud with that of Alexandria on this very question, and
maintained the more advanced estimate of the Homeric claims.
In consequence of this Strabo's judgment was hampered in a
prejudicial manner, and in describing Greece he makes Homer
his text-book, and employs himself chiefly with the examination
of his geographical statements. Even his general information
seems to have been to a great extent derived from commentators,
such as Apollodorus and Demetrius of Scepsis, rather than from
writers on topography. He made use, however, of the geographical
treatise of Ephorus, to which he refers in several passages. Fortunately, the remarkable physical geography of Greece attracted
his attention, and he has left us interesting notices, not only of
the striking conformation of land and sea which distinguishes its
coasts, but also of the subterranean drainage of particular districts,
especially the Arcadian valleys and the basin of the Copaic lake.
His principal error in this part relates to the position of the promontory of Sunium, which he supposed to extend nearly as far
south as that of Malea[1].

Veneration for Homer as a Geographical Authority.

In his eleventh book Strabo conducts us into Asia, the
boundary between which and Europe according
to him is the Tanais. He first notices the main
divisions of that continent, and the chain of the

Northern and Central Asia.

[1] 2. 1. 40.

Taurus as its leading geographical feature, including under that
name the Himalaya and other mountains which run through it
from west to east; and then surveys, first the lands which lie
between the Euxine and the Caspian and to the eastward of the
last-named sea, and afterwards the more central regions of Parthia,
Media, and Armenia. In his general geography of Asia he adopts
Eratosthenes as his authority, while for the western part of the
area which is specially treated in this book he relies on the
historians of the Mithridatic wars, and for the eastern on Patrocles
and the companions of Alexander. We have already noticed the
fulness of his account of the districts of Iberia and Albania, and of
the tribes inhabiting them, which is borrowed from Theophanes;
and we are also indebted to him for an accurate description both
of the mountain system of Western Asia, and of the upper courses
of the Euphrates and Tigris. He represents the Taurus—here
using that term in its more restricted sense—as running through
the south of Asia Minor, and at the eastern extremity of that
country throwing off the Anti-Taurus to the north, and the Amanus,
the commencement of the chains of Syria and Palestine, to the
south; then, as it pursues its course towards the east, forming a
marked boundary between Armenia and Mesopotamia, into both
which countries it ramifies, and increasing in elevation until it
culminates in Mount Niphates, near the brackish lake Arsene[1]
(Lake of Van). As regards the rivers—Strabo was not aware of
the fact, which modern geography has taught us, that both the
Euphrates and the Tigris have two sources, and flow for a considerable distance in two separate streams[2]: he confines the name
Euphrates to the western branch of that river, the modern Frat,
which rises near Erzeroum; and the only stream which he recognises
as the Tigris is its eastern branch, the river of Bitlis, with which
Xenophon also had identified it. But he rightly remarks, that the
Euphrates rises in the north, the Tigris in the south of the Taurus,
i.e. of Armenia; and he carefully distinguishes the provinces—
Sophene, Commagene and others—between which the Euphrates
flows in this part of its course[3].

---

[1] II. 12. 2; II. 14. 8.
[2] *v. supra*, p. 114.   [3] II. 12. 3.

As the geographer was a native of Asia Minor, it is only natural
that he should pay especial attention to that part of
the world, and accordingly we find that he devotes
to it three books—the twelfth, thirteenth, and fourteenth. The
contents of these are of great value, both because the writer is
frequently drawing on his own observation, and also on account
of the rich store of information which they provide about the
physical geography and products of the country, and the religious and political condition of the people.   These points
may best be illustrated by a few examples. Strabo notices the
absence of trees in Cappadocia, a feature of which he furnishes
the explanation when he says that this country, though lying
further south than Pontus, is the colder of the two[1]. He also
enlarges on the volcanic activity which at that period still existed
about the sides and base of Mount Argaeus in that province, and
on the strange craters of the Katakekaumene, or Burnt Country,
in Western Phrygia[2].   He mentions the valuable red earth, which
was called 'Sinopic earth,' because it was brought down from the
interior to Sinope for export[3]; and the gum of the storax-tree and
the 'orris-root,' which were found at Selge in Pisidia[4].   Observations, also, are frequently introduced on the strange religious
worship that prevailed in Asia Minor, with its orgiastic rites, the
numerous votaries that were attached to the temples, and the
elaborate festival processions[5].   Finally, the study of political
constitutions is illustrated by the descriptions that are given of
the federation which was known as the Lycian League[6], of the
tetrarchies of the Galatae with their elaborate system of government[7], and of the municipal organisation that was established at
Ephesus[8].

The remainder of Asia—that is, in the main, the lands which
lie to the southward of the dividing mountain
chain—is treated of in the fifteenth and sixteenth
books; the former embracing the eastern portion—
India, Persia, and the intervening districts; the latter the countries

Asia Minor. (margin)

Southern Asia. (margin)

[1] 12. 2. 7, 10.   [2] 12. 2. 7; 13. 4. 11.
[3] 12. 2. 10.   [4] 12. 7. 3.
[5] 12. 2. 3; 12. 3. 31, 32, 36, 37.   [6] 14. 3. 3.
[7] 12. 5. 1.   [8] 14. 1. 21.

to the west of these—Assyria, Syria, and Arabia.   His account of
India, which is very interesting, is compiled from the only authorities that existed at that time—the narratives of Nearchus, Aristobulus, Onesicritus, and others, who accompanied Alexander on
his eastern expedition, and the treatise of Megasthenes—and its
contents have already been noticed in connexion with them.   For
Ariana and Persia, too, sufficient materials were forthcoming from
the writings of Alexander's contemporaries and successors, and these
had already been reduced to a geographical form by Eratosthenes.
In describing Persia, Strabo rightly distinguishes according to
their climates the three regions into which that country is divided
between the coast of the Persian Gulf and the Median uplands:
the first being a parched and sandy tract, where only the date-
palm flourished; the next a well-watered and fertile district of the
interior, abounding in plains and lakes; while the northernmost
was mountainous and cold[1].   In the section which is devoted to
Babylonia there is an elaborate account of the system of canals
by which that country was intersected[2].   These were rendered
necessary by the periodical inundations of the Euphrates, which
were caused by the melting of the snows on the Armenian highlands; and they served, not only to divert the surplus water from
the river, but also as reservoirs in which the water could be
stored, so as to be used for irrigation during the dry season.
Accordingly, they were not mere channels cut in the soil, but
capacious water-courses, elevated on huge embankments to a considerable height above the surface of the ground; and the methods
are here described by which they were cleared from the silt which
accumulated in them, and were also closed by raising a dam, when
they were to be used as reservoirs.   As we approach nearer to the
Mediterranean, the historical interest of the narrative increases.
The cities of Phoenicia, from their remarkable sites, their famous
commerce, and the scientific discoveries and inventions which
proceeded from them, naturally attracted the geographer's attention; and he also notices the peculiar features of the Dead Sea[3],
and the palm-groves and balsam-gardens of Jericho[4], which were
presented to Cleopatra by Antony, and were first farmed for her,

[1] 15. 3. 1.   [2] 16. 1. 9, 10.
[3] 16. 2. 44.   [4] 16. 2. 41.

and then redeemed for himself, by Herod the Great. To judge
from the accounts of Palestine which are given by Pliny and
Tacitus, as well as by Strabo, the balsam-tree and the Dead Sea
seem to have been the objects in that country which chiefly attracted the attention of the Roman world in ancient times. The
description of Arabia, with which this part of the work concludes,
is as complete as the knowledge of that age allowed, and embodies
the additional information on the subject which Agatharchides
had collected. Strabo also relates the events of the campaign
which Aelius Gallus prosecuted in that country at the command
of Augustus, but in respect of geography that expedition did not
add much to what was already known.

The last book of the *Geography* is devoted to Africa, and the
larger portion of it is occupied with an account of
Egypt, of which country, as we have seen, Strabo
had personal knowledge. He commences with a
description of Alexandria, which is the most elaborate notice of any
city that is found in his work[1]—an honour which it fully deserved
from its importance as a commercial, geographical, and scientific
centre. The other famous places in Egypt are briefly depicted, in
accordance with the author's rule of confining his work within the
limits which he originally assigned to it; but his narrative in these
parts is sometimes enlivened by personal experiences, such as his
inspection of the bull Apis at Memphis[2], his witnessing the feeding
of the sacred crocodile at Arsinoë[3], and his own trepidation, when
being ferried across on a frail raft to the island of Philae[4]. Concerning the course of the Nile to the southward of that place he is
able to furnish some fresh information from the expedition of
C. Petronius in Aethiopia[5]. The remainder of Africa is somewhat briefly treated, and Strabo was not aware of the marked
projection formed by the northern coast near Carthage opposite
Sicily. About Mauretania he might have had more to say, if he
had used the treatise of his contemporary Juba, but with that
work he does not seem to have been acquainted.

Egypt and the Rest of Africa.

---

[1] 17. 1. 6—10, 13.   [2] 17. 1. 31.   [3] 17. 1. 38.
            [4] 17. 1. 50.   [5] 17. 1. 54.

CHAPTER XIII.

GEOGRAPHY FROM THE DEATH OF AUGUSTUS TO THAT OF TRAJAN (14—117 A.D.).

Roman Writers on Geography—Pomponius Mela—Pliny—His *Historia Naturalis*—Its Deficiencies—Its Statistical Geography—Notices of Places in Asia—The Jordan—The Dead Sea—The Essenes—Palmyra—The Tigris—Its Upper Course—Strabo's Account—The Lake of Van—Criticisms of the Ancient Accounts—Strabo's and Pliny's Stories—Disappearance of the Tigris—Common Source of the Tigris and Euphrates—Possible Explanation of the Fable—Pliny's Information about Taprobane—Ambassadors sent thence to Rome—Their Account of the Inhabitants—The *Periplus Maris Erythraei*—African Coast—Aromata Prom. (Cape Guardafui)—Menuthias (Zanzibar)—Arabian Coast—Arabia Eudaemon (Aden)—Syagrus Prom. (Cape Fartak)—Island of Dioscorides (Socotra)—Indian Coast—Baraces and Eirinon Inlets (Gulf and Runn of Cutch)—Barygaza (Baroche)—Bore of the Nerbudda—Nelcynda—The Direct Route to India—Voyage of Hippalus—Notices of Eastern Asia—This (China)—Dionysius Periegetes—His Date—His Geographical Poem—Its General Geography—Description of Africa—Of Europe—Of the Islands—Of Asia—General Remarks upon it—Progressive Knowledge of Britain—Conquests of Claudius, Suetonius Paullinus, Agricola, and Antoninus Pius—Germany and Scandinavia—Dacia conquered by Trajan—Suetonius Paullinus crosses the Atlas—Nero's Expedition to the Nile—The Marshy Region.

THE writers on geography of the period which immediately followed the Augustan age—Mela and Pliny—are of a completely different type from those of whom we have hitherto been speaking. They are the only Roman writers on this subject whose works we possess, and they forcibly illustrate the inferiority of the Roman to the Greek intellect in its manner of dealing with such a theme. It has been aptly remarked, that the task which Eratosthenes set himself of measuring the earth by means of the heavenly bodies, and that of Agrippa, who measured the Roman provinces by milestones, may be taken as typical of the genius of the two nationalities respectively[1]; and

Roman Writers on Geography.

---

[1] J. Partsch, quoted by Berger, *Geschichte der Erdkunde*, 4. p. 30.

certainly the contrast which is here drawn effectively illustrates the two points of view, scientific and practical, from which they regarded the study of geography.   In the two authors of whom we are now speaking the absence of anything like a comprehensive view of geography is eminently conspicuous.   Of the former of them in respect of date, Pomponius Mela, who wrote during the reign of Claudius, there is no need to speak at any great length, for his work was merely a popular compendium, and would hardly have attracted much attention had it not been the first formal treatise on the subject that was composed in Latin.   Its title is *De Chorographia*, and it professes to furnish a survey of the world as it was known in his age, while at the same time it is interspersed with notices of the manners and customs of various peoples, which are drawn without much judgment from earlier writers.   With regard to the shape of the inhabited world, and the continents and seas which diversified it, his opinions differ but little from those which had been held by his predecessors from the time of Eratosthenes, except that he affirms the existence of *antichthones*.   By this name he designated the inhabitants of another continent in the south temperate zone, which was separated from the known portion of the globe by the ocean and by the torrid zone; and he seems to have believed that Taprobane (Ceylon) was not an island, as was generally thought, but formed a part of this continent.   This southern region had long been recognised as habitable, but, in the absence of any evidence, it was mere guesswork to speak of it as inhabited.

Pomponius Mela.

The method which Mela pursued in his survey resembles that of a *Periplus*, for he follows round the coasts, first of the Mediterranean, and then of the Outer sea, describing the neighbouring countries as he passes.   The islands which lie in these seas he treats of separately.   One result of this mode of dealing with the subject is that some countries, such as Persia, Media, and Assyria, are excluded from consideration.   As he was a native of southern Spain, like Lucan, Seneca, and some other distinguished writers of the early Imperial period, it is not surprising that his notice of that country is the most valuable part of his work.   Of the Straits of Gibraltar, in particular, in the neighbourhood of

which his birthplace, Tingitera, lay, he has given a more accurate
account than any previous writer. He affirms that the name of
'Pillars of Hercules' was derived from the two lofty mountains of
Abyla (Ceuta) and Calpe (Gibraltar), which here face one
another; and he remarks on the manner in which both of them,
but especially Calpe, project into the sea, and on the deep caves
which form a striking feature of the Rock of Gibraltar[1]. He is
also more correct than his predecessors with regard to the outline
of Spain and Gaul. He is the first writer who mentions the
Magnum Promontorium; and whereas Strabo, as we have seen,
erroneously conceived of the coast between Cape Finisterre and
the mouths of the Rhine as deviating but little from a straight
line, Mela was well aware of the deep gulf formed by the Bay of
Biscay, of the great projection of the coast of Gaul towards the
north-west, commencing from the mouth of the Garonne, and of
the sharp angle formed by the Armorican peninsula.

The other Roman writer on geography, Pliny the Elder, however great his deficiencies may have been, was a
literary man of far greater importance. He was
Pliny.
born in the year 23 A.D., either at Verona or at Novum Comum
(Como) in North Italy, and came to Rome at an early age. He
served in the Roman army as a young man in Germany, in which
country he made the acquaintance of Vespasian; and he afterwards composed a history of the German wars in twenty books.
Towards the end of Nero's reign he was appointed procurator in
Spain. When Vespasian came to the throne, he was received by
him into the number of his friends, and this intimacy was continued by Titus, to whom he dedicated his *Historia Naturalis*.
The circumstances of his death, in connexion with the great
eruption of Vesuvius in 79 A.D., by which Herculaneum and
Pompeii were destroyed, are well known from the famous letter of
his nephew, the younger Pliny, to Tacitus the historian, in which
they are described[2]. From the same source we hear of his extraordinary assiduity in study—how, not only during every available
interval in his official duties, but even at his meals and when on
a journey, he used either to read, or be read to, all the while

---

[1] Mela, 2. 95.   [2] *Ep.* 6. 16.

making notes and extracts[1].   In this way he accumulated a vast amount of information on various subjects, out of which in the latter part of his life he compiled his great work.   The contents of this are valuable on account of the numerous facts which are thus communicated to us, and had Pliny been gifted with judgment and discrimination, as he was with diligence, he would have produced an encyclopaedic work of the highest order.   Unfortunately, it was exactly in those qualities that he was deficient, so that his materials are brought together with little method, and his treatise abounds in mistakes and contradictions, arising partly from want of scientific knowledge and of power of criticising the statements of his authorities, and partly from sheer carelessness.   These features are nowhere more conspicuous than in the portion of his *Natural History* which is devoted to geography—the latter part of Book II., and Books III.—VI. Here Pliny shews complete ignorance of scientific geography; and in describing the leading features of countries, such as mountains and rivers, instead of noting their distinguishing features, and their effect in determining the character of a land, he contents himself with lists of names, and in like manner the cities of any particular region he simply catalogues without remarking on their relative position.   This is not less noticeable in the case of Spain —a country with the nature and appearance of which he must have been well acquainted from having resided there as procurator—than in other parts of the world.   His carelessness is shewn by the way in which he occasionally introduces the same place twice over under different names.   Thus the island of Ustica, which is situated to the north of Sicily, and was also called Osteodes, is noticed twice under those two names, as if two separate islands[2].   A similar confusion arises in his account of a historic land like Greece, because he draws his details indifferently from authorities of widely different dates.   The natural result of this is that flagrant anachronisms are produced, and in some instances cities that no longer existed at the time when he wrote are mentioned side by side with others that were still flourishing.

His Historia Naturalis.

Its Deficiencies.

[1] *Ep.* 3. 5.

[2] Pliny, *H. N.* 3. 92 : see Bunbury, *Hist. of Ancient Geogr.*, 2. p. 397.

The fact is that, in order to estimate this portion of Pliny's *Natural History* in an appreciative spirit, we must regard it not so much from the point of view of geography as from that of statistics. For the illustration of the latter of these subjects he had access to the official records relating to the provinces of the empire, and especially to the smaller districts into which they were subdivided for administrative and judicial purposes. The material which was thus provided furnished him not only with the names of towns, but also with an account of their municipal status, as colonies or otherwise, when there was anything in this that called for notice.

Its Statistical Geography.

The most interesting additions to geographical knowledge which were made by Pliny are to be found in his description of Asia. He draws attention to the parallel courses of the ranges of Libanus and Antilibanus, and the origin of the Orontes near Heliopolis (Baalbec) in the interval between them[1]. His account of the Jordan also, with its source at Paneas, its passage through the lake of Gennesaret, and its final disappearance in the Dead Sea, is graphic and almost poetical, and in the same connexion he introduces a striking notice of the Jewish sect of the Essenes.

Notices of Places in Asia.

" The river Jordan rises from the fountain of Paneas, which has given its distinctive name to the city of Caesareia, of which we shall speak hereafter (*i. e.* Caesareia Paneas). It is a delightful stream, with many windings as far as the nature of the country allows, and is a blessing to those who dwell on its banks; so it seems to make its way unwillingly towards the Lacus Asphaltites (Dead Sea), a region of repellent aspect, by which at last it is absorbed, when its beneficent current loses itself in those noxious waters. This is why, as soon as a depression of the ground occurs, it discharges itself into the lake commonly called Genesara, which is sixteen miles in length and six in breadth, with charming towns on its banks on every side— towards the east those of Julias and Hippus, towards the south Tarichaea, a name which some persons apply also to the lake, and towards the west Tiberias, which is a health resort on account of its hot springs.

The Jordan.

[1] *H. N.*, 5. 77, 80.

"The Lacus Asphaltites produces only bitumen, from which also it receives its name. The bodies of animals float on its surface, and this is true even of bulls and camels; hence the story has arisen that nothing can sink in it. Its length is more than a hundred miles, its breadth where it is widest is seventy-five, where it is narrowest, six miles. To the east of it lies Arabia of the nomads, towards the south Machaerus, which in former days was the most important stronghold in Judaea after Jerusalem. On that side too there is a warm spring with medicinal qualities, the name of which, Callirrhoë or the Fair Stream, proclaims the celebrity of its waters.

The Dead Sea.

"On its western side, beyond the unhealthy strip of shore, dwell the Esseni, a solitary people, the strangest among the inhabitants of the world, for there are no women among them, and they have abjured all sexual pleasure, and possess no money, but abide in the palm-groves. Day by day the number of these refugees is renewed, being largely swelled by the accession of those whom the vicissitudes of fortune drive, weary of life, to adopt their usages. In this way, marvellous though it seems, a race exists perpetually in which no one is born, for it is propagated by other men's dissatisfaction with life."[1]

The Essenes.

These and other notices of Palestine and Syria which we find in Pliny may well have been due to his intimacy with Vespasian and Titus. He remarks also on the unique features of Palmyra—the fertility of its soil and its abundant fountains, its position in the midst of the sandy desert, as if it had been naturally set apart from the rest of the world, and its success in maintaining its independence on the confines of the two mighty empires of Rome and Parthia, though constantly exposed to danger owing to their quarrels[2]. Proceeding further towards the east, we find him affirming, on the authority of emissaries of Pompey at the time of his campaign against the Albani, the existence of an overland trade-route from India to Europe by way of the Oxus, the Caspian, and the Black Sea, which had previously been asserted by Strabo on the strength of the testimony of Patrocles[3]. He describes, too, the site of Margiana

Palmyra.

[1] *H. N.*, 5. 71—3.   [2] *Ibid.*, 5. 88.
[3] *Ibid.*, 6. 52; Strabo, 11. 7. 3.

(Merv), which like Palmyra was an oasis in the middle of a desert, and he speaks of that district as being favourable for the growth of vines[1].

The account which Pliny gives of the source and the upper waters of the Tigris—a subject which seems to have attracted the attention of the ancients— The Tigris. though the actual facts are much distorted, contains many points which are suggestive with regard to the features of the country in that neighbourhood.

"The Tigris," he says, "rises in the district of Greater Armenia, from a conspicuous source in a level spot. The name of the place is Elegosine; that Its Upper Course. of the river, where its course is slower, Diglito; from the point where its speed increases, it begins to be called Tigris from its rapidity, for this is the word for an arrow among the Medes. It flows into the lake of Aretissa, which supports whatever heavy substances are brought down into it, and exhales natron in clouds; it contains but one kind of fish, and these avoid the current of the river as it passes, and in like manner the fish from the Tigris do not pass into the lake. The river is distinguished from it, as it flows along, both by its current and its colour, and after passing through it, disappears into a chasm where Mount Taurus meets it, and after flowing underground, bursts out on the farther side at a place called Zoaranda. The identity of the stream is shewn by objects dropped into it being carried through. Subsequently it passes through a second lake called Thospites, and again descends into an underground passage; after a course of twenty-two miles it reappears near Nymphaeum[2]."

Before we examine this passage further, it may be well to compare with it the account of the same objects which is given by Strabo, with whose work Pliny was unacquainted, so that their testimony is independent. It will not be difficult to discover that the story as given by the latter of the two writers is an adaptation of the earlier one, with the amplifications which are usually found in a later version. Strabo writes thus:—

---

[1] Pliny, 6. 46.   [2] *Ibid.*, 6. 127, 128.

"There is too the lake Arsene, which is also called Thopitis, and this contains potash, and serves for cleansing and fulling clothes; and for this reason also its water is not drinkable. Moreover the Tigris flows through it, after rising in the mountain district over against Niphates, and preserves its stream unmixed owing to its swiftness, for among the Medes *tigris* means 'an arrow'; and whereas there are many kinds of fish in the river, in the lake there is one kind only. But at the extremity of the lake the river falls into a chasm, and after running underground for a long distance rises again in the district called Chalonitis[1]."

Strabo's Account.

The lake which Strabo here calls Thopitis, and which by Pliny and Ptolemy is more accurately called Thospites or Thospitis[2], is undoubtedly the lake of Van, for this is called by Armenian writers Lake of Dosp, from its being situated in the province of Dosp, of which the city of Van was the capital. The features of that piece of water are sufficiently noteworthy to have aroused the interest of the learned, as soon as it came within the range of their observation, for its water is salt, its extreme length is ninety miles, and it is more than five thousand feet above the level of the sea. Its conformation also is peculiar, for whereas the greater part of its surface forms an irregular oblong, at its north-eastern angle it throws off a long arm, which is in so many respects a separate piece of water, that it might easily be distinguished from the rest of the lake. This will account for Pliny's error, when he speaks of two lakes at some distance from one another, and confines to the easternmost of the two, which he calls Aretissa, the special features which Strabo attributes to the lake Thopitis. Here again the names come to our aid, for that of Arsene, which Strabo gives as an alternative name for Thopitis, is shewn to be the Aretissa of Pliny by the intermediate form Arsissa, which is found in Ptolemy[3], so that we may conclude that the application of this was originally restricted to the eastern arm of the Lake of Van. At the present day this arm is called the Lake Ardjish, from a town of that name

The Lake of Van.

Criticisms of the Ancient Accounts.

---

[1] Strabo, II. 14. 8.   [2] Ptol. 5. 13. 7.

[3] Ptol. 5. 13. 8.

on its northern shore, and in this perhaps the ancient name
survives, for it is found as early as the tenth century of our era,
when the place is mentioned by Constantine Porphyrogenitus[1].
Both Strabo and Pliny suppose the Tigris to rise at a point
higher up than the Lake of Van, and to pass through it, disappearing afterwards into a chasm at its further end, and rising
again after flowing for some distance underground.   This view is
erroneous, because no connexion is traceable between the Tigris
and the lake; but it is a perfectly natural one, because the source
of the Tigris above Bitlis, which we have already noticed in
speaking of the retreat of the Ten Thousand[2], though it is higher
than the level of the lake, and therefore could not be derived from
it, is only a few miles distant from it.   It is clear also that the
authorities from whom these writers drew their information had
rightly observed that the lake had no visible outlet for its waters.
Again, when it came to be believed that the river passed through
the lake, the stream which enters the lake at its head would be
regarded as the upper course of the Tigris.   This stream, which
is now called the Bende-Mahi su, rises in the mountain range to
the southward of Ararat.   The name Diglito, which Pliny gives
to it, is a genuine one, being an earlier form of the word Tigris,
which is found in the Biblical name of that river, Hid-dekel, and
is still in use, in the form Dijleh, among the inhabitants of
Mesopotamia[3].

The stories which are told about the river and the lake in the
passages quoted above are partly based on fact,   Strabo's and
and partly suggested by the phenomena which had   Pliny's
been observed in other lakes.   The statement that   Stories.
the water of the lake contains potash, and that this was used for
cleansing clothes, is equally true at the present day, for cakes of
that substance, which are made from the scum that is found on
the surface of the lake, are now used at Van for purposes of
washing.   The statement about the fish, that those which live in
the river and those which live in the lake will not pass from the
one to the other, may have been suggested by what still occurs;

[1] *De Administr. Imp.*, c. 44, vol. 3. pp. 191, 192 ed. Bonn.
[2] *v. supra*, p. 114.
[3] *Dict. of the Bible*, art. Hiddekel; cp. Gen. ii. 14.

viz. that the fish are found to congregate about the mouths of the streams, where they are caught in great quantities. On the other hand, the idea that the waters of the two refused to mingle —which is found elsewhere with regard to rivers passing through lakes—had its origin in the difference of colour which the stream presents for some distance below the point where it enters. The notion also that heavy substances can float on the surface of the lake probably arose from its saltness and incrustations, corresponding as they do to the peculiarities of other pieces of water, like the Dead Sea, where, as we have just seen, this takes place. The story of the disappearance of the Tigris underground became famous, and is referred to by other authors. Thus Seneca says of it: "The Tigris is swallowed up and remains long out of sight, but at last emerges at a far distant point, though there is no question about its identity[1]." And Lucan writes :—

Disappearance of the Tigris.

> —Tigris sinking from the sight of day
> Through subterranean channels cuts his way;
> Then from a second fountain springs again,
> Shoots swiftly on, and rushing seeks the main[2].

Milton also would seem to have had the same idea in his mind, when he made Satan enter Paradise—

> Where Tigris, at the foot of Paradise,
> Into a gulf shot underground, till part
> Rose up a fountain by the tree of life[3].

In the passage immediately following Pliny's account of the Tigris which we have been considering, that author goes on to say, on the authority of Claudius Caesar, that in the region of Archene the Tigris flows so close to the Arsanias (*i.e.* the eastern branch of the Euphrates), that when their streams are swollen they flow together, yet without mingling their waters, for the Arsanias, which is the lighter of the two, floats on the surface of the Tigris for a distance of about four miles, and then separates again from it, and falls into the Euphrates (*i.e.* the western

---

[1] Sen., *Nat. Quaest.*, 3. 26.
[2] Lucan, *Pharsal.* 3. 261—3 (Rowe's translation).
[3] *Par. Lost*, 9. 71.

branch of the river). If we eliminate the absurdly fabulous exaggerations which are found in this passage, there seems still to remain a tradition, which may not be wholly baseless, about the two rivers communicating somewhere in their upper courses. Elsewhere in Roman writers we meet with the still more definite statement that the Tigris and Euphrates rose from the same fountain. Thus Lucan says, in the lines immediately preceding those quoted above :—

Common Source of the Tigris and Euphrates.

> One spring the Tigris and Euphrates know,
> And joined awhile the kindred rivers flow;
> Scarce could we judge between the doubtful claim,
> If Tigris or Euphrates give the name[1].

The earliest author by whom the story is mentioned is Sallust, who is quoted to that effect by Isidore of Seville[2] (7th cent. A.D.); and it was chiefly through him that it obtained a wide acceptance during the middle ages, and was ultimately enshrined in Dante's great poem[3]. This writer places the two rivers in his Terrestrial Paradise, and says of them :—

> —the Tigris and Euphrates
> Methought I saw forth issue from one fountain,
> And slowly part, like friends, from one another[4].

Now, if there is any groundwork at all for these ideas, there is only one place where it can be discovered, and that is at the head waters of the Tigris above Bitlis, for at this point alone in the courses of the two rivers, until they finally join before entering the Persian Gulf, does any connexion exist between them. It is the fact, that the marshy ground in which the eastern branch of the Tigris rises is also the source of the highest tributary of the Kara-su, Xenophon's Teleboas, which flows into the Murad-su, or eastern branch of the Euphrates, in the neighbouring plain of Mush[5].

Possible Explanation of the Fable.

---

[1] Lucan, *Pharsal.*, 3. 256—9.

[2] *Origines*, 13. 21. 10; Sallustius, auctor certissimus, ita asserit Tigrim et Euphratem uno fonte manare in Armenia.

[3] See Moore's *Time References in the Divina Commedia*, p. 123.

[4] *Purg.* 33. 112—14.

[5] See the author's *Turkish Armenia*, pp. 297, 298.

In this way a community of origin may possibly have been assigned to the two great streams. The geographical feature which has been mentioned could hardly have failed to attract attention, because the pass between Kurdistan and Armenia, at the head of which this marsh is situated, has in all ages been an important line of communication. As to the passage in Sallust, which is our principal authority on the subject—though we are not told in what part of his works it occurred, yet, as that writer composed a history of the campaigns of Lucullus in Asia, which were partly carried on in Armenia, it seems probable that it was introduced in this. We know, moreover, that during the campaign of 68 B.C., Lucullus passed this watershed on his way from Tigranocerta to the upper valley of the Euphrates[1], so that information about the river-courses might have been obtained on that occasion, and in that case would easily have come to the knowledge of Sallust, who was a contemporary of Lucullus. If these facts are worthy of any attention, as a possible explanation of the fable which afterwards became so popular, they may also perhaps form the groundwork of the story in Pliny.

Another region, of which hitherto the Greeks and Romans had only heard through vague rumours, and about which Pliny had something more like authentic information to communicate, is the island of Taprobane (Ceylon). He tells us that in the reign of Claudius a freedman of one Annius Plocamus, who farmed the customs duties on the Red Sea, when sailing along the coast of Arabia was caught by a storm, and at the end of fifteen days reached the port of Hippuri in that island. There he was hospitably received by the king, and in the course of a stay of six months became sufficiently acquainted with the language of the country to be able to communicate with the natives. The king appears to have been greatly impressed by discovering that the *denarii* which were found on the person of his strange visitor, though struck in the reigns of different emperors, as the heads upon them shewed, were all of equal weight. From this circumstance he inferred that the administration of the Roman empire by which they were issued

Pliny's Information about Taprobane.

Ambassadors sent thence to Rome.

[1] Mommsen, *History of Rome*, vol. 4. pt. 1, pp. 69, 70 (Eng. trans.).

was characterised by justice ; and he was thus induced to despatch an embassy to Rome, consisting of four persons, the chief of whom was called Rachias.   It was from them that the details which Pliny relates were derived.   Unfortunately, owing either to mis-statements on the part of these envoys, or to the Romans having misunderstood their meaning, the geographical notices which we thus obtain are most unsatisfactory.   The exaggerated views of the size of the island which prevailed among the ancients are here countenanced, for it is said to have possessed five hundred towns, and the length of the side which faced India is estimated at not less than a thousand geographical miles.   The chief city, which was situated on a harbour on the southern coast, and had two hundred thousand inhabitants, was called Palaesimundus—a name which, either in this form or in that of Simundu, is attributed by the author of the *Periplus of the Erythraean Sea* and by Ptolemy to the whole island[1].   In the centre lay a vast lake called Megisba, and from this proceeded two rivers, which flowed towards the south and the north respectively, the former being named, like the city which was built at its mouth, Palaesimundus, the latter Cydara.   As no lake exists corresponding to this, it has been conjectured that we have here an exaggerated description of one of the gigantic tanks which were constructed by the early rulers of Ceylon, and are still the wonders of the island[2].   The promontory of Coliacum, by which Cape Comorin is evidently meant, and which was spoken of as four days' sail distant from Taprobane, was erroneously regarded as the nearest point of the Indian coast. The sea which intervened between the two countries is described as having a deep green hue, and we are told that vessels which passed that way met with trees growing from the bottom, the foliage of which they often broke with their rudders.   We here recognise the coral which abounds in the gulf of Manaar between Ceylon and the mainland.   The life of the inhabitants, as reported by the ambassadors, was characterised by its simplicity and its prosperity, and this account is corroborated by what we learn from native sources with regard to its history at this period.   Slavery was unknown among them, the dwellings were built on a moderate scale, the price of corn was

Their Account of the Inhabitants.

[1] *Periplus*, § 61; Ptol., 7. 4. 1.   [2] Tennent's *Ceylon*, p. 557.

not allowed to vary, and litigation did not exist. The king was elected, and careful provision was made that the office should not become hereditary; his power also was limited by the appointment of a council of advisers, and the imposition of capital punishment was still further restricted. The land was well cultivated and very productive, but the vine was not grown there. The natives were famed for their longevity, often exceeding a hundred years. But notwithstanding the sobriety of their manner of living, they were reported to have a thoroughly oriental appreciation of gold and gems, especially pearls, which were found there in great abundance; and the ambassadors remarked with some shrewdness that, while the wealth of their countrymen was greater than that of the Romans, the latter knew how to employ it more profitably[1].

We may now turn to a remarkable document, which was composed about ten years after Pliny's death, the *Periplus Maris Erythraei*. This is a manual of the coasts of Africa, Arabia, and India which border on the Erythraean sea; and as it introduces, not only the natural features of those coasts, together with the harbours and trading-stations, but also in great detail their exports and imports, it would seem to have been drawn up by a merchant for the use of merchants. Its great value for geography consists in the striking power of observation which its writer shews, and the accuracy of his statements, which have been amply verified by modern explorers. His name is not given, nor do we know anything about him beyond what may be gathered from internal evidence in the work itself; but from this it appears that he was a Greek residing in Egypt. His starting-point is the port of Myos Hormos on the Red Sea, and he first follows the African coast of that piece of water as far as the straits of Bab-el-Mandeb, mentioning on the way the places which had been established by the Ptolemies for purposes of commerce and elephant-hunting, and Adulis, the port of Auxuma (Axum), the capital of Aethiopia, which was situated in the interior of the country. Between the Straits and the promontory of Aromata (Cape Guardafui), also, the stations are carefully noted, with the products of the

The Periplus Maris Erythraei.

African Coast.

Aromata Prom. (Cape Guardafui).

---

[1] Pliny, *H. N.*, 6. 84 foll.

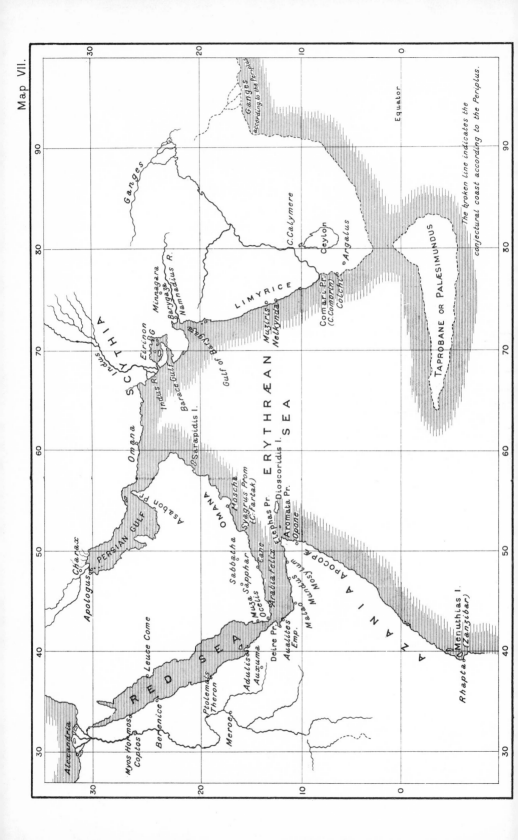

Map VII.

The broken line indicates the
conjectural coast according to the Periplus

neighbouring lands for which they were the *entrepôts*—ivory, tortoiseshell, cinnamon, and a variety of gums. After this we obtain our earliest information respecting the coast to the south-ward of that promontory, which is here rightly spoken of as the easternmost point of Africa. In particular, the peninsula, on the further side of which lay Opone—a considerable emporium, to which articles of commerce were brought even from India[1]—can be easily recognised in Ras Hafoun, a rocky headland, ninety miles south of Cape Guardafui, which is joined to the continent by a spit of sand. Beyond this point, perhaps, the writer himself had not advanced, for his narrative becomes less circumstantial; but the account which he gives must have been derived from other traders, since the spots which he names can in the main be identified. Almost the furthest of these which had been reached at that time was a low-lying island, rich in trees, called Menuthias[2]; and, according to the distances which are given, Menuthias this must correspond either to Zanzibar, or to the (Zanzibar). more northerly island of Pemba. The facts thus revealed give evidence of a great advance in the conception of the shape of Africa from what had previously existed, for whereas the coast of that continent was believed by Strabo and his predecessors to trend towards the west immediately after passing the Cinnamon country, it had now been proved to follow a southerly course at least as far as the equator. The writer, however, so far conforms to the traditional view, that he remarks (curiously enough) that beyond Menuthias, the ocean, 'which was unexplored,' makes a westward bend, and ultimately joins the sea on the other side of Africa[3].

Returning now to its original starting-point, the *Periplus* proceeds to trace in a similar manner the coasts of Arabia and India. Here, as before, we can only Arabian Coast. draw attention to the most marked points which

---

[1] *Periplus Maris Erythraei*, §§ 13, 14, in Müller, *Geogr. Gr. Minores*, vol. I. p. 267; Ἀπὸ δὲ Τάβαι μετὰ σταδίους τετρακοσίους παραπλεύσαντι χερσόνησον, καθ' ὃν τόπον καὶ ὁ ῥοῦς ἕλκει, ἕτερόν ἐστιν ἐμπόριον Ὀπώνη......Ἐξαρτίζεται δὲ συνήθως καὶ ἀπὸ τῶν ἔσω τόπων, τῆς Ἀριακῆς καὶ Βαρυγάζων, εἰς τὰ αὐτὰ τὰ τοῦ πέραν ἐμπόρια γένη προχωροῦντα ἀπὸ τῶν τόπων, σῖτος καὶ ὄρυζα, κ.τ.λ.

[2] *Ibid.* § 15.   [3] § 18.

are noticed. Shortly after passing the Straits we reach a

Arabia Eudaemon (Aden). port called Arabia Eudaemon, which, though at this time almost deserted, yet at an earlier period, when no direct traffic existed between India and Alexandria, had been of great importance as a station for the trans-shipment of goods[1]. This is undoubtedly the modern Aden, which at the present day under other influences has regained its early prosperity. Some distance again beyond this we meet with a conspicuous headland

Syagrus Prom. (Cape Fartak). called Syagrus (Cape Fartak), which is here dignified with the title of 'the greatest promontory in the world[2].' On its shore there was a depository of frankincense, for the neighbouring region of the interior of Arabia (the Hadramaut) has been in all ages the chief source of the supply of that article; but a more important cause of the celebrity of this cape was its being the starting-point for the direct sea-route to India, which was now beginning to be used by the more adventurous traders. The island of Socotra, which lies to the

I. of Dioscorides (Socotra). southward of this point and eastward of Cape Guardafui, and was called in ancient times the Island of Dioscorides, is noticed in this connexion, because it belonged to the sovereign of this part of Arabia. Beyond Syagrus we meet with another important emporium of frankincense, called Moscha, the mountains at the back of which were inhabited by cave-dwellers[3]; this neighbourhood is the region of Dhofar, and the account here given is corroborated by Mr Theodore Bent, who has recently explored it, and found the natives and their flocks living together in deep caves in the hill-sides[4]. The survey is then continued as far as the mouths of the Indus along the coasts of Arabia and Gedrosia, passing the entrance of the Persian Gulf. The lofty mountain-chain called

---

[1] *Periplus*, § 26; Εὐδαίμων δ' ἐπεκλήθη, πρότερον οὖσα πόλις, ὅτε, μήπω ἀπὸ τῆς Ἰνδικῆς εἰς τὴν Αἴγυπτον ἐρχομένων μηδὲ ἀπὸ τῆς Αἰγύπτου τολμώντων εἰς τοὺς ἔσω τόπους διαίρειν, ἀλλ' ἄχρι ταύτης παραγινομένων, τοὺς παρ' ἀμφοτέρων φόρτους ἀπεδέχετο, ὥσπερ Ἀλεξάνδρεια καὶ τῶν ἔξωθεν καὶ τῶν ἀπὸ τῆς Αἰγύπτου φερομένων ἀποδέχεται.

[2] § 30.

[3] § 32; ὑψηλὰ ὄρη πετρώδη καὶ ἀπόκοπα ἀνθρώπων ἐν σπηλαίοις κατοικούντων.

[4] *Geographical Journal*, vol. 6 (1895), p. 122.

Asabon, which is mentioned as rising at the last-named point, is the same as the promontory of Maceta which occurs in the narrative of Nearchus, now Cape Mussendum[1].

The description of the coast of India which follows is even more accurate in its details, and in the directions for sailing which it gives. Beyond the mouths of   Indian Coast. the Indus lay a large inlet called Eirinon, which was excessively dangerous on account of its currents and shoals; and on the farther side of it was another   Baraces and Eirinon Inlets bay called Baraces, enclosed by a long projecting   (Gulf and Runn cape[2]. The latter of these is evidently the Gulf of   of Cutch). Cutch, while the former, which lies to the northward of it, is the strange area known as the Runn of Cutch, which at the present time according to the season of the year is either a lake or a salt morass. The next gulf to this is that of Cambay, which leads up to the estuary of the Nerbudda. This river is called in the *Periplus* Namnadius, while the gulf took its name from the trading station of Barygaza, which was situated on the stream at a distance of thirty miles from the sea,   Barygaza (Baroche). and was the most famous emporium of all western India. Among its exports are mentioned perfumes, precious stones, ivory, muslin, and silk[3]. The bore of the Nerbudda, which presented the same features as   Bore of the Nerbudda. the corresponding inrush of the tide at the mouth of the Indus, which so greatly terrified Alexander's soldiers, is very vividly depicted, and the terms in which its effect on the vessels lying in the stream is described leave no doubt that the writer was an eye-witness of it.

" Throughout India there are numerous rivers, and the tide ebbs and flows in a remarkable manner, increasing for the space of three days towards the new moon and the full moon, but decreasing in the intervening periods. This is especially the case near Barygaza, insomuch that there the depths of the sea are on a sudden exposed to view, and while at one time portions of the mainland are covered with water, at another dry ground appears where vessels were but lately sailing; and owing to the inrush of the tide, the neighbouring sea being

---

[1] *m. supra*, p. 142.   [2] *Periplus*, § 40.   [3] § 49.

forced into a narrow space, the rivers are driven backwards for
many stadia contrary to the natural direction of their current.
In consequence of this, sailors who are unacquainted with these
waters and visit Barygaza for the first time run great risk in
approaching and quitting the port. For, since the rush of the
tide does not slacken its force, the anchors cannot hold ; and so
the vessels, which are carried away by its impetus, being driven
out of the straight course by the fury of the stream, run aground
on the sandbanks and are broken up, while the smaller ones are
even upset ; others, again, which to avoid the tide-wave have
betaken themselves to the neighbouring canals, are swamped by
the first onset of the stream, unless they are shored up, since the
bore comes suddenly upon them. So great indeed is the violence
with which the sea comes in at the new moon, especially during
the nightly flow of the tide, that, while at the commencement of
its advance, when the sea is calm, a sound like the shouting of an
army far away reaches the ears of those who dwell about the
estuary, shortly afterwards the sea itself with a rushing noise
comes sweeping over the shallows[1]."

Beyond Barygaza, the furthest point which was reached by
traders was Nelcynda—a place the position of
which is not certainly determined, but it seems
to have lain in the neighbourhood of the Malabar coast. It
was extensively resorted to in connexion with the pepper trade.
With regard to the shape of India the author of the *Periplus*
seems to have held truer views than any preceding geographer, as
we have already seen to be the case concerning Africa ; for he
remarks that from Barygaza onwards the direction of the coast is
from north to south, thus shewing that he was aware of the
existence of the peninsula of Hindostan. He also gives evidence
of being acquainted with the name of this region, which he says is
called Dachinabades because of its extension from north to south,
dachanos being the native word for the south wind[2]. This
etymology of the appellation ' Deccan ' is approximately right, for

Nelcynda.

---

[1] *Periplus*, §§ 45, 46.

[2] § 50; Μετὰ δὲ τὰ Βαρύγαζα εὐθέως ἡ συναφὴς ἤπειρος ἐκ τοῦ βορέου εἰς τὸν
νότον παρεκτείνει· διὸ καὶ Δαχιναβάδης καλεῖται ἡ χώρα· δάχανος γὰρ καλεῖται ὁ
νότος τῇ αὐτῶν γλώσσῃ.

dakkhina in Prakrit means 'south,' and *dakkhinâbadha* signifies 'the way towards the south[1].'

At this point the writer pauses to remark on the direct trade from the Arabian coast to the Indian ports; and by a comparison of the account which he gives with the notice in Pliny which has been already The Direct
Route to India. referred to we obtain a fairly clear view of the history of its development[2]. The first person who ventured to quit the ordinary route by the mouth of the Persian Gulf, and to steer across the open sea from the promontory of Syagrus to India, was a Greek navigator called Hippalus, Voyage of
Hippalus. who availed himself of the periodical blowing of the south-west monsoon for that purpose. Concerning the date of this voyage we have no information, but it was probably somewhat later than the Augustan age, for, while the manner in which it is spoken of implies that it was not a recent event, we gather from the silence of Strabo on the subject that it was subsequent to his time. The pioneering feat of Hippalus was commemorated by his name being attached to the south-west monsoon, as the *Periplus* informs us; and Pliny gives it this title, though he was unacquainted with its origin. It seems probable that the destination which he reached was the mouths of the Indus, and that subsequently to this other traders made their way, first to Barygaza, and afterwards to Nelcynda, though the direction of the monsoon was less favourable for the more southerly voyage. In any case, according to Pliny's account, there was an established line of traffic in his day between the frankincense region of southern Arabia and the last-named place—which, or rather the inhabitants of the neighbouring district, he calls Neacyndi—and also to the port of Musiris, which lay somewhat to the north of it; but he adds that it was necessary for the vessels, in addition to their crews, to be accompanied by bands of archers, on account of the pirates who infested those seas. The passage from Pliny may here be introduced with advantage for the purpose of comparison.

"For those who make the voyage to India the most convenient

---

[1] C. Müller, *op. cit.*, vol. I. p. 294.

[2] Pliny, 6. 100, 101, 104, 105; *Periplus*, § 57.

starting-point is Ocelis [in Arabia, near the straits of Bab el-Mandeb]. From that place a voyage of forty days before the wind called Hippalus brings them to Musiris, the first trading station which they reach in India, but not a desirable one, from the neighbourhood of the pirates, who occupy a spot called Nitrias. Nor, indeed, does it furnish many exports, and the roadstead is a long way from the coast, so that the freight has to be carried to and fro in boats. The name of the king at the time when I write is Caelobothras. A more serviceable port is that called Becare, in the territory of the Neacyndi. The ruler of the country, Pandion, dwells at Modura, a city in the interior a long distance from the trading station. The district from which pepper is brought to Becare by the natives in canoes is called Cottonara ; but as none of these names of tribes or stations or towns occur in any previous author, it is clear that the relative importance of the places is apt to change. The return voyage from India is made at the beginning of the Egyptian month Tybis, our December, or, at the latest, during the first six days of the Egyptian Mechiris, which fall within the Ides of January according to our computation ; thus they manage to reach home within the year. The wind which is favourable to the transit from India is the Vulturnus [SSE. wind], but after they enter the Red Sea the Africus [SW. wind] or Auster [S. wind][1]."

The remainder of the *Periplus* is devoted to notices of the coasts of Asia beyond Nelcynda. As no Greek navigators had as yet advanced so far, these must have been derived from the reports of native traders, and consequently we cannot be surprised if they are vague and inaccurate ; at the same time they contain certain elements of truth. Thus the name Comari, which the writer assigns to a place considerably to the southward of Nelcynda, is almost certainly that of Cape Comorin, though he does not associate it with that promontory[2]. He states that opposite the island of Taprobane the coast trends towards the east, after

Notices of Eastern Asia.

---

[1] Pliny, *H. N.*, 6. 104—6. In § 101 we are further told, 'omnibus annis navigatur sagittariorum cohortibus impositis ; etenim piratae maxime infestabant.'

[2] *Periplus*, § 59.

which it pursues for a time a northerly course, and then once more turns eastward towards the mouths of the Ganges. Beyond that point lay a district called Chryse, and an island of the same name, in both of which perhaps we may find an intimation of the Malay peninsula, which in Ptolemy's time was known as the Golden Chersonese[1]. Finally, the position of China is indicated, when we are told that far away This (China). towards the north, and bordering on the eastern ocean, there was a land called This, containing a great city named Thinae, from which silk was exported, both raw and spun and woven into textures[2]. To this statement is appended an interesting intimation of the two routes by which that article was brought from China into India, one being by the upper country through Bactria to Barygaza, the other by way of the Ganges to Musiris and Nelcynda. The name of Serica, which was given by the Romans to the northern region of China, is not mentioned in the *Periplus*. It seems to have originally signified the 'silk-producing country,' being derived from the old Chinese word for silk, which in Mongolian is 'sirkek.' From this again was formed the name of Seres to represent the inhabitants[3].

Another geographical work should here be mentioned, which, though it was of no real importance, at one period attained a considerable popularity—the *Periegesis* Dionysius Periegetes. or *Description of the World* of Dionysius, who from the title of his book was called Periegetes. The date of its composition has been much disputed, for it His Date. has been assigned to various periods from the Augustan age even down to the beginning of the fourth century of our era: but it seems now to be determined with a fair amount of certainty that it belongs to the reign of Domitian. That it cannot be earlier than Vespasian appears from the account there given of the Aegean islands, for the Cyclades are assigned to Asia, and it was under that emperor that they were first attached as a province to that continent[4]. And it is

---

[1] *Periplus*, §§ 61—63.   [2] § 64.

[3] Kiepert, *Lehrbuch*, p. 44; cp. Skeat, *Etym. Dict.*, s.v. Silk.

[4] Dionys., *Perieg.*, vv. 525 foll., in C. Müller's *Geogr. Gr. Minores*, vol. 2; where see the editor's note.

difficult to think that it is later than the age of Domitian, because
the writer goes out of his way to glorify the victory of the
prætor Flaccus over the Nasamones in Africa in 86 A.D.[1], of
which event Domitian wrote boastfully to the Senate, announcing
in the haughty language of divinity that he had 'forbidden the
Nasamones to exist[2]'; but the occurrence was one of so slight
importance, that it would hardly have been commemorated at
a later period—certainly not to the exclusion of more considerable successes of later emperors, of which no mention is
made. The work of Dionysius was composed in
Greek hexameters, and extended to 1189 lines.
Its brevity as a survey of geography, and the
metrical form in which it was written, seem to have commended
it to schoolmasters as a text-book for communicating a knowledge of the subject to their pupils, and in consequence of this
numerous copies of the work were made; afterwards, in proportion as learning declined, and the more important authors
ceased to be read, its authority came to be greatly overrated.

His
Geographical
Poem.

The *Periegesis* begins with general remarks on the shape of
the habitable world, which the writer compares to
that of a sling, and on its division into continents, a
choice being given for the boundary of Europe and
Asia between the Tanais and the Caucasian isthmus, and for
the boundary of Asia and Africa between the Nile and the
Pelusiac isthmus. It next describes the four sections of the
ocean by which this area is surrounded—the Atlantic to the
west, the Frozen sea to the north, the Indian Ocean to the east,
and the Erythraean or Aethiopian to the south; and also the
four principal gulfs which issue from it, and penetrate into the
land—the Mediterranean, the Caspian, the Persian, and Arabian
gulfs. Then follows a detailed account of the Mediterranean,
with all its subordinate bays and inlets, among which the Euxine
and the Palus Maeotis are included. The delineation of the

Its General
Geography.

---

[1] Dionys., *Perieg.*, vv. 209 foll.

[2] Zonaras *Annal.*, 11. 19; vol. 2, p. 500 ed. Bonn.; γνοὺς ὁ Φλάκκος τοῦτο
ἐπέθετο αὐτοῖς καὶ πάντας ἀπώλεσε καὶ τοὺς ἀπομάχους διέφθειρεν ἄπαντας· ἐφ'
ᾧ ὁ Δομετιανὸς ἐπαρθεὶς εἶπε πρὸς τὴν βουλὴν ὅτι "Νασαμῶνας ἐκώλυσα εἶναι."
ἤδη γὰρ καὶ θεὸς ἠξίου νομίζεσθαι.

three continents, to which Dionysius now proceeds, commences
with Africa, and the peoples and races which
occupied the northern part of that area are first   Description
of Africa.
described; next, those to the southward of them
in the centre of the country are enumerated, and the Aethiopians
in the neighbourhood of Cerne, which he regards, not, as former
writers had done, as an island, but as a district bordering on
the southern ocean.   The Nile, which flowed from the country of
these Aethiopians, he speaks of as bearing the name of Siris in
its upper course[1], though it would seem that in reality this appellation, so far as it was used at all, was restricted to a portion of the
stream between Meroë and Syene.   Descending this river he now
enters Egypt, which is the last section of Africa that he describes.
It is noticeable that in his account of it he mentions the statue
of Memnon as being still vocal[2]—a statement which might be
adduced as evidence to shew that the date of the *Periegesis*
cannot at all events be later than the end of the second century.
For, whereas the legs of that statue are covered with inscriptions
in Greek and Latin, recording that visitors had been present
when the sound was emitted, the date of the latest of these is
196 A.D., that is, shortly before the visit of Septimius Severus;
and, as the statue was repaired by that emperor, it is natural to
suppose that the work which was executed at that time caused
the cessation of the sound.

Proceeding now to Europe, Dionysius compares the shape of
that continent together with Africa to a cone, the
apex of which is towards the west, the base to-   Of Europe.
wards the east, bordering on Asia[3].   In this we find an exaggeration of the description of the world as tapering at its extremities,
which is given by Eratosthenes and Strabo; and the same form
is attributed by him to Asia[4], though this statement he modifies
in a subsequent passage, where he assigns to that area a quad-
rangular shape with one side facing east[5]—an inconsistency from
which his predecessors were not wholly exempt.   In enumerating
the various countries of Europe and their inhabitants he proceeds from west to east throughout the northern portion of the

[1] Dionys., *Perieg.*, vv. 221—4.   [2] v. 249.   [3] vv. 275—8.
[4] vv. 620—26.   [5] vv. 881 foll.

continent, and his ignorance of this shews how little he drew from Roman sources. Thus he seems to identify the Eridanus with the Rhone, and places the fountains of that river in the neighbourhood of the Pyrenees; while to the northward of the Euxine the names of the tribes that he mentions are mainly derived from Herodotus. A curious touch of mathematical geography is found in his account of the mouth of the Borysthenes, which he speaks of as lying 'over against the Cyanean rocks on the same meridian line[1]'; and he is also the first author to mention the tribe of Alans, whom he introduces in connexion with the Dacians and the Tauri in the south of Russia[2]. The name of the Huns too occurs in his description of Asia in the neighbourhood of the Caspian Sea[3], but whether these were the progenitors of the famous horde who overran Europe, or only an insignificant clan of the same name, it is impossible to say. The latter part of the section which is devoted to Europe treats of the three great peninsulas, or, as the writer quaintly calls them, 'pedestals,' which project into the Mediterranean.

At this point, before turning to Asia, the writer inserts a long section relating to the islands—first those of the Mediterranean, and afterwards those that lie in the outer sea. It is curious to notice the islands that have been selected for special mention under the latter head (vv. 555—611). He begins with Erytheia, a half-mythical name, which we find frequently associated with Gades, but which here is probably intended to designate one of the Fortunatae Insulae. Next to these are mentioned the Cassiterides, or, as he calls them, the 'Hesperides islands, whence tin comes,' and the position assigned to them is in the neighbourhood of the Sacrum Promontorium; but, as Dionysius says that this headland was the westernmost point of Europe, it has been conjectured that he really means the Armorican promontory, which was then believed to project farthest in that direction; and that, like some preceding writers, he identified the Cassiterides with Ushant and the other islands in that neighbourhood. Then follow the two British isles, and somewhere not far off from them the islands of the Amnitae, which were celebrated

Of the Islands.

---

[1] Dionys., *Perieg.*, v. 313; ὀρθὸν ἐπὶ γραμμῇ κατεναντία Κυανεάων.
[2] v. 305.   [3] v. 730.

on account of the orgiastic rites performed in them by the women
in honour of Dionysus. These observances are also related on
the authority of Posidonius by Strabo[1], who places these islands
off the mouth of the Loire, and calls the inhabitants Samnitae.
In Thule, which lies beyond Britain, the continuous duration of
daylight during the summer months is noticed. With regard to
the Arctic Sea, or Mare Pigrum, it is implied that there was unimpeded navigation through it as far as the Eastern Ocean, for the
writer supposes a vessel to sail in that direction from Thule as far
as the island of Chryse. His conception of the position of the
last-named place, indeed, is vague enough, but he seems to mean
the Aurea Chersonesus (Malay Peninsula). After this, Taprobane
(Ceylon) is introduced, with the usual exaggerated estimate of its
size; and the enumeration ends with two small islands in the
Persian Gulf, Ogyris and Icarus, the former of which is probably
the modern Ormuz[2], and was famed as the burial-place of king
Erythras, the eponymus of the Erythraean Sea; while the latter
contained a famous shrine of Artemis Tauropolos, which also is
mentioned by Strabo[3].

In his account of Asia Dionysius rightly follows his predecessors
in regarding the continent as divided in two parts
by the long chain of mountains, running from west
to east, to which they gave the name of Taurus. He starts from
the river Tanais and the Black Sea, and enumerates all the tribes
in the northern part of the country which lie to the eastward of
that line; then he returns to Asia Minor, and afterwards treats of
Syria, Arabia, and the peoples that lie to the eastward of them as
far as India. He traces accurately the courses of the Euphrates
and Tigris, and repeats the story which we have noticed above,
and which had now become well established, of the latter of these
two rivers flowing through the Lake of Van, and afterwards passing

Of Asia.

[1] Strab. 4. 4. 6; Ἐν δὲ τῷ ὠκεανῷ φησι [Ποσειδώνιος] εἶναι νῆσον μικρὰν οὐ
πάνυ πελαγίαν, προκειμένην τῆς ἐκβολῆς τοῦ Δείγηρος ποταμοῦ· οἰκεῖν δὲ ταύτην
τὰς τῶν Σαμνιτῶν γυναῖκας, Διονύσῳ κατεχομένας καὶ ἱλασκομένας τὸν θεὸν τοῦτον
τελεταῖς τε καὶ ἄλλαις ἱεροποιίαις.

[2] v. supra, p. 142.

[3] 16. 3. 2; ὁ παράπλους ἔχει προκειμένην νῆσον Ἴκαρον, καὶ ἱερὸν Ἀπόλλωνος
ἅγιον ἐν αὐτῇ καὶ μαντεῖον Ταυροπόλου.

for some distance underground[1]. The direction followed by the Indus is also carefully given, with the two branches into which it divides as it approaches the sea, and the district of Patalene which intervenes between them[2]. Of the fertility and valuable products of India he gives an enthusiastic account; but in no part of his poem is the writer's ignorance of recent discoveries more conspicuous than here, for he is unacquainted with the existence of the peninsula of Hindustan and the Bay of Bengal, and he still represents the Ganges as flowing into the Eastern Sea.

The geographical sketch of the world, which has thus been described in outline, is interspersed with notices of the peculiar features and products of the different countries, and of the customs of various tribes, together with legends and mythological stories which were associated with them. As may be supposed, it is not altogether homogeneous, for the store of facts which it contains has been gathered from various quarters, and from authorities widely differing in date, so that it does not represent the world as it existed at any one particular period. Callimachus and Apollonius Rhodius were among the author's geographical authorities. Still, this medley of information, clothed as it is in easily flowing metre, is even at the present day sufficiently pleasant reading, so that its popularity at the time when it was composed is easily accounted for. The permanent influence which it exercised is proved by its having been translated into Latin verse in the fourth century, for the benefit of readers unacquainted with the Greek language, by Avienus, the author of the *Ora Maritima*, which work has already attracted our attention as containing passages derived from the narrative of the voyage of the Carthaginian explorer, Himilco[3]. Another Latin translation, which was made at a later period by Priscian the grammarian, became a geographical text-book for school-boys in the middle ages[4]. The *Periegesis* was made the subject of an elaborate commentary by Eustathius of Thessalonica in the twelfth century, and in the West its statements reappear in later writers. An edition of it was issued at an early date after

General Remarks upon it.

---

[1] Dionys., *Perieg.*, vv. 987 foll.   [2] vv. 1088 foll.
[3] *v. supra*, p. 109.
[4] Bevan and Phillott, *Mediaeval Geography*, p. xxix.

the invention of printing, and it has several times been reprinted. To us at the present day it is chiefly of interest as shewing how greatly under the Roman empire the popular notion of geography lagged behind the scientific knowledge of the time. An acquaintance with this fact enables us to explain the existence at a later period of traditions on the subject which appear to us exceedingly primitive.

In no part of the world was greater advance made in the knowledge of geography during the first century and a half after Augustus than in Britain. Subsequently to the expeditions of Julius Caesar no serious attempt *Progressive Knowledge of Britain.* had been made by the Romans to conquer that country until the time of Claudius (43 A.D.), by whom and his lieutenants the southern part of the island was reduced *Conquests of Claudius,* to submission. Camulodunum, the capital of the Trinobantes, which was taken on this occasion, was afterwards occupied by a Roman colony—the first of many that were established in the island—and was consequently known as Coloniae Castrum (Colchester). The province which was now formed was gradually consolidated and extended, until in Nero's reign (61 A.D.) the conquests of Suetonius Paullinus carried its limits as far north as Lindum on the *Suetonius Paullinus,* one side and Deva on the other, which two places also became Roman settlements, and were called Lindum Colonia (Lincoln) and Devae Castrum (the fortress on the Dee, or Chester). Already at this time we hear of Londinium (London) as being the greatest and most populous commercial centre in the country on account of its favourable position at the mouth of the Thames, for Tacitus in his account of the campaign of Suetonius Paullinus speaks of it as the principal resort of traders and the chief depot for stores[1]. The next advance was made under Domitian by Agricola, who in the course of eight years (78—85 A.D.) extended the Roman dominion as far as the *Agricola,* Firths of Clyde and Forth, and defended the isthmus which lies

---

[1] Tac. *Ann.*, 14. 33; Londinium...copia negotiatorum et commeatuum maxime celebre.

between them by establishing a chain of forts across it[1]. He even penetrated into Caledonia to the northward of this line, and defeated the natives in two great battles. It was Agricola's good fortune to have his exploits recorded by Tacitus, who was his son-in-law, and through him we obtain an idea of the impression which the natural features of Britain produced on the foreigners. Thus, besides noticing the mildness and raininess of the climate, the shortness of the summer nights, and other peculiarities, he specially remarks on the depth to which the sea on these coasts penetrates into the land, and on the numerous estuaries which are formed in this manner[2]. Tacitus also records in his *Agricola* the expedition which was despatched by that commander to explore the shores of the island as far as its northern extremity, and he mentions that they reached the Orcades (Orkneys). The land which they saw in the distance beyond this point, but did not visit owing to the lateness of the season, and which they believed to be Thule, is no doubt the same to which Pytheas also assigned that name— Mainland, the chief of the Shetland islands[3]. In Hadrian's time (119 A.D.) the northern portion of these new conquests was abandoned, and that emperor fixed the line of the Eden and the Tyne as the limit of the Roman possessions, and constructed there the famous rampart, which is known at the present day as the Roman Wall. This continued to be the boundary until under

and Antoninus Pius. Antoninus Pius (142 A.D.) the country as far as the Forth and the Clyde was again occupied, and a continuous rampart of earth was built across the isthmus parallel to the line of forts which Agricola had erected. By means of these campaigns, and of the numerous settlements that were founded in the country, and the roads by which they were connected with one another, the Romans acquired a satisfactory knowledge of the characteristics of Britain, and of the position of the tribes by whom it was inhabited.

---

[1] Tac. *Agric.*, 23 ; Clota et Bodotria, diversi maris fluctibus per inmensum revectae, angusto terrarum spatio dirimuntur : quod tum praesidiis firmabatur.

[2] *Agric.*, 10; Unum addiderim, nusquam latius dominari mare, multum fluminum huc atque illuc ferre, nec litore tenus adcrescere aut resorberi, sed influere penitus atque ambire, et jugis etiam ac montibus inseri velut in suo.

[3] Müllenhoff, *Deutsche Altertumskunde*, 1. p. 388.

The acquaintance of the Romans with Germany derived from
personal observation decreased rather than otherwise after the
time of Augustus.   The rule which was laid down   Germany
by that emperor to the effect that the Roman arms   and Scandi-
should not advance beyond the Elbe was strictly   navia.
adhered to by his successors; indeed, so little did they attempt
to penetrate into the country at all, that Tacitus speaks of that river
as being known to his contemporaries only by hearsay[1].   At the
same time there arose a growing intercourse between the two
peoples, and from this was derived the enlarged knowledge of the
inhabitants of Germany which we find existing at a later period,
though we have no evidence whence it came.   Much of this
was embodied in the *Germania* of Tacitus; but that treatise,
interesting as it is from an ethnographical point of view, furnishes
us with but little information about the physical features of the
country, and even as to the situation of the various tribes.   It is
noticeable, as a proof of the ignorance which prevailed with regard
to the north-eastern part of the country, that the name of so important a river as the Viadrus (Oder) does not occur in any writer
before Ptolemy; and though the Vistula was known at an earlier
period, and was regarded as the boundary of Germany on its eastern
side towards Sarmatia, yet this was probably due to the trade-route
from the Baltic which passed through Pannonia, rather than to
any intelligence derived from Germany itself.   About the regions
in the north of Europe, however, some intelligence, though of an
imperfect character, was obtained.   In Mela the southern portion
of the Baltic is mentioned under the name of Codanus Sinus[2], and
the knowledge of this may have been acquired at the time of the
naval expedition of Tiberius, which sailed up the Elbe.   Mela also
is the first writer who mentions Scandinavia, but he regards it, not
as a peninsula, but as a large island[3]; this view is also found in

---

[1] Tac. *Germ.*, 41; in Hermunduris Albis oritur, flumen inclutum et notum
olim; nunc tantum auditur.

[2] Mela, 3. 31; super Albim Codanus ingens sinus magnis parvisque insulis
refertus est.

[3] *Ibid.* § 54; In illo sinu quem Codanum diximus eximia Scadinavia, quam
adhuc Teutoni tenent, et ut fecunditate alias ita magnitudine antestat.

Pliny[1], and was permanently maintained.   It is that country, no doubt, to which Tacitus also refers, when he speaks of an island lying out in the ocean off the northern coast of Germany, which was inhabited by a people called the Suiones[2]; for in that appellation the modern name of Swede is generally recognised.   Denmark, too, was known to Pliny under the name of the Cimbrian promontory as a great peninsula extending towards the north[3].

In eastern Europe the conquest of Dacia by Trajan opened out a considerable area, which was unexplored before that time.   The departure from the established policy of maintaining the Danube as the northern frontier of the empire, which the annexation of that tract involved, was in the first instance unavoidable.   During the reign of Domitian, Decebalus, a Dacian chieftain who had succeeded in concentrating in his own hands the government of the whole of that country, overran Moesia, and caused great injury to the Roman power.   At the conclusion of the war which followed a peace was concluded, which was far from advantageous to the Romans; and Trajan, when he came to the throne, in order to secure the neighbouring parts of the empire from attacks from that quarter, invaded Dacia, and in the course of his second campaign (104 A.D.) completely defeated Decebalus.   Dacia was now reduced to a Roman province, and its capital city, Sarmizegethusa, which was captured, received the name of Ulpia Trajana.   The territory which was comprehended in Dacia is that which is bounded on the east by the Dniester and on the west by the Theiss, including the modern kingdom of Roumania, with its wide plains extending to the Danube, the mountainous district of Transylvania and the lands to the northward of it as far as the Carpathians, and the adjoining portion of Hungary which is called the Banat.   A large number of military colonies were now established in the

Dacia conquered by Trajan.

---

[1] Pliny, 4. 96; sinum, qui Codanus vocatur refertus insulis, quarum clarissima est Scatinavia incompertae magnitudinis.

[2] Tac. *Germ.*, 44; Suionum hinc civitates, ipso in Oceano, praeter viros armaque classibus valent.

[3] Pliny, 4. 97; Promunturium Cimbrorum excurrens in maria longe paeninsulam efficit quae Tastris appellatur.

country, and in addition to these a multitude of civilians resorted thither from various parts of the empire, so that in the course of time Dacia became thoroughly Romanised. In order to secure the communication between these newly acquired domains and the neighbouring provinces, Trajan erected the famous bridge across the Danube that bore his name, the remains of which are still visible near Orsova below the rapids and narrow passage of the stream called the Iron Gate. A century and a half later than this, in the reign of Aurelian, it was found expedient to withdraw the Roman colonists into Moesia on the right bank of the river, where they were constituted into a new province, called the Dacia of Aurelian; but a clear evidence of their occupation of the northern district remains in the modern Roumanian language, which is as lineal a descendant of Latin as French and Italian are.

Some additional material was also contributed towards the knowledge of the interior of Africa by two ex-peditions which took place during the reigns of Claudius and Nero. In the year 42 A.D. Sueto-nius Paullinus—the same who, as we have seen, subsequently distinguished himself in Britain—having been appointed propraetor of Mauretania, carried his arms across the Atlas chain, which, as it was the winter season, he found covered with snow. He then advanced through the desert in burning heat, until he reached a river called Ger, the neighbourhood of which abounded with elephants and other wild beasts[1]. The name here given has induced some geographers to conjecture that the stream which was intended is the Niger; but there can be little doubt that it was one of those which run southwards from the Atlas and lose themselves in the Sahara, for the word *gir* in the Berber language, signifies 'running water,' and even at the present day it is attached to a river which follows that direction. The other expedition, for which Seneca is our chief authority, though it is also noticed by Pliny, was despatched by Nero, and was pacific in its character, being prompted by a spirit of enquiry. Its object was to explore the sources of the Nile; and it advanced in the first instance as far

Suetonius Paullinus crosses the Atlas.

Nero's Ex-pedition to the Nile.

---

[1] Pliny, *H. N.* 5. 14, 15.

as Meroë by way of Syene and Napata, which city has been already noticed in connexion with the campaign of Petronius against Candace.   Seneca, whose information (so he tells us) was obtained directly from two centurions employed on the mission, states that they were furnished with an escort by the king of Aethiopia, and with introductions to the neighbouring chiefs, and thus advanced far into the interior.   The furthest point in the Nile valley that was attained they described as occupied by vast marshes, where the water was clogged with herbage so muddy and tangled as only to afford a passage for boats of the smallest size.   In these we recognise the extensive swampy region of the White Nile, which is first met with above the junction of that river with the Sobat, about 400 miles to the southward of Khartoum[1].   The discovery, however, was not entirely new, for, little as this district was known in antiquity, yet Aristotle had heard of it, since he mentions it in connexion with the race of Pygmies[2].

The Marshy Region.

---

[1] Sen. *Nat. Quaest.* 6. 8. 3, 4; Ego quidem centuriones duos quos Nero Caesar, ut aliarum virtutum ita veritatis in primis amantissimus, ad investigandum caput Nili miserat audivi narrantes longum illos iter peregisse, cum a rege Aethiopiae instructi auxilio commendatique proximis regibus penetrassent ad ulteriora. 'Equidem,' aiebant, 'pervenimus ad immensas paludes, quarum exitum nec incolae noverant nec sperare quisquam potest, ita inplicatae aquis herbae sunt et aquae neque pediti eluctabiles nec navigio, quod nisi parvum et unius capax limosa et obsita palus non ferat. Ibi,' inquit, 'vidimus duas petras, ex quibus ingens vis fluminis excidebat.'   Cp. Pliny, 6, 184—6.

[2] *v. supra*, p. 29.

CHAPTER XIV.

ROMAN FRONTIER DEFENCES AND ROADS.

Natural Limits of the Roman Empire—Frontier Defences—Chiefly organised by Hadrian—The *Periplus* of Arrian—Dio's Account of Hadrian's System—The German Limes—Chains of Military Posts—Defences of the Upper Euphrates—The Roman Roads—The Via Aurelia—Via Aemilia Scauri—Via Julia—Road through Southern Gaul and Spain—The Via Flaminia—Via Aemilia—Passes of the Alpes Cottiae, Graiae, and Penninae—Roman Roads in Gaul, and in Britain—Watling Street—Fosse Way—Ermine Street—Icknield Street—Passes of the Alpes Rhaeticae and Juliae—Road through Pannonia to Byzantium—The Via Appia—The Via Egnatia—Main Roads through Asia and Africa—Roman Itineraries—The Antonine Itinerary—Its Probable Date—Not a completely Homogeneous Document—Its Contents—The *Itinerarium Maritimum*—The Jerusalem Itinerary—The Peutinger Table—Its Transcription, and probable Date of Composition.

THE reign of Hadrian, at which we have now arrived, affords a suitable opportunity for surveying the boundariés of the Roman empire when it had reached its utmost limits, and the defences by which it was protected. The limits which, as Gibbon remarks, *Natural Limits of the Roman Empire.* appeared to have been permanently placed for that purpose by nature, were on the west the Atlantic Ocean; the Rhine and Danube on the north; the Euphrates on the east; and towards the south the sandy deserts of Arabia and Africa[1]. These boundaries were recommended by Augustus to his successors; and they were observed by subsequent emperors, except in Britain, and in two districts into which Trajan carried his victorious arms—Mesopotamia, which for a short time, and Dacia, which for a longer period, became subject to Rome. It was only by gradual stages, however, that a system of frontier defence grew up along these lines. *Frontier Defences.* In some instances a belt of allied native states,

[1] *Decline and Fall*, vol. I. p. 139, ed. Smith.

such as Commagene, Cappadocia, and Pontus on the side towards the Euphrates, were allowed to remain, so as to separate the Roman provinces from the nations outside; and it was only after a time that these were annexed to Rome, and were formally recognised as part of the Roman dominion.   There can be little doubt that the development of the frontier defences, which followed on this, was quickened by a growing fear of danger arising from the incursions of barbarians from without. The emperors, whose policy was especially devoted to this end, were those of the Flavian and Antonine dynasties, and the sovereign in particular, with whom above all others it should be associated, is Hadrian[1].   Not only does the Roman Wall in

Chiefly or-
ganised by
Hadrian.

Britain bear his name, but in other parts of the empire also we find evidence of the attention which he paid to this question.   On the site of the camp constructed by his orders for the Third Legion at Lambaesis in the interior of Numidia, fragments remain of an inscription recording the address which he made to the troops stationed there; and in the course of this Hadrian expresses his admiration of the walls that had been built, and eulogises the excellence of the training of the soldiers, notwithstanding the few opportunities of drilling which they had had owing to their being stationed for long periods continuously in remote posts on the frontiers[2].   Similar testimony with regard to the care expended on the frontier stations and garrisons on the south-eastern coast of the Black Sea is contained in the report

The *Peri-
plus* of Arrian.

on that subject addressed to Hadrian by Arrian the historian, who was præfect of the province of Cappadocia.   The date of this document—which is known as the *Periplus Ponti Euxini,* and was written in Greek —is 131 A.D.; and it formed a supplement to a Latin official report, such as was regularly sent by these officers to their master,

---

[1] For many of the remarks which are introduced in connexion with this subject I am indebted to Prof. Pelham's paper on *The Roman Frontier System* in vol. XIV. of the *Transactions* of the Cumberland and Westmorland Antiquarian and Archæological Society: see also his *Outlines of Roman History,* pp. 490—492.

[2] *Corp. Inscript. Lat.,* vol. VIII. no. 2532.

the emperor. Throughout it we meet with accounts of the condition of the fortifications along that line, in which the writer mentions that he had replaced earthwork embankments and wooden towers by brick walls, and had everywhere examined the fortifications and trenches; the entire statement being drawn up in such a manner as to imply that the defences were a question of primary interest to the person to whom the letter was addressed[1].

Indeed, Hadrian is spoken of quite plainly by Dio as having been the chief organiser of this system. The following is his account :

'Hadrian used to travel from province to province, visiting both the country districts and the cities; and in the course of his inspections of the forts and walls he transferred some to more suitable positions, while others he dismantled or erected at new points. He also personally superintended and examined every detail; not merely the condition of the camps in general—their arms and military engines, their trenches, ramparts and palisades—but also what affected the individual soldiers, the rank and file as well as the officers—their manner of life, and dwellings and habits; and in many cases, where novel arrangements had been introduced tending to greater comfort, he remodelled and amended them. Besides this, he exercised the men in all kinds of fighting, approving some and censuring others, and instructing them all in their duties. And in order that they might profit by his example, wherever he went he led a hardy life, and never at such times availed himself of a carriage or four-wheeled chariot, but always walked or rode; nor did he protect his head, either in

Dio's Account of Hadrian's System.

---

[1] Arrian, *Periplus Ponti Euxini*, § 12, in C. Müller's *Geographi Graeci Minores*, vol. I. p. 376: Καὶ τάφρος διπλῆ περιβέβληται τῷ τείχει, εὐρεῖα ἑκατέρα. Πάλαι μὲν οὖν γήϊνον τὸ τεῖχος ἦν καὶ οἱ πύργοι ξύλινοι ἐφεστήκεσαν, νῦν δὲ ἐκ πλίνθου ὀπτῆς πεποίηται καὶ αὐτὸ καὶ οἱ πύργοι, καὶ τεθεμελίωται ἀσφαλῶς, καὶ μηχαναὶ ἐφεστᾶσι, καὶ ἑνὶ λόγῳ, πᾶσιν ἐξήρτυται πρὸς τὸ μηδὲ πελάσαι ἄν τινα αὐτῷ τῶν βαρβάρων, μήτιγε δὴ εἰς κίνδυνον καταστῆσαι πολιορκίας τοὺς ἐν αὐτῷ φρουροῦντας. Ἐπειδὴ δὲ καὶ τὸν ὅρμον ἐχρῆν ἀσφαλῆ εἶναι ταῖς ναυσὶ, καὶ ὅσα ἔξω τοῦ φρουρίου κατῳκεῖτο ὑπὸ τῶν τε πεπαυμένων τῆς στρατιᾶς καὶ τινων καὶ ἄλλων ἐμπορικῶν ἀνθρώπων, ἔδοξέ μοι ἀπὸ τῆς διπλῆς τάφρου, ἡ περιβέβληται τῷ τείχει, ἄλλην τάφρον ἐκβαλεῖν ὡς ἐπὶ τὸν ποταμὸν, ἡ τό τε ναύσταθμον περιέξει καὶ τὰς ἔξω τοῦ τείχους οἰκίας. Cp. §§ 7, 14, &c.

heat or cold, but went about with it uncovered both in the snows of Gaul and under an Egyptian sun. In a word, throughout the whole empire he so trained and disciplined the entire military force both by action and precept, that even at the present time the appointments which he then made are their rule of service. This was the main reason why during the greater part of his reign he was at peace with foreign nations: they were aware of his means of defence, and inasmuch as they suffered no ill-treatment, and even received presents of money, they maintained the existing order of things. For his soldiers were so well trained, that the cavalry of the so-called Batavi swam across the Danube with their arms: on seeing which the barbarians were impressed with fear of the Romans, and when they fell out with one another they called in that power to arbitrate in their mutual disputes[1].

The most famous of these frontier fortifications was that which served for a defence to the empire against the Germanic tribes, who from their proximity to Italy and their threatening attitude were the enemies whose sudden attacks were most formidable to Rome. The name by which it was known to the Romans was, as long as it skirted the frontiers of Vindelicia, the Limes Rhaetiae, and afterwards the Limes Germaniae: in modern times—for the wall, or at least its foundations, can still be traced almost continuously—it is called the Pfahlgraben or Teufelsmauer. Leaving the left bank of the Danube at Kelheim between Ratisbon and Neustadt, it describes a curve westward as far as Lorch, at which place the Limes Rhaetiae comes to an end after a course of 108 miles. Here the direction which the fortification pursues turns at right angles, and follows the stream of the Neckar as far as Wimpfen, whence it runs due north until it meets the Main at Wörth. Descending that stream to the parallel of Frankfort, it then bends round until it meets the northern extremity of the Taunus chain, and after passing those mountains gradually approaches the Rhine, which river it finally reaches between Andernach and Remagen. This section, which formed the Limes Germaniae, measured 228 miles. In respect of construction the Limes Germaniae was greatly superior to the Limes Rhaetiae.

The German Limes.

[1] Dion Cass. *Hist. Rom.*, Epitome, l. 69, c. 9.

The former of these consisted of a succession of forts, placed as a rule about nine miles from each other. In certain portions of the line thus formed, the rivers along whose courses the forts were built, the Neckar and the Main, were themselves a sufficient limit to prevent ingress into the Roman territory; elsewhere a boundary wall was erected, not indeed connecting the forts with one another, but running in front of them at a distance seldom exceeding one-third of a mile. This was protected by a fosse on the outside, and had watchtowers built in it at short intervals on the inner side. In the Rhaetian Limes, on the other hand, the forts were constructed without any regular succession, and the barrier was not only destitute of a fosse and watch-towers, but was formed of stones rudely piled together[1].

Walls and embankments, however, such as those just described, by no means formed a necessary part of a frontier fortification. We find them, indeed, in the north of Britain, but there is no trace of them along the Numidian border, nor where security was afforded by the presence of a great river, such as the Rhine in its lower course, the Danube, or the Euphrates. What was essential to the system of defence was the chain of military posts; and so independent was this, that, even where a legion was established in the adjacent territory, its camp did not necessarily form part of the chain, but might lie at some distance towards the rear. Such was the case with York and Chester in Britain, with Mogontiacum (Mainz) behind the German Limes, and with Lambaesis in Africa; in all which instances the legion that was stationed there was connected by roads with the outlying posts, so that it was able to support them when necessary. The opposite plan, where the camp was included in the system of defence, is found on the lower Rhine and on the Danube. A certain extent of territory both within and without the line of defence was appropriated by the defenders, so that no barbarians were allowed to occupy it—a precautionary measure which was quite reasonable, since the position to be guarded was so exposed. It is not improbable that all the district between the German Limes and the Upper Rhine, and also the region of Britain north

Chains of Military Posts.

[1] Mommsen, *The Provinces of the Roman Empire*, vol. I. pp. 154, 155.

of the Humber, and the southern portion of Numidia, were treated as 'march-land.' A tendency soon arose for the soldiers of a certain legion to become the permanent occupants of a particular camp. Thus the Twentieth Legion is found at Chester, the Sixth at York, and the Third Augustan Legion in Africa. The outlying fortresses were garrisoned by auxiliary troops, and these could be more easily transferred from one station to another; yet the evidence goes to prove that they also frequently continued to occupy the same positions[1].

A marked instance of the method of defence by means of a succession of military posts is found on the frontier which followed the upper course of the Euphrates. The importance of this line arose

Defences of the Upper Euphrates.

from its commanding the approaches to the Roman dominion on its eastern side, where it bordered on Armenia, which country had become a debateable land between the Romans and the Parthians. The most central point in the military system in this quarter was Melitene (Malatia), which town lay at no great distance from the junction of the river Melas, which flows from the Anti-Taurus, with the Euphrates. To it led the great high-road which traversed Asia Minor from Ephesus by way of Caesareia in Cappadocia; and from it again two other roads diverged to south and north respectively. The former of these passed over the Taurus range to Samosata (Samsat), the position of which city was considerably lower down the course of the great river, where there is an important crossing place of the stream. Here was the permanent station of the Sixteenth legion (Flavia Firma), while at Melitene the Twelfth legion (Fulminata) was quartered. A Roman bridge of magnificent construction still remains near Kiakhta, at some distance to the northward of Samsat, to testify to the existence of this line of communication. The other road, which ran northward from Melitene, was carried to Satala, where were the *stativa* of the Fifteenth legion (Apollinaris). The recent discovery of inscriptions containing the name of that legion at the modern village of Sadagh—at which considerable remains of an ancient fortified town were previously known to exist—renders certain the

---

[1] Pelham, *The Roman Frontier System*, pp. 180, 181.

identification of that place with Satala[1].   It lay near the head-waters of the river Lycus, due west of Theodosiopolis (Erzeroum), but separated from that place, and from the Euphrates valley, by a range of mountains.   Afterwards the road was prolonged from Satala to Trapezus, which was also a Roman military station; and ultimately a line of posts guarded by troops was established along the entire route from Samosata to the Euxine.

The communications between the capital and the frontier provinces of the empire were maintained by means of the great system of military roads, the construc- **The Roman Roads.** tion of which everywhere followed in the wake of the Roman conquests.   The starting-point for these, from which the measurements along them were calculated, was in each case the gate by which the road issued from the walls of Rome; and the distances to which they respectively extended were recorded on the Miliarium Aureum, or Golden Milestone, which was set up for that purpose by Augustus in the Forum at the foot of the Capitoline Hill.   Through the facilities which they offered for speedy transit the intelligence which was constantly required by an elaborately centralised system of administration was transmitted to headquarters, and provision was made for the rapid passage of the Roman armies, and for the conveyance of merchandise from distant countries.   The massive construction of these roads is made evident by the terraces, raised above the level of the neigh-bouring ground and paved with solid masonry, which remain in part both in our own country and in other lands which were formerly subject to Rome; and the system of milestones by which they were measured is represented by numerous specimens which are found in all the three continents.   We will now proceed to trace the principal lines which were followed by these great arteries of communication, beginning from the western provinces.

The great western road at its commencement was called the Via Aurelia, under which name it extended **The Via Aurelia.** from Rome to Pisae (Pisa) by way of Cosa and

[1] See Mr V. W. Yorke's paper, *A Journey in the Valley of the Upper Euphrates*, in the *Geographical Journal*, vol. 8 (1896), p. 460.   The whole of this paper contains valuable information about the line of Roman defences here spoken of.

Populonium, passing through the unhealthy coast-land of Etruria, which is now known as the Maremma.   In the
Via Aemilia Scauri.   year 109 B.C. it was continued by Aemilius Scaurus over the difficult ground which skirts the head of the Gulf of Genoa, as far as Vada Sabatia (Vado); and this portion was called the Via Aemilia Scauri, to distinguish it from the more famous Aemilian Way in Cisalpine Gaul.   During
Via Julia.   the reign of Augustus it was again extended under the name of Via Julia along the Ligurian coast to Cemenelum (Cimiez, at the back of Nice), thus reaching the frontier of Gaul.   The principal places which it passed in this part were the native towns of Albium Ingaunum (Albenga) and Albium Intemelium (Ventimiglia), and the old Greek colony of Portus Herculis Monoeci (Monaco).   At Cemenelum the road
Road through Southern Gaul   was brought into connexion with the great Roman way through the Provincia, which passed by way of Forum Julii (Fréjus) and Aquae Sextiae (Aix) to Arelate (Arles) at the head of the delta of the Rhone; and from that place, first to Nemausus (Nîmes), and then by Narbo (Narbonne) to the foot of the Pyrenees.   That
and Spain.   chain was crossed between Ruscino (Roussillon) and Gerunda (Gerona); and from the latter place the road proceeded to Tarraco (Tarragona), and after crossing the Iberus continued along the coast to Valentia and the mouth of the Sucro (Jucar).   It there turned inland, and after passing the watershed which separates the streams that fall into the Mediterranean from those which reach the Atlantic, entered the basin of the Baetis (Guadalquivir), and traversed the province of Baetica by way of Corduba (Cordova), and Hispalis (Seville), until it arrived at the ocean, with which in this way Rome was connected[1].

The Via Flaminia, which was the great northern road from Rome, was constructed in 220 B.C. by Gaius
The Via Flaminia.   Flaminius during his censorship, with the object of maintaining the communications between the capital and Cisalpine Gaul, which country he had previously subjugated.   Leaving Rome by the Porta Flaminia, it crossed

[1] Mommsen, *The Provinces of the Roman Empire*, 1. p. 74.

the Tiber at the Milvian bridge, two miles distant from the walls of the city, and passing the foot of Mount Soracte entered Umbria near Ocriculum, from whence by way of Narnia and Mevania it reached the foot of the Apennines. On the further side of that chain it descended the valley of the Metaurus to the Adriatic at Fanum Fortunae (Fano), and then followed the coast as far as its terminus at Ariminum (Rimini). About half a century later this road was continued as far as Placentia (Piacenza) by M. Aemilius Lepidus, and from him this additional portion obtained the name of the Aemilian Way. It was carried through the plains of Cisalpine Gaul, skirting the northern spurs of the Apennines, and connected with one another and with its two termini the important cities of Bononia (Bologna), Mutina (Modena) and Parma. From Placentia, where it crossed the Po, it was subsequently prolonged to Mediolanum (Milan). The places thus reached formed the starting-points for the lines of communication which connected Italy with the central regions of Gaul. From Placentia by way of Ticinum (Pavia) and the valley of the Po a road was constructed to Augusta Taurinorum (Turin), whence it ascended along the Duria Minor (Dora Riparia) to the pass over the Alpes Cottiae (Mont Genèvre), and on the western side of these mountains followed the course of the Druentia (Durance) downwards to Arelate. Again, from Mediolanum another route led by Eporedia (Ivrea) and the valley of the Duria Major (Dora Baltea) to Augusta Praetoria (Aosta), which place formed the point of divergence of two other Alpine passes. To the west a way conducted over the Alpes Graiae (Little St. Bernard) to the upper waters of the Isara (Isère) ; and the course of that stream was pursued as far as Cularo (Grenoble), shortly after passing which the road turned to the north-west and made for the Rhone, which river it struck at Vienna (Vienne) and then followed upwards to Lugdunum. To the north—on the further side of Mont Blanc, the great mass of which is here interposed—was the pass of the Alpes Penninae (Great St. Bernard), which led to the upper valley of the Rhone and the Lake of Geneva. The

Marginal notes:

Via Aemilia.

Passes of the Alpes Cottiae,

Graiae,

and Penninae.

road then traversed Helvetia, and after crossing the range of the Jura met the Rhine at Augusta Rauracorum, a few miles above Bâle.

In Gaul the chief highways started from Lugdunum, the Roman capital city, which is called by Strabo on account of the importance of its position the acropolis of the country[1]. As we have already observed in connexion with Agrippa's work in organising the provinces of Gaul, four great roads diverged from this point in different directions, three of which communicated with three different seas.   One ran due south along the course of the Rhone to Arles and the Mediterranean.   A second pursued a westerly course through the territory of the Arverni (Auvergne) and by Augustoritum (Limoges) to the mouth of the Garonne, after which it penetrated southward into Aquitania.   A third went northward up the valley of the Arar (Saône) to Cabillonum (Châlon), thence by Augustodunum (Autun) and across the upper waters of the Yonne and Seine and Marne to Durocortorum (Reims), the capital of the Remi, and from that point north-westward to Samarobriva (Amiens) and Gesoriacum (Boulogne), which was the ordinary place of transit for Britain. Again, from Cabillonum a fourth route diverged from the one just described, and followed the stream of the Doubs upwards throughout a great part of its course, but ultimately crossed a watershed into the valley of the Rhine, not far from where the road from the Pennine pass entered it.   From this point to the German Ocean a continuous line of road maintained the communications of the Romans throughout the two provinces of Upper and Lower Germany, passing the important stations of Mogontiacum (Mainz) and Colonia Agrippina (Cologne), and reaching at last Lugdunum Batavorum (Leyden) near the mouth of the stream.

Roman Roads in Gaul,

We may now proceed to Britain; and in speaking of the lines of road in this country it may not be amiss to retain the familiar names that have been attached to them.   The principal landing-place, which from a Roman point of view was the starting-point for communications

and in Britain.

[1] Strabo, 4. 6, 11.

with the interior, was Rutupiae (Richborough), the massive fortifications of which testify at the present day to the importance
that was attached to it as securing the line of transit from the
continent. Between Rutupiae and Londinium a road ran by way
of Durovernum (Canterbury) and Durobrivae (Rochester); and
the great commercial centre was also connected with the south
coast on the side of Sussex by another road (Stone Street), which
started from Regnum (Chichester). The Midlands
were traversed from south-east to north-west by   **Watling Street.**
Watling Street, which reached from Londinium
by way of Verulamium (St. Albans) to Viroconium (Wroxeter),
not far from Shrewsbury at the confluence of the Tern and
the Severn. Wroxeter, the numerous Roman remains at which
have obtained for it the name of the English Pompeii, was the
station of the Fourteenth legion; and its importance from a
military point of view arose from its proximity to the Welsh
border, where the mountain tribes maintained their independence
after the rest of the country had been brought under the Roman
rule. The other fortresses on the same frontier were Deva
(Chester), further to the north, where, as we have already remarked, the Twentieth legion was posted, and towards the south
Isca (Caerleon in Monmouthshire), the station of the Second
legion. Transversely to the line of Watling Street   **Fosse Way.**
the Fosse Way followed a direction from south-
west to north-east. Commencing at Isca Dumnoniorum (Exeter),
it passed across Somersetshire to the Roman township of Aquae
Sulis (Bath), and then took a straight course by Durocornuvium
(Cirencester) to Lindum (Lincoln). The last-named place was
reached also by a road called Ermine Street,
which started from Camulodunum (Colchester),   **Ermine Street.**
the seat of the earliest Roman colony which was
established in Britain, and traversed the eastern part of the
country: this was continued beyond Lindum by Danum (Doncaster) to Eburacum (York), and ultimately reached Luguvallium
(Carlisle), which was situated on the line of Hadrian's wall.
Finally, a road which is known as Icknield Street
ran in a direction almost parallel to the Fosse   **Icknield Street.**
Way from Glevum (Gloucester) to Doncaster. It

may be remarked that the names of highways which have been given above are in several cases assigned also to roads in other parts of the country.   Thus the title of Ermine Street is attached to the line of way that leads from Silchester by Cirencester to Gloucester; and that of Icknield Street to the road between Dorchester near Oxford, and Chesterford to the southward of Cambridge: while the road which for a time joined the wall of Hadrian to that of Antonine is known as Watling Street.

The Via Aemilia in Cisalpine Gaul, the connexion of which

Passes of the Alpes Rhaeticae and Juliae. with the lines of communication in north-western Europe has been traced above, was also the parent of other important roads, which led northward and eastward through the Roman empire.   From Milan a branch reached Verona, from which city there was a way by the valley of the Adige to the Brenner pass over the Rhaetian Alps, which led to Augusta Vindelicorum (Augsburg), the Roman outpost in the direction of Germany.   From Verona again another road ran eastward to Aquileia at the head of the Adriatic, and through the Julian Alps to Aemona (Laibach) in Pannonia.   Here it divided in two, one part following the old line of the Baltic traffic northwards by Poetovio (Pettau) to Carnuntum on the Danube, the other

Road through Pannonia to Byzantium. descending the valley of the Save by way of Sirmium (Mitrovitsa) to the junction of that river with the Danube at Singidunum (Belgrade).   The latter of these routes continued along the right bank of the Danube as far as Viminacium (Kostolatz), and then turned southwards up the valley of the Morava to Naissus (Nisch), and through the passes of the Balkan by Serdica (Sophia) and Philippopolis to Byzantium.

An earlier line of transit, however, from Rome to the Bosporus, and at all times a shorter and more convenient one,

The Via Appia. than that just mentioned, was the route by way of southern Italy and the Egnatian Way.   The first part of this was formed by the Via Appia, the earliest of all the Roman highways, the construction of which was due in the first instance to the censor Appius Claudius Caecus in 312 B.C.   By him it was conducted as far as Capua, but from that place it was afterwards continued to Beneventum, and finally by two different

lines to Brundisium.   One of these led to this port through the
centre of the country by Venusia and Tarentum, while the other,
passing at once through the Apennines into Apulia, took a more
northerly course by Canusium and the coast of the Adriatic.   On
the farther side of that sea, opposite Brundisium,
the Egnatian Way commenced at two points,   The Via
Dyrrachium towards the north, and Apollonia   Egnatia.
towards the south.   The highways which started from these
converged at a place in the interior called Clodiana; and from
that station the road threaded the difficult defiles of the Illyrian
mountains as far as the Lacus Lychnitis (Lake of Ochrida); after
which it crossed the Scardus range to Heraclea (Monastir), and
passed by Edessa and Pella to Thessalonica.   This portion of the
route was sometimes known by the separate name of the Via
Candavia.   The remainder of the Egnatian Way proceeded by
Amphipolis and Philippi to Byzantium.

In Asia Minor the main road from the Asiatic shore of the
Bosporus led by way of Nicomedia to Ancyra   Main Roads
(Angora) in the upland levels of Galatia, and after   through Asia
crossing Cappadocia descended through the Cilician   and Africa.
Gates in the Taurus range to Tarsus; from that place it proceeded
round the head of the gulf of Issus and over the Mons Amanus to
Antioch. From northern Syria there was a choice of routes by which
to reach Seleucia on the Tigris at the eastern extremity of the Roman
dominion.   One of these, which was at once the longer and the
easier way, traversed Mesopotamia, after crossing the Euphrates at
the Zeugma, or bridge of boats, which was situated in the neighbourhood of the modern Biredjik, where that stream approaches
nearest to the Mediterranean; for this place of passage had
superseded the earlier transit by Thapsacus, which was two
hundred miles lower down the course of the river.   The other
route, which was more direct, led across the Arabian desert by
way of Palmyra.   Syria and Palestine, again, were intersected
by a highway which ran from Antioch to the frontier of Egypt;
and in the latter country a road was carried up the valley of the
Nile as far as Coptos, the central trading-station of the country,
somewhat to the northward of Thebes. From thence lines of
communication reached to the ports of Myos Hormos and

Berenice on the Red Sea. Finally, the provinces of northern Africa were connected with one another by a continuous road which skirted the shore of the Mediterranean ; and in the western portion of that region, where there is a wider belt of cultivated land, this was supplemented by other highways, which approached nearer to the southern frontier of the empire.

Let us now notice the specimens which have come down to us of the documents by which information was fur-

Roman Itineraries. nished with regard to the roads in the Roman empire. We have already seen[1] that these documents were of two kinds, (1) *Itineraria adnotata*, which contained lists of the principal stations on the roads, accompanied by computations of the distances between them, but without any geographical remarks or explanations, so that they somewhat resembled the Railway Guides of the present day; and (2) *Itineraria picta*, where the same details were given in a form more nearly approaching that of a map, with the addition of various geographical features, especially the courses of the rivers. The wall-map of Agrippa would seem to have been the original source from which the main facts in both of these were drawn ; but we cannot doubt that much additional material was from time to time embodied in them, which was furnished by the Roman archives, for these could not fail to possess a catalogue of the Roman roads, with measurements of their length according to the milestones, and this catalogue would be gradually enlarged. The former of the two classes is represented at the present day by

The Antonine Itinerary. the Antonine Itinerary, or, to give its full title, *Itinerarium Provinciarum Antonini Augusti.* The emperor to whom the first publication of this work is here referred, is commonly supposed to have been either Antoninus Pius, or Marcus Aurelius Antoninus, but some writers are disposed to ascribe it to Caracalla, who also bore the name of Antoninus.

Its Probable Date. It is clear, however, that the edition of it which we possess is not earlier than the time of Diocletian, since the name of the city of Diocletianopolis, which was so called after him, occurs in it, and Perinthus is here called Heraclea—a name which it did not receive until shortly before

[1] *v. supra*, p. 236.

the reign of that emperor.   At the same time in its main features
it is hardly later than Constantine's era.   Thus Cirta in Numidia,
which at that time became Constantina, and Ostudizum in Thrace
and Antaradus in Phoenicia, which thenceforward were called Nice
and Constantia, here appear under their earlier names ; and, what
is still more important, Constantinople is not treated as the
starting-point or terminus of roads in the same way as Rome is,
though this was subsequently the case.   In one passage, where the
distances on the route between Sirmium and Nicomedia are being
computed, the great city on the Bosporus, which was necessarily
passed on the way from the one to the other, is not even noticed.
Elsewhere it is introduced under the name of Byzantium, that of
Constantinopolis being added by a later hand.   Mannert, indeed,
maintained, that the date of this document was not earlier than
364 A.D., because Mesopotamia is unnoticed in it, and that country
first ceased to be a Roman province in that year, when it was
ceded by the emperor Jovian to Sapor, king of Persia[1].   This
omission, however, is equally well explained by supposing that
this part of the Itinerary was either lost, or intentionally removed
after Mesopotamia had passed out of the hands of the Romans.
At the same time, though we may approve the conclusion which
has been stated above as to the approximate date of the bulk of
the work as we now possess it, points are not
wanting which intimate a plurality of authorship
and difference in date of composition in certain
parts.   Thus in some of the lists the distinctive
character of the halting-places, according as they were colonies, or
garrisons, or villages, is stated, while in others this is not done.
A similar irregularity is noticeable in respect of the insertion or
omission, at the end of the description of a certain route, of the
total of the number of miles which it contains.   Again, the same
name, when it recurs in different places, is apt to be spelt in
different ways.   In the account of the roads through Sicily we
meet with the entry, *Item a Catina Agrigentum mansionibus nunc
institutis ;* here the form of expression seems to suggest that it is
a later insertion.   Finally, the notice of the route through Thrace
is introduced out of its natural position, being placed between

Not a completely Homogeneous Document.

[1] Mannert, Introd. to *Tabula Peutingeriana,* p. 7.

those of Egypt and of Asia. Variations such as these are hardly reconcilable with the view that the whole Itinerary belongs to one period; indeed, a certain amount of accretion is only what we should expect in the formation of such a document.

The contents of .the Itinerary may be thus briefly summarised. First the roads throughout the north of Africa are given, reaching from the extremity of Mauretania to Alexandria. Next come those in Corsica, Sardinia, Sicily, and part of Italy. Then follows the whole route from Rome to Hiera Sycaminus, on the Nile to the southward of Pselcis, which was the limit of the Roman empire in that direction: this passed by way of Pannonia, Moesia, Thrace, Asia Minor, Syria, and Egypt. From Egypt again we are conducted back by the way of Syria, Armenia Minor, and the Balkan peninsula, after which an excursus is made into Italy. The concluding portion treats of the lines of communication in the northern provinces, and westward through Gaul and Spain, ending with Britain at the limit of the Wall of Hadrian. The order here assigned to the countries traversed by these roads is different from that usually found in ancient geographers, but it will be seen that it has a convenience of its own. To students of ancient geography the chief value of such an itinerary consists in its furnishing a more accurate knowledge of the position of towns, especially in the interior of countries, than would otherwise be obtainable.

Another and shorter Itinerary, which is usually regarded as forming a continuation of the one just mentioned, is the *Itinerarium Maritimum*. In the first of the three parts into which this is divided the same method is pursued as in the *Itinerarium Provinciarum*, for it gives the distances of the coast-towns from one another by sea, and measures of the sea-transits (*trajectus*) from one country to another. This is for the most part, though not entirely, confined to the shores of the Mediterranean. As the distances are here computed in stadia, it seems probable that it was originally the work of a Greek, and that the information was drawn from Greek sources, though it was subsequently modified. The second part, which appears to be a fragment of an unfinished work, enumerates in great detail the ports and roadsteads from the Portus Augusti

at the mouth of the Tiber along the coasts of Italy, Liguria, and
Gaul to the mouth of the Rhone, and up the course of that river
to Arelate. The third part is devoted to the islands. In this the
distances are computed either from one island to another, or from
an island to the nearest point on the mainland; but in some cases
they are omitted altogether.

Another roadbook of the same kind as the Antonine Itinerary,
though planned on a smaller scale and for a dif-
ferent purpose, is the Jerusalem Itinerary (*Itinera-*   The Jerusa-
rium Hierosolymitanum). This was drawn up in   lem Itinerary.
333 A.D., and was the work of a Christian, being intended for the
use of pilgrims on their way from western Europe to Jerusalem.
Its starting point is Burdigala (Bordeaux), from which place it
passes by Arles, Turin, and Milan to Aquileia, and afterwards by
the way of Sirmium and Sardica to Constantinople. On the
further side of the Bosporus it is continued across Asia Minor by
Ancyra to Tarsus, and finally by Antioch to Jerusalem. Two
supplementary routes are added for the return journey—one from
Heraclea (Perinthus) on the Propontis, where the road diverges
from that previously given, to Rome, by Thessalonica and the line
of the Egnatian Way, crossing the Adriatic from Avlona to Otranto;
the other from Rome to Milan by Ariminum. One feature in
which this Itinerary differs from the Antonine is that, while the
other has no comments, geographical or otherwise, appended to
the names of places, in the Jerusalem Itinerary these are occasionally introduced. Thus of Viminacium in Moesia, on the
Danube, we are told (not quite accurately) that it was the place
ubi Diocletianus occidit Carinum; of Tyana it is said, *inde fuit
Apollonius magus;* and of Tarsus, *inde fuit apostolus Paulus.*
These remarks are few and far between in the earlier part of the
route ; but when Palestine is reached, as might be expected, they
become more numerous. The account of Jerusalem itself and the
sites in its neighbourhood has a peculiar interest, because it is the
earliest description which we possess of the Holy Places. The
document in general is useful because it mentions numerous
minor stations—whether post-stations for changing horses (*muta-
tiones*) or night-quarters (*mansiones*)—which are omitted in the
Antonine Itinerary. This arose from the pilgrims belonging to a

poorer class, and therefore travelling more slowly, than the state officials, for whom in the first instance the Roman Itineraries were intended[1].

The *Tabula Peutingeriana*, which is our sole existing representative of the *Itineraria picta*, received its name

The Peutin-
ger Table.
from Conrad Peutinger, a scholar of the first half of the sixteenth century, to whom it was bequeathed by his friend Conrad Celtes, having been previously purchased by him. This original is now in the imperial library at Vienna, but it has several times been copied and edited, the most important editions being that of Mannert (Leipzig, 1824), to which a valuable introduction is prefixed, and that of Desjardins (Paris, 1869, &c.), an elaborate and sumptuous work, which is still unfinished. This map represents, not merely the Roman empire, but the world as known to the Romans, extending from the mouth of the Ganges towards the east to Spain on the west; in the latter direction, however, it is imperfect, only the south-eastern corner of Britain and a fraction of Spain appearing upon it. As it is 21 feet in length by about one foot wide, thus forming a long strip, it neces-sarily follows that the shapes of countries and other geographical features are extravagantly distorted: the Mediterranean Sea, for instance, assumes the form of a long canal. This however was a matter of no importance to the author, whose primary object was to trace the lines of roads throughout the empire, marking the stations and the distances. For the same reason the natural objects in each district, such as rivers, lakes and mountain chains, though they are not altogether neglected, are treated as subsidiary. In order to distinguish the various kinds of places a number of different symbols are introduced. Ordinary towns are marked by small houses, while those of unusual importance, such as Aquileia, Thessalonica and Nicomedia, are dignified with a circuit of walls and towers. Great prominence is given in all three continents to the watering-places, which are indicated by a bath-house with a tank in the centre. Important public works are also conspicu-ously delineated; among these may be mentioned the dike which

---

[1] On the subject of the Itineraries see Parthey and Pinder's Introduction to their edition of them; also Forbiger, *Handbuch der alten Geographie*, vol. I. pp. 465—9.

was cut by Marius at the mouth of the Rhone, or Fossa Mariana, the Port of Augustus at Ostia, and the Pharos of Alexandria. The highest distinction is reserved for the three cities of Rome, Constantinople, and Antioch, each of which is represented by a figure seated on a throne, which is inscribed within a circle; but whereas the first and last of these are crowned, the figure of Constantinople wears a plumed helmet. These vignettes are elaborately ornamented, so that, while in other parts of the map six colours are introduced, and these are used to discriminate certain classes of objects, they are all combined in the illuminations of the three cities. The most probable explanation of the prominence which is thus assigned to them is, that the figures, or at least their prototypes, were introduced during the period subsequent to the death of Constantine the Great, when the Roman empire was for a while partitioned between his three sons, Constantine, Constantius and Constans.

The existing copy of the Tabula dates from the thirteenth century, for it was made by a monk of Colmar in 1265; but notwithstanding a few insertions of his own, and numerous misspellings of the names of places, such as Riger for Liger, Igeum for Aegeum, the copyist appears in the main to have faithfully transcribed the older map which he had before him. To him we may probably attribute the introduction of *Mons Oliveti*, which is in close juxtaposition to *antea dicta Herusalem, nunc Helya Capitolina;* and other Scriptural names, such as *Mons Syna*, and *Desertum ubi quadraginta annis erraverunt filii Israel ducente Moyse.* M. Desjardins has also pointed out, that only two forests are represented in the Tabula, viz. that of the Vosges (*silva Vosagus*), and the Black Forest (*silva Marciana*); and that both these would no doubt be visible from the windows of the monastery in Colmar. With regard to the date of composition of the original document it is less easy to make a definite statement. Mannert has adduced strong evidence to shew that it was drawn up in the reign of Alexander Severus (222—235 A.D.), or at least between that time and the end of the third century. Thus (to take one or two points in his argument) it must have been later than the overthrow of the Parthians by the Persians in 226 A.D.,

Its Transcription,

and Probable Date of Composition.

for Parthia is marked merely as a province, while an ample space is assigned to the Persian empire, which extends from Babylonia to India.   On the other hand, as Palmyra is introduced, this would seem to imply a time earlier than its destruction by Aurelian (273 A.D.).   The same thing may be inferred from the delineation of Dacia, which appears with its cities and roads as it was arranged by Trajan, without any intimation of the withdrawal of the Roman colonists from thence across the Danube by Aurelian.   Mannert also notices the great care and accuracy with which the details of Mesopotamia are given, and remarks that this may well be due to the campaign of Alexander Severus in those parts in 232, when he defeated the Persians[1].   Still, if we concede this writer's conclusion, it does not necessarily follow that no part of the Tabula existed before that time, and that no additions were subsequently made.   A closer inspection has led M. Desjardins to believe, that some portions of it can be distinguished as belonging to the epoch of Augustus, and others to other periods—to the reign of Trajan, to the middle of the fourth century, to the year 435 under Theodosius II., and finally to the time of Justinian[2].

---

[1] Mannert, Introd. to *Tab. Peut.*, pp. 12—16.

[2] *Revue Historique*, vol. I. p. 184.

CHAPTER XV.

ESTIMATES OF MOUNTAINS IN ANTIQUITY.

Hadrian's Mountain Ascents—Indistinct Conception of Mountain Summits—
Strabo on Alpine Features—Use of Crampons and Tobogganing—Moun-
tains differently viewed by the Ancients and the Moderns—Religious
Feeling in Antiquity—Ascents of Etna prompted by Research—Strabo on
the Summit of Etna—The Poem of *Aetna*—Ascents of Mount Argaeus—
Of Tmolus—Ascents for the Sake of the Panorama—Sunrise seen from
Mt. Ida—Lucian on a Mountain View—Description of a Mountain
Climb—Mountains regarded as Look-out Places—Story of Lynceus—
Mountains as Signalling Stations—The Beacon-fires in Aeschylus, probably
corresponding to a Real Line of Stations—The Shield at Marathon—
Mountain Telegraphy in Thucydides, Xenophon, and Polybius—Develop-
ment of the Art of Signalling—Estimates of the Heights of Mountains—
Scientific Measurement by Dicaearchus, and Xenagoras.

THE mountain ascents which are recorded as having been
made by the emperor Hadrian may serve, at the
present stage of our subject, as a starting-point
for a review of the notices that are found in
classical writers of this form of geographical exploration, which
has been quaintly, and not unsuitably, called 'vertical advance'
in geography, as compared with 'lateral extension.' Hadrian,
as we have seen, was much more than a 'tourist monarch,'
for the constant journeys in which the greater part of his
reign was spent were undertaken by him with the view of
making himself personally acquainted with the administration
of the provinces, and with the condition of the defences of the
empire. At the same time the inquisitiveness of his disposition
led him to make use of every opportunity that presented itself of
investigating the countries through which he passed, and of
noting their peculiarities. From this point of view the summits
of high mountains, and the extensive panoramas which they
afforded, were naturally attractive to him. His biographer

Hadrian's
Mountain
Ascents.

Spartianus informs us that he ascended Etna to see the sunrise from thence[1], and it has been conjectured that the *Torre del Filosofo*—as the building of Roman construction, the ruins of which still remain high up on the shoulder of that mountain, is called from its supposed connexion with Empedocles—was erected on that occasion to afford a night's lodging to the emperor[2]. From this writer also we learn that Hadrian with the same object in view reached the summit of the Mons Casius in Syria near Antioch and the mouth of the Orontes[3]. And Arrian tells us, that he made his way to the point which was affirmed by tradition to be that from which Xenophon and his companions first beheld the Euxine after quitting the highlands of Armenia[4].

In speaking of the ideas entertained by the ancients with reference to mountain ascents, it is well to remember that an accurate appreciation of what constitutes a summit is a thing of comparatively recent growth. At a time when peaks were not regarded as objects to be studied for their own sake, it was not unnatural that the highest point that was usually accessible in a chain should not be distinguished in name, or ordinarily even in thought, from the true summits; and thus it happened that the top of a pass was commonly spoken of as if it were the top of the mountain which that pass traversed. This mode of thought prevailed, not only in antiquity, but to a great extent also in modern times, until the establishment of Alpine clubs and the development of the art of mountaineering caused more accurate notions to prevail. When regarded from this point of view, the passage of the Pylae Persicae by Alexander after the battle of Arbela, and his crossing the Paropamisus on his way to Bactria, were mountain

Indistinct Conception of Mountain Summits.

[1] Spart., *Hadrianus*, 13. 3 : Post in Siciliam navigavit, in qua Aetnam montem conscendit, ut solis ortum videret arcus specie, ut dicitur, varium.

[2] See Friedländer, *Sittengeschichte Roms*, vol. 2, p. 203. The references on the subject of mountain ascents in antiquity which are given in the following pages are largely taken from that volume.

[3] Spart. *op. cit.*, 14. 3 : In monte Casio, cum videndi solis ortus gratia nocte ascendisset, imbre orto fulmen decidens hostiam et victimarium sacrificanti adflavit.

[4] Arrian, *Periplus*, 1. Addressing the emperor, Arrian says, καὶ τὴν μὲν θάλασσαν τὴν τοῦ Εὐξείνου ἄσμενοι κατείδομεν, ὅθενπερ καὶ Ξενοφῶν ἐκεῖνος καὶ σύ.

ascents; and still more so was the achievement of Hannibal in leading an army over the Alps. It was by these experiences, at all events, and by the knowledge acquired in the course of the construction of the mountain roads, that the features of Alpine scenery came to be familiar. The clearest description of these that occurs in any ancient writer is found in Strabo's account of Alpine passes. Speaking of the tribes in those parts he says:—

'Some of them have been exterminated, and others have been completely civilised, so that the passes of the mountain-chain through their territory, which formerly were few and difficult, now lead from every quarter, and are safe from attack, and have been rendered easy, as far as may be, by the engineering works. For Augustus Caesar, besides putting down brigandage, constructed roads to the best of his ability; for it is not possible everywhere to overcome nature in traversing rocks and prodigious precipices, some of which overhang the track, while others descend beneath it, so that but a slight deviation involves inevitable danger, since the fall is into unfathomable ravines. Indeed, in some parts the road is narrow enough to cause giddiness to foot-passengers, and to their beasts of burden too, if they are unaccustomed to it, though the native packhorses convey their burdens in security. It is impossible to provide against these risks, and against the huge layers of ice which slide down from above, with such force as to cut off a whole company, and carry them along with them into the gorges beneath. For there are numerous layers one on the top of the other, because the *névé* is converted into ice again and again, and those on the surface are easily detached from those within before they are completely melted in the sunlight[1].'

Strabo on Alpine Features.

The same geographer, in a passage derived from Theophanes of Mytilene, the scientific companion of Pompey in his Mithridatic campaigns, describes the mountaineering habits of the natives of some parts of the Caucasus, who wore crampons and practised a kind of tobogganing.

Use of Crampons and Tobogganing.

'The summits of the range,' we are told, 'are inaccessible in the winter-time, but in the summer men make their way thither

[1] Strabo, 4. 6. 6.

shod with flat plates of untanned ox-hide, like timbrels, furnished with spikes on account of the ice and snow. They make the descent by lying on skins together with their property, and sliding down; the same thing is done in the part of Media called Atropatene, and in Mount Masius in Armenia, but there they also place beneath the hides small wooden wheels furnished with spikes[1].'

A crampon, resembling that which is described in this passage, was found not long ago in an ancient grave near Vladikavkas at the northern foot of the Caucasus, and was brought to England by Mr Douglas Freshfield, who describes it as being 'very similar to the crampons depicted by De Saussure as worn 100 years ago by the natives of Chamonix, when they wanted to go over the glaciers of Mont Blanc[2].' The wheels, which were said to have been used for tobogganing, probably correspond to those that were attached to the 'cyclopodes,' by the help of which—as we learn from Theophanes the Byzantine historian—Leo the Isaurian, the future emperor of Constantinople, crossed the snows of the Caucasus in the spring-time[3]. We hear of tobogganing again in Plutarch's *Life of Marius*, where he describes the Cimbri as shewing off in the presence of the enemy, by placing their shields underneath them, and letting themselves be carried down steep places, where there were slides and openings in the cliffs[4].

To return, however, to the question from which we originally started of the confusion between the highest accessible and the highest actual points, it is noticeable that this prevailed to a greater extent among the Romans than among the Greeks, on account of the greater individuality of structure of the mountains in the country inhabited by the last-named people. This was the case, not only with many of the higher peaks, such as Ossa, Cyllene and Taygetus, but with those which attained a lower

---

[1] Strabo, 11. 5. 6.

[2] *R. Geogr. Society's Magazine*, vol. 12, p. 463.

[3] Theoph. p. 604, ed. Bonn.: ὁ σπαθάριος......ὑπερβὰς μετὰ κυκλοπόδων Μαΐου μηνὸς τὰς χιόνας τῶν Καυκασίων.

[4] Plut. *Marius*, c. 23 : ἄνωθεν δὲ τοὺς θυρεοὺς πλατεῖς ὑποτιθέντες τοῖς σώμασιν, εἶτα ἀφιέντες αὐτοὺς ὑπεφέροντο κατὰ κρημνῶν ὀλισθήματα καὶ λισσάδας ἀχανεῖς ἐχόντων.

elevation, like Ithome, Maenalus, and the Acrocorinth. The sight of these was a continual object-lesson to remind the beholder what was meant by the real summit of a mountain.

The feelings also which were inspired by mountains in antiquity were different from those which are associated with them in modern times. The sentimental and romantic ideas with which we invest them are a growth of late years, and when such impressions are mentioned in connexion with external nature, especially among the Romans, they are almost always introduced with reference to pleasant and gentle, and not to wild, scenery. Thus Cicero, speaking of the influence which habit exercises over men, remarks—as if it was altogether an exception to the general rule—that we take pleasure even in mountainous and wooded regions, if we have dwelt a long time in them[1]. And again, when he makes his friend Atticus sing the praises of the island in the river Fibrenus, a tributary of the Liris, in the neighbourhood of which Cicero had a villa, he represents him as saying that he had been agreeably disappointed in it, for he had expected to find there nothing but mountains and rocks[2]. Virgil, indeed, in a fine simile, compares Aeneas exulting in the prospect of battle with the grandeur of the mountains— 'great as Athos, great as Eryx, or as father Apennine himself, when he roars with his gleaming oak-forests, and rejoices in lifting his snowy summit to the skies[3]'; but this passage is almost unique in the poet's works; and in the Georgics, when he celebrates the numerous points in which the superiority of Italy over other lands consists, he says not a word about its mountains[4].

Mountains differently viewed by the Ancients and the Moderns.

But while the charm of romance, which has attached itself so strongly to solitary peaks during the present century, was wanting in ancient times, its place was taken by the feeling of awe, which gathered round them, and pointed them out as suitable places for the worship of the divinities.

Religious Feeling in Antiquity.

[1] *De Amicit.* § 68: cum locis ipsis delectemur, montuosis etiam et silvestribus, in quibus diutius commorati sumus.

[2] *De Legg.* § 2: nihil enim his in locis nisi saxa et montes cogitabam.

[3] *Aen.* 12. 701—3.   [4] *Georg.* 2. 136 foll.

> Not vainly did the early Persian make
> His altar the high places, and the peak
> Of earth-o'ergazing mountains, and thus take
> A fit and unwall'd temple, there to seek
> The Spirit, in whose honour shrines are weak,
> Uprear'd of human hands[1].

Thus wrote Byron, and his words seem like an echo of those of Herodotus, who says of the Persians, 'their custom is to ascend to the highest mountain-tops, and there offer sacrifices to Zeus, calling by that name the whole vault of heaven[2].' Among the Greeks there is ample evidence of the same form of observance. Thus, to take three instances from different parts of the land which they inhabited : on the summit of Mount Atabyrion, the highest and most central mountain in Rhodes (4070 feet), there remain the foundations of a temple of grey limestone dedicated to Zeus, of whom Pindar speaks as 'holding sway on the ridges of Atabyrion[3].' Mela mentions altars as existing on the peak of Athos[4] (6350 feet); and for this reason, it would seem, Aeschylus calls that summit 'the Athoan height sacred to Zeus[5].' On the highest point of Lycaeum in Arcadia, also (4695 feet), there was an altar; and on a somewhat lower peak of the same mountain, which was known as the Sacred Summit, stood a grove and altar of Zeus Lycaeus, together with a hippodrome and stadium, where games called Lycaea were celebrated in honour of that God. The love of 'high places,' as has often been remarked, has been perpetuated in a striking manner in Greece during Christian times, and this is true in particular of all three of the spots which have just been mentioned. The site of the temple on Atabyrion was afterwards occupied by a chapel of St John the Evangelist; the summit of Athos is the scene of the festival of the Transfiguration, which is observed on the sixth of August; and a not less remarkable celebration takes place on Mount Lycaeum on

---

[1] Byron, *Childe Harold*, 3. 851—6.   [2] Herod. 1. 131.

[3] Pind. *Ol.* 7. 159—161 : ὦ Ζεῦ πάτερ, νώτοισιν 'Αταβυρίου μεδέων.

[4] Mela, 2. 2. 31 : Atho mons adeo altus est, ut credatur altius etiam quam unde imbres cadunt surgere. Capit opinio fidem, quia de aris quas in vertice sustinet non abluitur cinis, sed quo relinquitur aggere manet.

[5] Aesch. *Ag.* 285 : "Αθωον αἶπος Ζηνός.

the twentieth of July.   The last-named peak is now called after
the prophet Elijah, to whom, under the name of Hagios Elias,
the great majority of the high mountains in Greece are dedicated.

Of the other motives besides religious feeling which prompted
visits to mountain-tops in antiquity, inquisitiveness
perhaps is the most prominent, whether taking the   *Ascents of
Etna*
form of mere curiosity or of scientific research.   *prompted by
Research.*
It is in this strain that Seneca writes about Etna
(10,874 feet) to his friend Lucilius, who was procurator in Sicily,
and whom he had already requested to investigate for him the
currents of Charybdis.   'When you have given me your answer
on these points,' he says, 'I shall make bold to give you a further
commission, namely, that you should do me the favour of making
the ascent of Aetna; for persons argue that the mountain is
wasting and gradually sinking, because at one time it used to
be visible to mariners from a greater distance than at present.
Now the reason of this may be, not the diminution of the height
of the mountain, but because its flames are not seen, being
emitted with less force and volume; and that would account
too for the smoke being more slack in the day-time.   Still, there
is nothing incredible in either supposition—in the mountain
which is being consumed lessening from day to day, or in the
fire abating; for this is not generated of itself, but overflows
after it has been ignited in some depression in the lower regions,
and gets its aliment from elsewhere: what the mountain itself
provides is not a supply of fuel, but a passage[1].'

A similar account of the object with which ascents of
Etna were undertaken is found in the following   *Strabo on
the Summit
of Etna.*
interesting passage of Strabo relating to that mountain.

'Near Centuripa is the small town of Aetna just mentioned,
which is the halting and starting place for those who make the
ascent of the mountain, for there the upland district commences.
Now the elevated parts are bare and cindery, and are snow-
covered in the winter-time, while those below are diversified
with oak-forests and a variety of growths.   But the summits of
Aetna seem to undergo numerous changes owing to the fire

[1] Sen. *Ep.* 79. 2, 3.

distributing itself, since at one time it converges towards a single crater, and at another time it is parted, and sometimes sends forth lava-streams, at other times flames and smoke, and then again ejects red-hot masses; and of necessity the underground passages, too, correspond in their changes to these movements, and so do the vents, the number of which at times increases on the surface of the mountain all round. The account which we received from those who had recently made the ascent was as follows. They found at the top a level plain about twenty stadia in circumference, enclosed by a ridge of ashes as high as a wall, so that those who desired to advance into the plain had to leap down; and in the midst of this they saw a hill of ashen colour, in which respect it resembled the surface of the plain, and over the hill a column of cloud rising steadily—for there was no wind—to the height of about 200 feet, which they compared to smoke. Two of their number ventured to advance into the plain, but when the sand on which they trod became increasingly warm and deep, they returned without having any further account to give of what was to be seen than those had who observed them from a distance. It was from some such appearance, they thought, that many stories had arisen, especially what was reported of Empedocles, that he leapt down into the crater, and left there in evidence of his fate one of the bronze sandals which he wore; for this was found outside at a short distance from the rim of the crater, as if it had been thrown up by the violence of the fire. But these must have been fancies, for it was impossible either to approach the spot or to view it, and they did not conceive that any object could even be thrown down there owing to the opposing force of the winds ascending from below, and to the heat which would naturally meet them before they came near the crater's mouth; and if it were cast down, it would be destroyed before it could be thrown up again in the same condition. No doubt, there might be a temporary cessation of the currents of air and jets of fire, when the material which produced them failed; yet the change would not be so great or continue so long, as to admit of a man's approaching the place. The part of the coast nearest to Aetna is that from the Sicilian strait to Catana, but the mountain also overlooks that which faces the Tyrrhenian sea and the Lipari islands. By night bright jets of flame may be seen emerging from the summit, but in the day-time it is covered by clouds and smoke[1].'

The poem of *Aetna*, which has sometimes been attributed to Seneca's friend, Lucilius, describes the mountain almost entirely from the scientific point of view, and illustrates many of the points which are referred to in Strabo's narrative; especially the small cone of eruption in the middle of the great crater[2], and the cloud which rises vertically from it, and is said to 'look down from on high on the work going on within the vast receptacle[3].'

The Poem of Aetna.

In the account which is given by Strabo of a still higher mountain than Etna, Mount Argaeus in Cappadocia (13,150 feet), he seems to imply that it was ascended for the sake of the view. Speaking of the city of Mazaca, which was also called 'Eusebeia by Argaeus,' he remarks, 'It lies beneath Mount Argaeus, which is the highest mountain of all, and has perpetual snow on its upper parts; and those who make the ascent (though but few do so) say that from these on cloudless days both the seas, that of Pontus and that of Issus, are visible.' He then proceeds to notice the volcanic character of the mountain. 'At a little distance from the town there are plains with igneous soil, full of burning hollows for the distance of many stadia, so that the necessaries of life have to be brought from afar, and what seems to be an advantage brings danger in its train; for, whereas there are hardly any trees elsewhere in Cappadocia, Argaeus has a belt of oak-forest, so that wood can be procured close at hand, but there are numerous fiery spots even in the region below the forest, and other places have cold water beneath, though neither the fire nor the water emerge, so that the greater part is covered with verdure; and

Ascents of Mount Argaeus.

---

[1] Strabo, 6. 2. 8.

[2] *Aetna*, v. 182; penitusque os erigit ultra.

[3] *vv.* 332—6:

> Quamvis caeruleo siccus Jove fulgeat aether
> Purpureoque rubens surgat jubar aureus ostro,
> Illinc obscura semper caligine nubes
> Pigraque defuso circumstupet humida vultu,
> Prospectans sublimis opus vastosque receptus.

here and there the surface is marshy, and by night jets of inflammable gas proceed from it. Thus, while those familiar with the neighbourhood take precautions when they are wood-cutting, the majority are exposed to risk, and this is especially the case with the beasts of burden, which fall into hidden pits

Of Tmolus.
of fire[1].' In another passage of the same writer there is a description of a sort of belvedere, constructed on one of the summits of Mount Tmolus in Lydia, which appears to have been a legacy from the time of the Persian occupation of the country. 'Above Sardis rises Tmolus, a fertile mountain, which has on its ridge a look-out place, consisting of an arcade of white stone, the work of the Persians, from which the surrounding plains are in view, and especially that of the Cayster[2].' The geographer himself scaled the Acrocorinth, and viewed the panorama from it, which is one of the finest and most interesting in Greece. Of this he introduced a description into his work, but unfortunately it has reached us in a mutilated condition[3].

Ascents for the Sake of the Panorama.
Towards the conclusion of this survey of mountain ascents we have once more met with the same motive for undertaking them by which, as we saw at starting, Hadrian was influenced—namely the desire of obtaining a panorama over a widely extended tract of country. In Livy we find a curious account of an expedition which was made by Philip V. of Macedon to the highest peak of the Haemus range, with the object of reconnoitring from thence in connexion with the war which he had in hand against the Romans, because it was widely believed that it commanded a view over the Danube and the Alps, and both the Adriatic and the Euxine seas. Three days, we are told, were occupied by the king and his companions in ascending from the foot of the mountains to the summit. With regard to the view the historian cautiously remarks, that after their return they said

[1] Strabo, 12. 2. 7.

[2] Strabo, 13. 4. 5; ὑπερκεῖται δὲ τῶν Σαρδέων ὁ Τμῶλος, εὔδαιμον ὄρος, ἐν τῇ ἀκρωρείᾳ σκοπὴν ἔχον, ἐξέδραν λευκοῦ λίθου, Περσῶν ἔργον, ἀφ' οὗ κατοπτεύεται τὰ κύκλῳ πεδία, καὶ μάλιστα τὸ Καϋστριανόν.

[3] 8. 6. 21.

nothing in contradiction to the traditional view, but that this was, in all probability, rather to save themselves from being laughed at for the fruitlessness of their enterprise, than because it was possible to see from one point seas and mountains and rivers so far distant from one another[1]. As the district from which they originally started was about the head-waters of the Axius, and it took them seven days to reach the base of Haemus, we may conclude that the point intended was towards the middle of the range. Strabo contradicts the statement about the two seas being visible, attributing it to Polybius, who was probably the original authority[2]; but such fancies are not easily extinguished, and the same idea reappears at a later time in Mela[3]. We have already noticed the similar belief with regard to Argaeus, and here the mistake probably arose from a misconception as to the width of the eastern part of Asia Minor, which was regarded as an isthmus both by Herodotus and Strabo, and by the former of these writers was estimated as only five days' distance across for a vigorous walker[4]. A glance at the map will show that the space of country and the intervening mountain chains render this impossible, and the testimony of modern travellers who have made the ascent is to the same effect[5].

Two passages remain to be mentioned, in which the habit of ascending mountains seems to be indirectly referred to. One of these, which is found in Diodorus, is a description of a phenomenon which was said to be visible in the summer time from the summit of the Trojan Ida. 'A strange and peculiar occurrence,' the historian

Sunrise seen from Mt. Ida.

---

[1] Livy, 40. 21, 22; Tertio demum die ad verticem perventum. Nihil vulgatae opinioni degressi inde detraxerunt, magis, credo, ne vanitas itineris ludibrio esset, quam quod diversa inter se maria montesque et amnes ex uno loco conspici potuerint.

[2] Strabo, 7. 5. 1: τὸ Αἷμον......, ἀφ' οὗ φησι Πολύβιος ἀμφοτέρας καθορᾶσθαι τὰς θαλάττας, οὐκ ἀληθῆ λέγων.

[3] Mela, 2. 2. 17; e quis Haemos in tantum altitudinis abit, ut Euxinum et Hadrian ex summo vertice ostendat.

[4] Herod. 1. 72; ἔστι δὲ αὐχὴν οὗτος τῆς χώρης ταύτης ἁπάσης· μῆκος ὁδοῦ, εὐζώνῳ ἀνδρὶ πέντε ἡμέραι ἀναισιμοῦνται. Strabo, 11. 1. 7: ὁ διείργων ἰσθμὸς τήν τε Ποντικὴν καὶ τὴν Κιλικίαν θάλασσαν.

[5] See the author's *Turkish Armenia*, p. 126.

remarks, 'is wont to happen in connexion with this mountain. On the summit of the peak, about the time of the rising of the dogstar, owing to the stillness of the surrounding atmosphere the highest point is far above the current of the winds, and while it is still night the sun is seen to rise, emitting its rays not in a spherical form, but so that its brilliancy is dispersed in various directions, with the appearance of a number of flames striking the horizon. After a while these contract into a single area, until they cover a space of three hundred feet, and at last when the daylight has spread, the disk of the sun fully manifests itself, and imparts to day its wonted character[1].' The process of change which is here depicted in somewhat inflated language is not altogether easy to explain, but the description seems to have been suggested by something which was seen from a lofty ridge. The height of Ida is about 5,000 feet. A humorous notice of a panorama viewed from a mountain summit

Lucian on a Mountain View.

is found in the Dialogue of Lucian which is entitled *Contemplantes* or 'The Sight-seers.' In this, Charon, who has been allowed a day's holiday from his usual occupation as ferry-man of the dead, requests Hermes, on the strength of their common interest in introducing the shades to the lower regions, to act as his *cicerone* to explain to him the unfamiliar sights of the world of the living, with which he was only acquainted through the grief for the loss of former enjoyments manifested by those who made the passage in his boat. When Hermes consented to this, it was agreed that a high mountain would be a suitable point from which to take a survey of the earth; and accordingly, following the suggestion of Homer, they pile Ossa and Pelion on Olympus. The mass thus formed, however, proved too low for their purpose, so they proceeded to add Oeta and Parnassus also, and took their seats respectively on the two summits of the last-named mountain. In this detail, we may remark, Lucian betrays the influence of Roman poetry, for when the Greek poets spoke of the 'twin peaks' of Parnassus, they meant the two cliffs which rise above Delphi, and it was only through misinterpretation on the part of the Romans that it came to be thought that the mountain itself

[1] Diodor. 17. 7. 4—7.

had more than one summit.   However, from this point of vantage
the two divinities study the lives and fortunes of mankind, until
Charon—egotistically, as it might seem to some, but here lies the
moral or sarcasm of the story—concludes with remarking on the
small space which he, Charon—or, as we might say, Death—
seems to occupy in the thoughts of those who play their parts on
this stage.   Before leaving the earth, the climbers, from fear of
punishment, if not from a sense of propriety, replace in their
original positions the mountains which they had removed in order
to facilitate their ascent and extend their prospect.

The following unusually careful description of a mountain
climb deserves to be quoted from Sallust.   The
scene of it was a Numidian fort, situated on a
precipitous rock, which Marius was besieging.

Description
of a Mountain
Climb.

'After spending much time and toil on the attempt, Marius
seriously debated in his mind, whether he should give it up as
hopeless, or wait for the chances of fortune, which had so often
favoured him.   Now while he was thinking this over unde-
cidedly for several days and nights, it chanced that a Ligurian, a
common soldier of the auxiliary cohorts, who had left the camp
to fetch water, at no great distance from that side of the fort
which faced in the opposite direction to the combatants, noticed
snails crawling among the rocks; and as he was picking first one
or two, and afterwards more of these, gradually, being absorbed
in his occupation, he made his way almost to the top of the
mountain.   Now when he found that the place was deserted, he
proceeded to examine it, with the usual desire of the human mind
to investigate the unknown.   It happened that just there a great
holm-oak had sprung up among the rocks; this at first inclined
downwards, but afterwards bent round and rose upwards, as is
the way with growing things: so the Ligurian soldier, supporting
himself sometimes on its boughs, sometimes on jutting rocks,
took a survey of the level of the fort, all the Numidians being
intent on watching the combatants.   When he had examined
every point which he thought might afterwards be serviceable, he
returned the same way, not in the random manner in which he
had ascended, but testing and scrutinising everything.   Thereupon
he at once betook himself to Marius, and after telling him what he

had done, urged him to assail the fort from the side by which he had ascended, and undertook to shew the way and to be foremost in the danger.

'Marius sent some of those about him with the Ligurian to examine his proposal; and these reported the matter as easy or difficult according to their prepossessions. Still, the consul's interest in it was to some degree aroused; and accordingly he chose five of the most active of his force of trumpeters and hornblowers, accompanied by four centurions to act as guards, and placed them all under the command of the Ligurian, appointing the following day for the adventure. When the time agreed upon arrived, he set out for the place with everything prepared and in order. Those, however, who were to make the ascent, according to the instructions of their leader had put off their arms and equipment, baring their heads and feet, so as to have a freer view and a firmer foothold among the rocks, and carrying on their backs their swords and shields; but the latter were Numidian bucklers made of leather, both for the sake of lightness, and in order that when they struck any object they might give out less sound. So the Ligurian went in front, and fastened nooses round the rocks and any old roots that jutted out, that by the help of these the soldiers might climb more easily. From time to time he gave them a hand, if they were discouraged by so unusual a mode of progress, and when the gradient was steeper than usual, he sent them on one by one in front of him without their arms, and then followed bearing them. Where the ground appeared untrustworthy, he shewed the example of testing it, and by frequently going up and down the same way, and now and then on the sudden varying the route, inspired the rest with confidence. In this way, with much expense of time and labour, they reached the fort, which was undefended on that side[1].'

If any additional proof be required, beyond that which has been already given, of the frequency with which mountains were ascended in antiquity—at least at an early period—for the sake of the views which they commanded, it may be found in the recurrent

Mountains regarded as Look-out Places.

---

[1] Sall. *Bell. Jugurth.* 93, 94: cp. *The Alpine Journal*, vol. II. pp. 180, 181.

use, both in Greek and Latin, of the words for 'a look-out
place' (σκοπιά, *specula*) to signify 'a mountain height.' In the
Iliad we meet with two similes in which this occurs:—"as
when a goatherd from a place of outlook seeth a cloud coming
across the deep before the blast of the west wind"[1]; and again—
"as far as a man seeth with his eyes into the haze of distance as
he sitteth on a place of outlook and ga eth over the wine-dark
sea[2]." In the *Odyssey*, also, Ulysses says—"I went up a craggy
hill, a place of outlook[3]." And Simonides speaks of the summits
of Cithaeron as "lonely watch-towers[4]." The Latin word is similarly used in Virgil, though this usually occurs in passages where
he is imitating the Greek poets. Thus in the *Bucolics* he makes
the despairing lover say—"I will fling myself headlong into the
waves from the watch-tower of a soaring mountain summit"[5];
and in the *Aeneid* Turnus when he goes to encounter Pallas is
compared to "a lion, that from a lofty place of outlook hath caught
sight of a bull which stands afar off on the plains contemplating
fight[6]." Again, in a picturesque passage in the same poem, where
a mountain glen has just been described, we are told that "above
it, in the midst of the watch-towers which form the summit of a
mountain, there lies a table-land withdrawn from view[7]." The
same thing appears in legend in the story of Lynceus (the

[1] *Il.* 4. 275, 6;
   ὡς δ᾽ ὅτ᾽ ἀπὸ σκοπιῆς εἶδεν νέφος αἰπόλος ἀνὴρ
   ἐρχόμενον κατὰ πόντον ὑπὸ Ζεφύροιο ἰωῆς.
[2] *Il.* 5. 770, 771;
   ὅσσον δ᾽ ἠεροειδὲς ἀνὴρ ἴδεν ὀφθαλμοῖσιν
   ἥμενος ἐν σκοπιῇ, λεύσσων ἐπὶ οἴνοπα πόντον.
[3] *Od.* 10. 97;
   ἔστην δὲ σκοπιὴν ἐς παιπαλόεσσαν ἀνελθών.
[4] Simon. 130; Κιθαιρῶνός τ᾽ οἰονόμοι σκοπιαί.
[5] *Ecl.* 8. 59;
   Praeceps aërii specula de montis in undas
   Deferar.
[6] *Aen.* 10. 454;
   Utque leo, specula cum vidit ab alta
   Stare procul campis meditantem in praelia taurum.
[7] *ibid.* 11. 526, 7;
   Hanc super, in speculis summoque in vertice montis
   Planities ignota jacet.

'lynx-eyed' man), who was noted for his power of sight in distinguishing distant objects. By Pindar he is represented as watching from the summit of Taygetus, 'for of all men on the face of the earth he had the keenest eye'[1]; and elsewhere we are told that 'he went to Taygetus, trusting to his speed of foot, and climbed to the summit, where he overlooked the whole island of Pelops the son of Tantalus[2].' That mountain, as being the highest in the Peloponnese and rising in the immediate vicinity of Sparta, was considered to be the natural point of view for a panorama in that neighbourhood; hence Aristophanes in the *Lysistrata* makes the Lacedaemonian woman say that she would mount to the top of Taygetus to get a sight of peace[3]. Of Lynceus it is further related that, when the daughters of Danaus at Argos by the desire of their father slew their husbands in one night, and Lynceus only was spared through the fidelity of his wife Hypermnestra, he escaped to Lyrceia, a town seven miles to the north-westward of Argos, and from the hill on which it was built displayed a burning torch, to certify to her that he had reached a place of safety. She 'n return, according to their agreement, shewed a corresponding signal from the Larissa, or lofty citadel of Argos, in token that she also had escaped from danger[4]. This story may serve to introduce to our notice another and more practical aspect from which mountains were regarded in ancient times, viz. as signalling stations.

Story of Lynceus.

The passage which most readily suggests itself to the mind of a scholar in this connexion is the famous description in the *Agamemnon* of Aeschylus of the line of fire-beacons by which the poet imagines Agamemnon to have transmitted to Clytaemnestra at Argos the news of the capture of Troy.

Mountains as Signalling Stations.

The Beacon-fires in Aeschylus,

'From Ida's top Hephaestus, lord of fire,
Sent forth his sign; and on, and ever on,
Beacon to beacon sped the courier flame.

---

[1] Pind. *Nem.* 10. 61—3.

[2] Stasinus, *Cypria*, in Düntzer, *Die Fragmente der epischen Poesie der Griechen bis zur Zeit Alexanders des Grossen*, p. 13.

[3] Aristoph. *Lysist.* 117, 118.   [4] Pausan., 2. 25. 4.

From Ida to the crag, that Hermes loves,
Of Lemnos; thence unto the steep sublime
Of Athos, throne of Zeus, the broad blaze flared.
Thence, raised aloft to shoot across the sea,
The moving light, rejoicing in its strength,
Sped from the pyre of pine, and urged its way,
In golden glory, like some strange new sun,
Onward, and reached Macistus' watching heights.
There, with no dull delay nor heedless sleep,
The watcher sped the tidings on in turn,
Until the guard upon Messapius' peak
Saw the far flame gleam on Euripus' tide,
And from the high-piled heap of withered furze
Lit the new sign and bade the message on.
Then the strong light, far-flown and yet undimmed,
Shot thro' the sky above Asopus' plain,
Bright as the moon, and on Cithaeron's crag
Aroused another watch of flying fire.
And there the sentinels no whit disowned
But sent redoubled on, the hest of flame—
Swift shot the light, above Gorgopis' bay,
To Aegiplanctus' mount; and bade the peak
Fail not the onward ordinance of fire.
And like a long beard streaming in the wind,
Full-fed with fuel, roared and rose the blaze,
And onward flaring, gleamed above the cape,
Beneath which shimmers the Saronic bay,
And thence leapt light unto Arachne's peak,
The mountain watch that looks upon our town.
Thence to th' Atrides' roof—in lineage fair,
A bright posterity of Ida's fire.
So sped from stage to stage, fulfilled in turn,
Flame after flame, along the course ordained,
And lo ! the last to speed upon its way
Sights the end first, and glows unto the goal[1].'

The stations of the fire-beacons which are mentioned in this passage are (1) Mt. Ida, to the southward of the Plain of Troy (5750 ft.); (2) Mt. Hermaeus, the north-eastern promontory of Lemnos; (3) Mt. Athos, the most conspicuous point in the north of the Aegean (6350 ft.); (4) Mt. Macistus in the north-west of Euboea (3967 ft.); (5) Mt. Messapius, on the coast of Boeotia opposite Chalcis (3363 ft.); (6) Mt. Cithaeron, which separates that

---

[1] Aesch. *Ag.* 281—314 (Morshead's translation).

country from Attica (4629 ft.); (7) Mt. Aegiplanctus, in the range of Geraneia to the northward of the Isthmus of Corinth (3465 ft.); and, finally, (8) Mt. Arachnaeus in Argolis, which is visible from Argos (3934 ft.). All these, with the exception of the Mons Hermaeus in Lemnos, which was chosen on account of its intermediate position between Ida and Athos, are conspicuous summits; and it will be seen that the line of beacon-fires which were lighted upon them traversed the northern and western sides of the Aegean. The points thus chosen are visible, successively, one from the other. The longest interval is that from Athos to Macistus; but this is considerably less than that between Samo-thrace and Pelion or Scyros, both which places can clearly be seen from the former island[1]. It has also been proved that a fire-beacon can be seen by the naked eye at a much greater distance than that here implied[2]. The whole description in Aeschylus is, no doubt, imaginary; but the choice of the stations was determined by the knowledge of the writer's own time, and all this geographical detail would hardly have been given, had the audience not been supposed to be in some degree acquainted with it. That they were so follows almost necessarily from the fact that the islands of Imbros and Lemnos, which lay in the remotest part of this area, had for some time been in the possession of the Athenians, and were in constant communication with Athens. It is, moreover, by no means improbable that a line of signalling stations, corresponding more or less closely to that of which we are speaking, was actually used before this date. Herodotus, in his account of the commencement of the campaign of Mardonius in Greece which ended in the battle of Plataea, states that one of the chief causes which rendered that general anxious to capture Athens a second time was, that he might be able to report to Xerxes

probably corresponding to a Real Line of Stations.

[1] See the author's *Islands of the Aegean*, p. 348.

[2] See the late Mr A. C. Merriam's paper on 'Telegraphing among the Ancients,' p. 26, in the *Papers of the Archaeological Institute of America*; Classical Series, III. No. I. The present writer is indebted to this valuable essay for most of the information on that subject which is given in the following paragraphs.

at Sardis by means of fire-beacons by way of the islands that
he was in possession of that city[1]. Now it has been justly
remarked that the line of communication here intended could
not have been the direct one across the Aegean through the
Cyclades, since that was not at this time in the hands of the
Persians, because after the battle of Salamis the Greeks were
masters of the sea[2]. It is probable, therefore, that the elevated
positions which were then used lay in the neighbourhood of
the land-route by which the Persians had advanced into Greece;
and from that point of view none would be so convenient as
a line which passed from Boeotia by way of Athos and Lemnos
to the coast of Asia Minor.

We may now proceed to notice some other instances of the
employment of mountain heights as stations for
signalling. The first of these that occurs in Greek   The Shield
history is the graphic incident, which is narrated in   at Marathon.
the story of the battle of Marathon, of the shield which was displayed on that occasion as a signal to the Persians—probably from
the summit of Pentelicus, a position which was admirably suited
for such a purpose[3]. Herodotus, who is our informant on this
subject, mentions the rumour which was current in his time with
regard to it, that it was a treasonable act on the part of the Alc-
maeonidae, who were supposed to be in collusion with the enemies
of their country. This charge he himself regarded as unfounded,
and at the present day the opinion of the learned seems to incline
towards the same view. It is quite possible that this point of
vantage had been occupied by a detachment of the Persians, who
by means of a shield, the surface of which flashed in the sunlight,
communicated some intelligence to their comrades. On this
subject, however, the historian gives us no definite information;
but with regard to the shield having been employed in some way
as a signal—and this for our present purpose is the important
point—he says there was no doubt whatsoever[4]. Mountain
In Thucydides, again, we meet with an instance of   Telegraphy in
mountain telegraphy in connexion with an incident   Thucydides,

[1] Herod. 9. 3.
[2] Rawlinson, note on Herodotus *ad loc.*; Merriam, *op. cit.*, p. 4.
[3] Herod. 6. 115.   [4] Herod. 6. 115, 121, 124.

of the Peloponnesian war, when the Lacedaemonians in 429 B.C. had planned an attack on the Piraeus by sea, taking Nisaea the port of Megara as their starting-point. This project they failed to accomplish, either through faint-heartedness, or—as they themselves asserted by way of excuse—owing to an unfavourable wind; and instead, they made a descent on Salamis and ravaged that island. In order to convey the intelligence of this to Athens (we are told), fire-signals of an enemy's approach were displayed[1]; and the position of these, there can be little doubt, was on the north-eastern heights of the island, which are in view from the Acropolis. Xenophon also mentions that in 367 B.C.

Xenophon, the city of Phlius, which lies in the upland country that intervenes between the territory of Sicyon and the Argive plain, was attacked by a hostile force aided by some exiles from their own state; but that the citizens were on their guard, having been forewarned by watchers on Mt. Tricaranon, the neighbouring height towards the east, who signalled to them that the enemy were advancing[2]. It is noticeable that Aeneas Tacticus—the writer on the art of war, whose probable date corresponds closely with that of the event just mentioned—in his work on the defence of besieged cities, or *Commentarius Poliorceticus*, recommends that such look-out men—three at least in number, and experienced persons—should be stationed on a height in the neighbourhood of a city, when there was a prospect of an attack, in order that they might signal the numbers and movements of the enemy. He adds, that the signals should be changed from time to time, lest the enemy should come to understand them[3]. At a later period again

and Polybius. we hear of a system of beacon-stations which was organised by Philip V. of Macedon in 207 B.C., when he was opposed by the forces of the Aetolians on one side, and by the fleet of the Romans and Attalus in the Aegean on the other. Polybius informs us that that monarch, in order to obtain information with regard to the movements of his adversaries, had given orders to the Phocians, to the inhabitants of Euboea, and to the natives of Peparethus—the furthermost of those islands stretching from the extremity of Pelion—that they should acquaint him,

---

[1] Thuc. 2. 94; cp. Diodor. 12. 49.

[2] Xen. *Hellen.*, 7. 2. 5.   [3] *Comment. Poliorc.*, 6. 1.

by means of beacon-fires displayed on elevated positions, with what was taking place in their neighbourhood. The central post, towards which their signals were to be directed was the lofty, and from this point of view central, peak of Mt. Tisaeus, which rises between the Straits of Artemisium and the Pagasaean Gulf, and was in full view from the city of Demetrias near the head of that gulf, which at this time was Philip's place of residence[1].

It is interesting to trace the progress which appears to have been made in the art of signalling during the period which has just been noticed. In the narrative of Thucydides mentioned above, which speaks of the transmission of intelligence from the heights of Salamis to Athens, the expression used for the signals which intimated the nearness of the enemy is 'hostile fire-signals'[2]; and the Scholiast on that passage remarks in explanation of this term that, when the news of hostile movements was communicated, the signals—which in this case must have been torches—were waved to and fro; whereas, if they referred to the approach of a friendly force, they were held steady[3]. Elsewhere in the same author—in the account which he gives of the movements of the Lacedaemonian and Athenian fleets in connexion with the Corcyrean seditions—we are told that the Peloponnesians were made aware by fire-signals of the approach of sixty ships of the Athenians[4]. If this passage is interpreted literally, it would imply that the number of the vessels was signalled; but, as Thucydides is fond of condensed expressions, it does not perhaps signify more than that an Athenian fleet was signalled, and that it proved to be composed of sixty ships. Half a century later than this, in 373 B.C., we find that a somewhat more advanced system was in use. The scene again is Corcyra, and the Athenians and Lacedaemonians are the combatants. On this occasion Iphicrates, who commanded the fleet of the former of the two states, hastened to that island, in order to save it

Development of the Art of Signalling.

---

[1] Polyb. 10. 42. 7, 8; cp. Livy, 28. 5.

[2] φρυκτοὶ πολέμιοι.

[3] Schol. Thuc. 2. 94; καὶ ὅταν μὲν φίλους ἐδήλουν, ἐβάσταζον τοὺς φρυκτοὺς ἠρεμοῦντες· ὅταν δὲ πολεμίους, ἐκίνουν τοὺς φρυκτούς, δηλοῦντες τὸν φόβον.

[4] Thuc. 3. 80; ὑπὸ νύκτα αὐτοῖς ἐφρυκτωρήθησαν ἐξήκοντα νῆες Ἀθηναίων προσπλέουσαι.

from the rival power; and on his arrival he heard that ten triremes, which Dionysius of Syracuse was sending to the assistance of the Spartans, were expected shortly to arrive there. Accordingly he proceeded to inspect in person the points from which he might receive notice of the approach of these vessels; and there can be little doubt that the post which he selected was in the neighbourhood of the modern Pass of Pantaleone among the mountains in the north of Corfu, since from it the city is visible on one side, and on the other the sea in the direction of Italy. Xenophon, from whom our knowledge of these events is obtained, tells us that look-out men were stationed there, and that a system of signals was agreed upon, by which they should inform Iphicrates when the ships were in sight, when they were mooring, and so forth. The result was, that the vessels of Dionysius when they arrived were captured, and their crews who had disembarked were made prisoners[1]. From Polyaenus, the author of the *Strategemata*, we further learn that the information was conveyed by fire-signals, and that the scene of the capture of the ships was one of the group of small islands which lie off the north-western angle of Corcyra[2]. It was at a still later period, however, that the art of telegraphy received its greatest development. A full account of this is given by Polybius in connexion with the story of Philip V. of Macedon which has been mentioned above. He begins by remarking that the old system of signalling by beacon-fires was comparatively inefficient, because the things to be signalled had to be agreed on beforehand. Hence, while ordinary occurrences could be notified in this manner, the case was not the same with anything unusual, and thus the most important emergencies were unprovided for. He then goes on to notice an intricate plan elaborated by Aeneas Tacticus, which rendered it possible to signal words and short sentences. Finally, he describes in full detail the method devised in the first instance by Cleoxenus and Democleitus, and afterwards brought to perfection by Polybius himself, which approximated in many respects to the system of signalling in use at the present day. By this scheme the letters of the alphabet were represented, according to the rules of a prearranged code, by means of raising torches, varying in number, sometimes on the right hand and sometimes

[1] Xen. *Hell.* 6. 2. 33–5.   [2] Polyaen. *Strateg.* 3. 9. 55.

on the left, to denote the letter intended : in this way it was possible to transmit any form of intelligence[1]. Whether either of the two last-named plans was ever actually employed we have no certain evidence to shew.

The attempts which the ancients made to determine the height of mountains were of necessity little more than guesswork. In some cases there was not even a pretence of scientific measurement, the estimate being made either by the eye, or by the comparison of one mountain with another; in other instances, where greater accuracy was attempted, either the perpendicular height is given, or the distance on foot, or the time usually occupied in the ascent. Thus Polybius is quoted by Strabo as comparing the Alps in respect of their elevation with the highest summits in Greece—Taygetus, Lycaeum, Parnassus, Olympus, Pelion and Ossa, together with Haemus and Rhodope in Thrace; and he is represented as saying that every one of these mountains might be scaled in little more than a day by a good walker, while more than five days were required to ascend the Alps[2]. Strabo himself speaks of the highest summits of the Alpine chain, which he places in the country of the Medulli (in the neighbourhood of St. Jean de Maurienne), as being regarded as 100 stadia (12½ Roman miles) in direct ascent—from the use of which expression it is evident that perpendicular height is not intended[3]. Pliny estimates the elevation of Haemus at six Roman miles[4]. The geographer, however, to whom the credit is due of having first attempted the scientific measurement of the height of

Estimates of the Heights of Mountains.

---

[1] Polyb. 10. 43—47.

[2] Strabo, 4. 6. 12 ; ὁ δ' αὐτὸς ἀνὴρ (Πολύβιος) περὶ τοῦ μεγέθους τῶν Ἄλπεων καὶ τοῦ ὕψους λέγων παραβάλλει τὰ ἐν τοῖς Ἕλλησιν ὄρη τὰ μέγιστα, τὸ Ταΰγετον, τὸ Λύκαιον, Παρνασσόν, Ὄλυμπον, Πήλιον, Ὄσσαν· ἐν δὲ Θρᾴκῃ Αἶμον, Ῥοδόπην, Δούνακα· καὶ φησιν, ὅτι τούτων μὲν ἕκαστον μικροῦ δεῖν αὐθημερὸν εὐζώνοις ἀναβῆναι δυνατόν, αὐθημερὸν δὲ καὶ περιελθεῖν, τὰς δ' Ἄλπεις οὐδ' ἂν πεμπταῖος ἀναβαίη τίς.

[3] Strabo, 4. 6. 5 ; Μετὰ δὲ Οὐοκοντίους Ἰκόνιοι καὶ Τρικόριοι καὶ μετ' αὐτοὺς Μέδουλλοι, οἵπερ τὰς ὑψηλοτάτας ἔχουσι κορυφάς· τὸ γοῦν ὀρθιώτατον αὐτῶν ὕψος σταδίων ἑκατὸν ἔχειν φασὶ τὴν ἀνάβασιν, κἀνθένδε πάλιν τὴν ἐπὶ τοὺς ὄρους τοὺς τῆς Ἰταλίας κατάβασιν.

[4] Pliny, H. N. 4. 41 ; Haemi excelsitas sex mil. pass. subitur.

mountains, is Aristotle's pupil, Dicaearchus, to whom, as we
have seen, other discoveries also have been attri-

Scientific Measurement by Dicaearchus,

buted[1]. From a passage in Geminus the astronomer
we learn that Dicaearchus accomplished this by
geometry[2], and the same thing is affirmed by Pliny,
who speaks of Dicaearchus as a man of distinguished learning, and
implies that he undertook the investigation of this question in the
service of the Macedonian monarchs[3]. The results of his calculations, however, were anything but satisfactory. Geminus tells us
in the passage just referred to, that he estimated the vertical height
of Cyllene in Arcadia as less than 15 stadia (9,000 feet), and that
of Atabyrium (or, as he calls it, Satabyrium) in Rhodes as less
than 14 stadia (8,400 feet); whereas in reality their heights are
7,789 feet and 4,070 feet respectively[4]. Again, Pliny says that
the highest mountain measured by Dicaearchus was Pelion, which
reached 1250 *passus*, or 6,250 feet[5]. The error in this case was
all the more remarkable on account of the neighbourhood of
Olympus, the summit of which mountain is 9,754 feet high, while
that of Pelion is only 5,310 feet. It seems strange that the observation of the snow-line did not of itself suggest a more accurate
estimate. From Plutarch we learn in his *Life of Aemilius Paullus*

and Xenagoras.

that Olympus was measured on scientific principles
by one Xenagoras. Speaking of the town of Py-
thium at the foot of that mountain he says, 'at that
point Olympus rises to the height of more than 10 stadia; and
this is intimated by the inscription of the person who measured it,
which runs thus—"On the summit of Olympus the shrine of
Pythian Apollo stands at the height of 10 stadia and a plethrum
less four feet (and it was measured vertically). This inscription
was set up by Xenagoras son of Eumelus as the measurement of

---

[1] *v. supra*, pp. 170, 180.

[2] Geminus, *Element. Astronom.* § 14, in Petav. *Uranologia*, p. 55 E; καὶ
ἔστι μὲν τῆς Κυλλήνης τὸ ὕψος ἔλασσον σταδίων ιε΄, ὡς Δικαίαρχος ἀναμετρικῶς
ἀποφαίνεται. τοῦ δὲ Σαταβυρίου ἐλάσσων ἐστὶν ἡ κάθετος σταδίων ιδ΄.

[3] Pliny, *H. N.* 2. 162; Cui sententiae adest Dicaearchus, vir in primis
eruditus, regum cura permensus montis, ex quibus altissimum prodit Pelion
MCCL passuum ratione perpendiculi.

[4] *v. supra*, note 2.   [5] *v. supra*, note 3.

the distance; hail, O King, and grant us thy blessing." For all this,' Plutarch continues, 'the geometricians maintain that no mountain is of greater height, nor any part of the sea of greater depth, than 10 stadia; yet Xenagoras does not seem to have made his computation carelessly, but strictly with the help of instruments[1].' About the height of Cyllene also there were other, and widely divergent estimates, besides that already given. Apollodorus reckoned it at 80 feet less than nine stadia[2] (5,320 feet). And Strabo says that by some it was computed by perpendicular measurement as 20 stadia (12,000 feet), by others as about 15 stadia[3] (9,000 feet). By the latter of these two numbers the calculation of Dicaearchus was probably meant. Strabo also records the elevation of the Acrocorinth, which he says was estimated as three stadia and a half (2,100 feet) in vertical height[4]. This is approximately true, for the real measurement is 1,887 English feet.

---

[1] Plut. *Aemil. Paull.* c. 15; Ἐνταῦθα τοῦ Ὀλύμπου τὸ ὕψος ἀνατείνει πλέον ἢ δέκα σταδίους· σημαίνεται δὲ ἐπιγράμματι τοῦ μετρήσαντος οὕτως·

> Οὐλύμπου κορυφῆς ἔπι Πυθίου Ἀπόλλωνος
> ἱερὸν ὕψος ἔχει (πρὸς τὴν κάθετον δ' ἐμετρήθη)
> πλήρη μὲν δεκάδα σταδίων μίαν, αὐτὰρ ἐπ' αὐτῇ
> πλέθρον τετραπέδῳ λειπόμενον μεγέθει.
> Εὐμήλου δέ μιν υἱὸς ἐθήκατο μέτρα κελεύθου
> Ξειναγόρης· σὺ δ', ἄναξ, χαῖρε καὶ ἐσθλὰ δίδου.

Καίτοι λέγουσιν οἱ γεωμετρικοὶ μήτε ὄρους ὕψος μήτε βάθος θαλάσσης ὑπερβάλλειν δέκα σταδίους. Ὁ μέντοι Ξεναγόρας οὐ παρέργως, ἀλλὰ μεθόδῳ καὶ δι' ὀργάνων εἰληφέναι δοκεῖ τὴν μέτρησιν.

[2] Steph. Byz. s.v. Κυλλήνη: Eustathius *in Hom. Od.* p. 1951, ed. Rom. 1542.

[3] Strabo, 8. 8. 1; μέγιστον δ' ὄρος ἐν αὐτῇ [τῇ Πελοποννήσῳ] Κυλλήνη· τὴν γοῦν κάθετον οἱ μὲν εἴκοσι σταδίων φασίν, οἱ δ' ὅσον πεντεκαίδεκα.

[4] Strabo, 8. 6. 21; ὄρος ὑψηλὸν ὅσον τριῶν ἥμισυ σταδίων ἔχον τὴν κάθετον, τὴν δ' ἀνάβασιν καὶ τριάκοντα σταδίων, εἰς ὀξεῖαν τελευτᾷ κορυφήν· καλεῖται δ' Ἀκροκόρινθος. On the subject of these measurements see Bunbury, *Hist. of Anc. Geography*, vol. I. p. 618; Berger, *Geschichte der Erdkunde*, Pt. 3, p. 53.

CHAPTER XVI.

PTOLEMY AND LATER GEOGRAPHERS.

Marinus Tyrius—His Attempt to reform the Map of the World—Its Deficiencies—Ptolemy—His Great Reputation—His Error about the Circumference of the Earth, and the Length of the Habitable World—The Fortunate Isles his Prime Meridian—His System of Projection—His Geographical Treatise—His Maps—His Corrections of Previous Maps—His Chief Errors—His Account of Britain—Accurate Delineation of the Coast—Erroneous Position of Scotland—Possible Explanation of this—Ptolemy's Tables of the Coast of Britain—The Southern Coast—The Western Coast—The Eastern Coast—Ireland—Other Additions to Geographical Knowledge—The Volga (Rha)—The Altai Chain (Imaus)—Direct Trade Route to China—Sources of the Nile—Mountains of the Moon—The Soudan—Rivers Gir and Nigir—Pausanias—His Resemblance to Herodotus—His Illustrations of Physical Geography—Fountains—Their Different Colours—Warm Springs—Fountain of Deine—Caverns—The Corycian Cave—Trees—Cotton—Pausanias' Researches in Greece—His Descriptions of Olympia and Delphi—Routes which he followed—Contents of his Book—The Question of his Veracity—The View Adverse to Pausanias—Explanations of his Statements—Difficulties involved in the Supposition—Recent Testimonies in his Favour—Stephanus Byzantinus—His *Ethnica*—Character of its Contents—Solinus—His *Memorabilia*—Mediaeval Estimate of him—Modern Estimate—Orosius—His *Historiae*—Its Geographical Section—Transient Character of Ptolemy's Influence—Earlier Errors revived—Retrospect and Summary—Continuous Advance of Knowledge of General Geography, and of Scientific Geography.

In the middle of the second century of our era there arose two remarkable geniuses, by whom the coping-stone was placed on the geographical study of the ancients. The former of these, Marinus of Tyre, is comparatively little known, his fame having been eclipsed by that of his successor, Ptolemy ; and of his writings nothing has come down to us, except what is imbedded in the works of that author. Yet Ptolemy is unstinting in his acknowledgment of the debt which he owed him, and he professes to come forward himself rather as the corrector of points in which the work of Marinus was deficient

Marinus Tyrius.

than as the originator of an independent scheme[1]. The particular
form which this remarkable revival of scientific geography assumed
was largely due to the practical spirit which the Roman temperament had infused into the study—in other words, to the encouragement which the imperial government had given to map-
making—for Marinus professes that it was the ob-
ject of his treatise to reform the map of the world; His Attempt
to reform the
indeed, from the terms in which Ptolemy speaks of Map of the
World.
it, we seem to gather that this was declared in its
title[2]. In doing this, it is true, he was only following in the steps of
Eratosthenes, who had put forward the same project as his primary
aim in the study of geography[3], but there was this difference in their
points of view, namely, that, while scientific questions of general
import, such as the measurement of the circumference of the
earth, which are of the highest value for exact cartography, held
the first place in the scheme of the earlier writer, in the hands of
Marinus they fell into the background in comparison with the
design of rendering maps more accurate in detail. Still, the fact
remains that Marinus was, as far as we know, the first person
after the time of Hipparchus who resumed the task—which that
great astronomer had suggested as the ultimate aim of scientific
geography—of subdividing the surface of the globe by meridians
and parallels, and inscribing within the spaces formed by their
intersections the places and districts about which information had
been attained, their position being determined as far as possible
by means of astronomical observation. We have seen that in
Hipparchus' age the execution of this was impracticable owing to
the limited amount of knowledge that was available for the purpose, and even Marinus could not fail to recognise that the
materials at his command were insufficient to enable him to deal
with it with any completeness; yet, during the period of nearly
three centuries which had elapsed since Hipparchus wrote, a great
mass of facts had gradually been accumulated, and the attempt
was worth making, though the result might be imperfect. That

---

[1] Ptol., *Geographia*, I. 6. 2.

[2] *Ibid.*, I. 6. I, where it is called ἡ τοῦ γεωγραφικοῦ πίνακος διόρθωσις.

[3] *v. supra*, p. 180.

it was imperfect we gather from Ptolemy, who, while he extols
the diligence of Marinus in collecting and sifting
his data, and notes that in the successive editions
of his work he had done his best to amend and
supplement it, remarks also that much was left for himself to
accomplish in correcting and improving it. To this must be
added a more serious deficiency arising from want of method, for
the continuity of the treatise was much broken up by the insertion
of discussions of disputed points. The map also left much to be
desired, because the parallels of latitude and meridians of longitude were represented upon it throughout by straight lines, and
the meridians of longitude were drawn parallel to one another—
a system, of the faultiness of which Marinus shewed himself to be
aware in the criticisms which he passed on the attempts of his
predecessors to delineate the spherical surface of the globe on a
plane map[1].

Its Deficiencies.

Of the life of Claudius Ptolemy hardly anything is known, but
it is probable that he studied and wrote at Alexandria, where the renowned school of letters which
had been founded by the Greek rulers of Egypt still flourished.
His treatise on geography was published subsequently to the
completion of his astronomical works, and its date may be fixed
approximately at 150 A.D. The greatness of his
fame as a mathematical geographer, which is
superior to that enjoyed by any other ancient
writer on the subject, has arisen from several causes. In the first
place it is to be attributed to the age in which he lived, for it
coincided with the decline of learning among the Greeks and
Romans, and in consequence of this he towered so conspicuously
above the writers who followed him, that an undue importance
was attached to his statements. No doubt, also, the renown of
Ptolemy as an astronomer was reflected on his geographical
studies, and heightened the estimation in which they were held.

Ptolemy.

His Great Reputation.

---

[1] Ptol. I. 20. 3, 4; ὅπερ Μαρῖνος εἰς ἐπίστασιν οὐ τὴν τυχοῦσαν ἀγαγών, καὶ
πάσαις ἀπαξαπλῶς μεμψάμενος ταῖς μεθόδοις τῶν ἐπιπέδων καταγραφῶν, οὐδὲν
ἧττον αὐτὸς φαίνεται κεχρημένος τῇ μάλιστα μὴ ποιούσῃ συμμέτρους τὰς διαστά-
σεις· τὰς μὲν γὰρ ἀντὶ τῶν κύκλων γραμμὰς τῶν τε παραλλήλων καὶ τῶν μεσημ-
βρινῶν εὐθείας ὑπεστήσατο πάσας.

But the cause which contributed more than any other to produce this result was the completeness of his system, which communicated to his statements an appearance of finality that did not really belong to them. The evidence on which Ptolemy relied in determining the position of places on the face of the globe was largely derived from the same source which had been used by his predecessors—the computations of distances made by travellers and navigators, whose estimates were from the nature of the case inaccurate. But when the evidence was withdrawn from view, as it was in Ptolemy's work, and the results were embodied in maps and tables of distances symmetrical in form, the definite character which they thus acquired caused them in the course of time to be regarded in the light of exact statements, as if they were based on scientific observations. It should be remembered, however, that Ptolemy himself is not responsible for this result of his mode of treating his subject, for in his Introduction he makes no secret of the imperfection of his materials[1] : nor ought the mistakes in his work which are revealed by modern discovery and modern science to blind us to its preeminent merits.

With regard to the measurement of the circumference of the earth Ptolemy followed Marinus in accepting Posidonius' erroneous estimate of 180,000 stadia[2], which fell short of the reality by one-sixth. It resulted from this that, as he adopted from Hipparchus the division of the equator and other great circles into 360 degrees, he made every degree only . 500 stadia (50 geographical miles) instead of 600 stadia (60 geographical miles), which is the true computation. This mistake at once affected his calculation of distances on his map, for in consequence of it he overestimated them: thus, if he discovered from his authorities— itineraries or otherwise—that the interval between two places was 500 stadia, he would express this on his map by a degree, which in reality is 600 stadia; and when the estimate was made on a large scale, the error in excess became very great. This was especially felt when he came to deal with the second important question of general scientific geography, that of the length of the habitable

His Error about the Circumference of the Earth,

and the Length of the Habitable World.

world, because he greatly over-estimated this relatively to the true circumference of the earth. There was, however, another cause which contributed even more largely to this error—namely, the tendency to exaggerate distances on the part of seamen and traders, on whose reckonings, as we have seen, in default of astronomical observations, which were few in number, he was forced to depend. It is greatly to Ptolemy's credit that, whereas all previous geographers had accepted these without qualification, he clearly perceived the necessity of making allowance for the deviations from the direct line, and the varying rate of progress, which were produced by the windings of roads or the irregular force and direction of winds, and of reducing the distances on the map accordingly[1]; his only fault was that his corrections were made on too limited a scale, so that a very considerable excess still remained. On the other hand, a certain error in defect in his calcula-

The Fortunate Isles, his Prime Meridian. tion arose from his assuming the Fortunate Isles (the Canaries) as the point from which his longitudes were to be reckoned. The westernmost island of this group, Ferro, long continued to be treated as the prime meridian, and is so among some German geographers at the present day; but in Ptolemy's time the position of those islands was not determined, and accordingly it was only by conjecture that he placed them two degrees and a half to the westward of the Sacred Promontory (Cape St. Vincent), instead of about nine degrees, which is the true estimate. The total result which he produced for the length of the known world, from the Fortunate Isles in the west to the city of Sera in China towards the east, was 180°, whereas the reality is about 130°. In one respect this mistake was advantageous in the consequences which proceeded from it at a later period, for by diminishing the interval between the eastern and western extremities of the world it encouraged the idea that the passage from the one to the other might be accomplished, and thus indirectly contributed to the discovery of America by Columbus. Its breadth he estimated at 80°, from the parallel of Thule (the Shetlands) to that of the Prasum Promontorium (perhaps Cape Delgado) on the eastern coast of Africa to

[1] i. 2. 4.

the south of Zanzibar. As the interval between these is 70°,
Ptolemy's computation in this case exceeded the reality by 10°.
In connexion with the extension thus assigned to the known
world from west to east and from south to north respectively, we
may remark that Ptolemy (or Marinus) is the first writer who uses
the Greek words for 'length' and 'breadth' ($\mu\hat{\eta}\kappa\text{os}$ and $\pi\lambda\acute{a}\tau\text{os}$) in
the technical sense of 'longitude' and 'latitude,' *i.e.* to signify the
distance of a place from a fixed meridian line, or from the
equator.

In cartography the great advance which Ptolemy made on the
work of his predecessors consisted in his system of
projection, which in many respects approximates   **His System
of Projection.**
to that which is in general use at the present day.
We have seen that former geographers, including Marinus, had
drawn the parallels of latitude and meridians of longitude in
straight lines, parallel to one another; and in his special maps of
the separate countries Ptolemy continued to do this, because, when
the area was limited, the inaccuracy thus produced was of small
importance.   But in a general map of the whole known world he
recognised that the error arising from this cause was very great,
and that it was necessary to make allowance for the spherical
character of the earth, and for the inclination of the meridians to
one another.   With a view to this he represented the lines of
latitude by parallel curves, while, in order to avoid too elaborate a
scheme, he represented the meridians of longitude in the first
instance by straight lines, converging towards a point outside
the limits of the map.   Subsequently, however, he reduced the
meridians also to a curved form, so as to make them correspond
more nearly with the reality.   From intimations which are found
in various writers it seems probable that Hipparchus in some
degree anticipated this method, but there is no reason to believe
that he constructed any such complete scheme as is found in
Ptolemy.   The map on which this network of lines was drawn
was not in shape a perfect hemisphere, because it represented the
portion of the globe then known; and this, while it extended some
distance south of the equator, did not include the regions about
the pole.   The *climata* of Ptolemy, which also were marked on
his map, were—like those spaces on the surface of the globe to

which, as we have already seen, Hipparchus assigned that name[1].—
the intervals between two parallels of latitude. The width of
these intervals, however, was not measured by degrees, as was
the case with the *climata* of Hipparchus, but by the increase in
the length of the longest day, proceeding northwards from the
equator. From this line as far as the 45th degree of N. latitude,
where the longest day was of $15\frac{1}{2}$ hours, the breadth of a
clima was determined by the difference of a quarter of an hour in
the length of the longest day ; but beyond the 45th degree by the
difference of half an hour[2]. The reason for this change in the
system of measurement, no doubt, was that a more elaborate
division was required for the better known parts of the world,
where it was necessary to fix the position of a large number of
places, while for the remoter regions towards the north a smaller
number of boundary lines was necessary.

The geographical treatise of Ptolemy was intended to elucidate
and explain his maps. His aim was to make mathematical geography as complete as possible, and
consequently such questions as more properly belong
to physical and historical geography are excluded from consideration. In order to understand his work aright, we must remember
that the maps preceded the description, and that this is adapted
from them. It is divided into eight books, the first of which treats
of the principles of mathematical geography and of the projection
of maps, together with a discussion of the length and breadth of
the habitable world, while the six following books contain tables,
which give the names of the places marked on the maps of the
separate countries, and the latitude and longitude of each, and are
accompanied by notices of the boundaries of the countries, and
other remarks which are required for purposes of explanation.
These tables were extremely serviceable for purposes of reference,
and they also enabled the student who did not possess the author's
maps to reconstruct them for himself. The eighth book is written
rather from the point of view of astronomy than from that of
geography. In it the writer takes the most important positions
which had already been determined on his maps, and deduces
from their latitudes and longitudes such results as the length of

His Geo-
graphical
Treatise.

---

[1] *v. supra*, p. 175.   [2] Ptol. *Geogr.* I. 23.

the longest day at each, and, for those that were situated within the tropics, the course of the sun with respect to them. It is a difficult matter to decide whether we still possess the actual maps which Ptolemy constructed. Such   **His Maps.** maps are found in some of the manuscripts of his work, and are there attributed to one Agathodaemon of Alexandria; but since nothing further is known about that person, it is impossible to determine whether he was a contemporary of the geographer, who delineated them under his supervision, or whether he reconstructed them several centuries later, when owing to the negligence of copyists the original ones had been omitted from the text. The question is less important than it would otherwise be, because, as we have remarked, the instructions which Ptolemy has provided furnish the means of reproducing them, and this task has been accomplished by various scholars from the fifteenth century onwards.

When we proceed to examine Ptolemy's map of the world in detail, we discover that, while he has corrected   **His Correc-** certain mistakes which defaced the maps of his pre-   **tions of Pre-** decessors, he has introduced several serious errors of   **vious Maps.** his own. The great southward extension which Strabo attributed to the promontory of Sunium is now avoided, and Taenarum is rightly treated as the southernmost point of the Peloponnese. The eastern coast of Africa is no longer represented as turning towards the west after passing Cape Guardafui; and, what is still more important, the Caspian, which ever since the time of Alexander the Great had been regarded as an inlet from the ocean, is once more recognised as being, what Herodotus had believed it to be, an inland sea. On the other hand, Ptolemy advances the Palus Maeotis and the mouth of the   **His Chief** Tanais much too far towards the north—as high, in   **Errors.** fact, as the southern shore of the Baltic. In India, he ignores the discoveries which had been embodied in the *Periplus Maris Erythraei*, and places the southernmost point of the peninsula only four degrees south of Barygaza. The size of the island of Taprobane, which had been over-estimated by earlier writers, is exaggerated by him to an enormous degree, so that he makes it about fourteen times as large as the reality. But these mistakes were of slight importance in comparison with those which he introduced in the eastern and south-eastern portion of his map, and for which he was largely indebted to Marinus. The great extension which had come to be attributed to eastern Asia, owing to reports which had reached the West of distant countries in that quarter, induced him to refuse to believe in the existence of a sea which formed the boundary in that direction. Again, when traders extended their voyages beyond India, and intelligence was brought of a great gulf on the further side of the Golden Chersonese—by which perhaps the gulf of Siam may have been meant—and it was further rumoured that the coast of Asia in this part, instead of turning northwards, as had previously been supposed, trended towards the south; on the strength of these intimations Ptolemy adopted the view, not only that the land advanced still further in that direction, but that Asia was connected by an unbroken line of continent with the south-east of Africa. From this assumption it followed that the Indian Ocean was surrounded by land—a view which had long before been advanced as a hypothesis by Hipparchus, but after his time had been generally rejected.

Ptolemy commences his tables with the British Islands, Ivernia and Albion, the native name being used in the latter case instead of that of Britannia apparently for the sake of distinction. In the account which is here given we trace a striking advance in the knowledge of Britain, corresponding to the more intimate acquaintance of the Romans with the island, which was the natural result of the progress of their arms, and of the numerous settlements which they had established there[1]. A marked distinction, however, in respect of accuracy is to be drawn between the geography of the coast and that of the interior. The two were evidently derived from different sources, and those which furnished the materials for the latter were of a decidedly inferior character.

His Account of Britain.

Accurate Delineation of the Coast.

If we construct a map from the latitudes and longitudes furnished by Ptolemy, we find that the outline of Britain which is thus drawn corresponds very

---

[1] Ptol. 2. 3.

MAP X

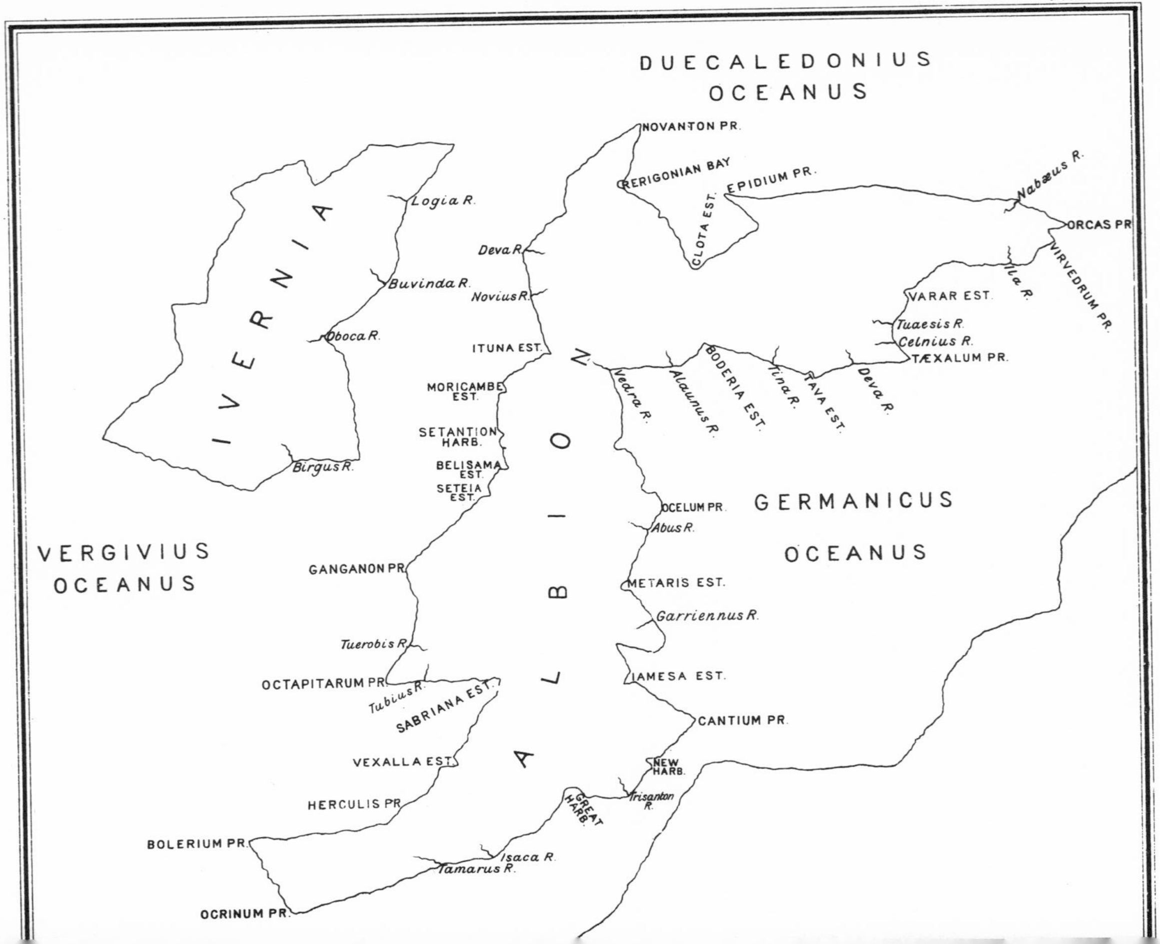

DUECALEDONIUS OCEANUS

DUECALEDONIUS OCEANUS

GERMANICUS OCEANUS

VERGIVIUS OCEANUS

IVERNIA

ALBION

NOVANTON PR.

CERIGONIAN BAY

EPIDIUM PR.

CLOTA EST.

ORCAS PR.

VIRVEDRUM PR.

Nabæus R.

Ila R.

VARAR EST.

Tuaesis R.

Celnius R.

TÆXALUM PR.

Deva R.

TAVA EST.

Tina R.

BODERIA EST.

Alaunus R.

Vedra R.

OCELUM PR.

Abus R.

METARIS EST.

Garrienus R.

IAMESA EST.

CANTIUM PR.

NEW HARB.

Trisanton R.

GREAT HARB.

Tamarus R.

Isaca R.

OCRINUM PR.

BOLERIUM PR.

HERCULIS PR.

VEXALLA EST.

SABRIANA EST.

Tubius R.

OCTAPITARUM PR.

Tuerobis R.

GANGANON PR.

Birgus R.

Oboca R.

Logia R.

Buvinda R.

Novius R.

Deva R.

ITUNA EST.

MORICAMBE EST.

SETANTION HARB.

BELISAMA EST.

SETEIA EST.

closely with the reality. The gradual southward slope of the
southern coast as it proceeds from east to west clearly appears.
The most important inlets—the Bristol Channel, the Solway Firth
and that of Clyde, above all the marked indentation produced by
the Moray Firth—are all strikingly delineated. The same thing
is true of the promontories. The two separate capes at the south-
western angle, the Lizard and the Land's End, St David's Head and
the extremity of Cardiganshire in Wales, and the Mull of Galloway
and that of Cantire on the western side of Scotland, are carefully
distinguished. The general accuracy which is thus apparent
makes it the more surprising that in one important particular,
namely the position of Scotland relatively to England, Erroneous
Ptolemy's map should be extravagantly in error. Position of
                                                  Scotland.
For, whereas the southern part of the island as far
as the line of the Solway Firth is correctly orientated, the northern
portion is twisted round towards the east, so that the mouth of the
Clyde, instead of lying to the westward of the Firth of Forth, is due
north of it, and the farthest extremity of the country, the promontory of Orcas, instead of pointing northward faces due east. On
the same principle the western and eastern coasts of Scotland are
called by Ptolemy in this part of his tables the northern and
southern coasts. It is difficult to account for this extraordinary
mistake. The latest, and at the same time the most Possible
probable explanation of it is that of Mr Henry Explanation of
                                                 this.
Bradley, who would attribute it, not to defective
information, but to an error in the construction of the map.
Either Ptolemy or one of his predecessors, he suggests, had before
him three sectional maps, representing severally the countries
which we call England, Scotland, and Ireland, and drawn approximately to scale, but without meridians or parallels. It was, no
doubt, then, as now, usual for a map to be enclosed in a rectangular
frame, with sides towards the four cardinal points. In fitting the
three maps together, Ptolemy (or his predecessor) fell into the
mistake of turning the oblong map of Scotland the wrong way.
Mr Bradley further points out, in explanation of the origin of this
mistake on Ptolemy's part, that he had assigned to Ireland a
latitude so much too high, that if he had given to the map of

Scotland its proper orientation, a portion of that country must have fallen right across the western island[1].

It may be worth while, in order to illustrate the contents of Ptolemy's work, and to test its accuracy in a par- ticular instance, to follow him in his enumeration of the features of the coast of our island, in order to see how far they correspond with what we find at the present day, omitting those localities about the identification of which much uncertainty exists. In making this comparison we have to depend, in some cases on the similarities of the ancient and modern names, when these are corroborated by the positions which Ptolemy assigns to them, and in others either on certain geographical features being the only ones which can correspond to his data, or on their situation being determined by their occurring in his enumeration between places already known. The majority of the localities which he mentions are the mouths or estuaries of rivers; and the names which he assigns to these are in so many instances traceable in those which are now attached to them, that we discover in them an illustration of the principle embodied in the witty saying that local names, in order to be permanent, should be "writ on water."

Ptolemy's Tables of the Coast of Britain.

Let us take first the southern coast of Britain, commencing from the promontory of Cantion, the north-eastern point of Kent. The first place to the westward of this which Ptolemy mentions is the New Harbour, and this according to his measurements corresponds to Hastings, where a harbour is known to have existed formerly, though there is none at the present day. Again, the Great Harbour can be confidently identified with Portsmouth Harbour, both on historic grounds and because of the longitude which Ptolemy assigns to it. Between these two havens a river Trisanton is introduced, the name of which is the original form of Trent or Tarrant; and

The South- ern Coast.

---

[1] See Mr Henry Bradley's article, "Ptolemy's Geography of the British Isles," in *Archæologia*, vol. 48. (1885), pp. 382, 383. The contents of this valuable paper have been used in what follows, though the author has not been able in every case to accept Mr Bradley's conclusions: the map also which is here inserted is based on that by which his paper is illustrated.

we thus discover that it represents the Arun, for that stream appears in old maps as Tarant[1]. Plymouth Sound is determined by the mouth of the Tamarus (Tamar) being given. The river Isaca, which is placed to the eastward of it, might be, as far as the name is concerned, either the Exe or the Axe, but the former of these is the more likely to have been mentioned on account of its importance, because the town of Isca (Exeter) was situated on its banks. The two south-western promontories have each of them, for some unknown reason, a double name, the Lizard being called on Ptolemy's table Damnonium or Ocrinum, the Land's End Antivestaeum or Bolerium Promontorium.

On the western side of the island, following the coast northward from this angle we first pass the Herculis Promontorium (Hartland Point), and then reach the Vexalla estuary, which corresponds to Bridgewater Harbour; while the main inlet in this neighbourhood takes its name of Sabriana from the Severn. On the southern coast of Wales the mouth of the river Tubius (Towey) is noted, and on the western coast that of the Tuerobis (Teify); between these the promontory of Octapitarum (St. David's Head) intervenes, and further to the north a striking projection is formed by the cape of the Gangani, which is the extreme point of Carnarvonshire. In the interval between the north-west angle of Wales and the Ituna estuary (Solway Firth) we meet with the estuaries of Seteïa (or Segeïa) and Belisama, the harbour of the Setantii (or Segantii), and the Moricambe estuary: the position of these identifies them with the well-marked mouths of the Dee, the Mersey, and the Ribble, and with Morecambe Bay. The name Ituna is undoubtedly that of the Eden, which river flows into the Solway Firth; and the original of the appellation Solway itself can be discovered in that of the neighbouring tribe of the Selgovae. On the northern side of this inlet the river Novius (Nith) and the Deva (the Dee of Kirkcudbright) are also mentioned. From this point onward Ptolemy's great error about the coast of Scotland begins to be apparent, for the peninsula of Galloway, which in reality advances westward opposite the

The Western Coast.

---

[1] Bradley, *op. cit.*, p. 390.

Irish coast, on his map is made to project northwards. He
calls it the promontory of the Novantae—a tribal name which
seems to be connected with that of the Novius; and in its
immediate vicinity he places the Rerigonius Sinus, both the
name and the position of which identify it with Loch Ryan.
Then follow the entrance of the Clota (Clyde), the Lemannonius
Sinus (Loch Fyne), and the marked promontory of Epidium
(Mull of Cantire), which also is represented as extending into
the northern sea. The coast beyond this point was evidently
little known, for very few places are marked, but in the far
north we can recognise the river Nabaeus both by its name
and its position as the Naver in Sutherlandshire. Cape Orcas,
to which Ptolemy attaches a second name, Tarvedum, had been
regarded from the time of Pytheas as the extremity of Britain in
this direction, and therefore must be identified with Dunnet
Head. From this it follows that the Vervedrum Promontorium
on the further side of it must correspond to Duncansby Head.

The eastern (from Ptolemy's point of view the southern) coast
of Scotland gives evidence of being better known.
The river Ila is the Ullie in the east of Sutherlandshire. The Varar estuary is the Moray Firth, and
its name is identical with that of the Farrar river, which finds its
way into the Beauly Basin and Inverness Firth at the head of
that inlet. Between this and the headland of Taexalum, the
north-eastern angle of Aberdeenshire, the river Tuaesis is the
Spey, and the Celnius, which lies beyond it, appears from its
name to be the stream which runs by the town of Cullen. On
the further side of Taexalum we find the Deva (the Dee at
Aberdeen), the estuary of Tava (Firth of Tay), and that of
Boderia (Firth of Forth), the Bodotria of Tacitus. The river
Tina, which is placed between Tava and Boderia, can only be
the Eden, which enters the sea between the two firths. As we
advance southward along the English coast we recognise the
Alaunus as the Alne, the Vedra as the Wear, and the Abus
as the Humber; and since the promontory of Ocelum occurs
between the two last-named of these, it is probably Flamborough
Head. Then follow the Metaris estuary (the Wash), and the
river Garriennus, the name of which corresponds to that of the

The Eastern
Coast.

Yare at Yarmouth; and finally our survey ends at the mouth of the Thames, which in the text of Ptolemy (probably through an error in writing) is called Iamesa.

In Ptolemy's notice of Ireland in like manner the number of the places that are mentioned gives evidence of an increased knowledge of that island on the part **Ireland.** of the Romans during the period subsequent to the Augustan age[1]; and this confirms the statement of Tacitus in the *Agricola*, to the effect that its trade and communication with the sister island had increased in that interval[2]. There are but few of the names which he gives, however, that we can identify with any certainty, and these are mainly river-names on the eastern coast. The Logia of Ptolemy is probably the Lagan at Belfast, the Buvinda is the Boyne, the Oboca is the Avoca in Wicklow; and the Birgus corresponds both in position and name to the Barrow, which flows into Waterford Harbour. But Ptolemy's knowledge of the position of Ireland relatively to England is a great advance on that of Strabo and others, who placed it to the northward of the latter island.

We may now proceed to notice the principal additions which Ptolemy made to the map of the world in other countries. In eastern Europe he mentions for **Other Additions to Geographical Knowledge.** the first time by name the Carpathians (Mons Carpatis), with the existence of which the Romans had become acquainted through Trajan's conquest of Dacia; and he rightly fixes them as the boundary between that country and Sarmatia[3]. The great river Volga also, the absence of all notice of which in the works of **The Volga (Rha).** former geographers is so remarkable, here appears under the name of Rha, and is described as discharging its waters into the Hyrcanian or Caspian Sea[4]. In his account of Asia we meet with the earliest notice of the great Altai chain, which, commencing from the central group **The Altai Chain (Imaus).** of the Pamirs, diverges from the Himalaya, and

---

[1] Ptol. 2. 2.

[2] Tac. *Agric.* 24; melius aditus portusque per commercia et negotiatores cogniti.

[3] Ptol. 3. 5. 6.   [4] 5. 9. 12, 13.

follows a north-easterly direction through Central Asia. To
it Ptolemy appropriates the name of Imaus, which had hitherto
been assigned to a portion of the Himalaya; and it is from
this that the distinction is derived, which is commonly introduced in maps of the ancient world, between Scythia intra
Imaum and Scythia extra Imaum[1]. He furnishes information,

Direct Trade
Route to
China.

too, with regard to the trade-route which traversed
the interior of Asia from the passage of the Euphrates to Sera in Northern China. The distances
along this, he says on the authority of Marinus, had been computed by a merchant of Macedonian extraction, called Maës,
though not from his own observations, but from information
which he obtained from his travelling agents[2].

In the account of Africa which follows, it is highly interesting,

Sources of
the Nile.

in the light of recent discoveries, to read of the
sources of the main stream of the Nile as being
found in two lakes which lay to the southward of
the equator[3]; and that these lakes were fed by the snows of a

Mountains of
the Moon.

mountain range which lay beyond them, called the
Mountains of the Moon—a name which was
destined to be a source of perplexity to travellers
and geographers down to our own times[4]. The intelligence
which is contained in these statements was probably transmitted, not by way of the Nile valley, which was not followed
by traders beyond the marshy region which has been already
noticed, but from the coast in the neighbourhood of Zanzibar,
where the station of Rhapta had been established. On this
supposition it is not improbable that the lakes here spoken of
are the Victoria and Albert Nyanza, and the mention of so
unusual a phenomenon as snow-covered mountains in the
neighbourhood of the equator supports the conjecture that the
Mountains of the Moon are none other than Mounts Kilimanjaro
(19,700 ft.) and Kenia (18,370 ft.), which lie between those

The Soudan.

lakes and the sea. With regard to the central districts of Africa also Ptolemy furnishes us with fresh
information, for he notices—though with a somewhat tantalising

[1] 6. 14, 15.   [2] 1. 11. 4—7.
[3] 4. 7. 23, 24.   [4] 4. 8. 3.

brevity which gives no clue to the dates—two expeditions in that direction which were reported by Marinus. The starting-point of these was the land of the Garamantes (Fezzan), which had been already reached by Cornelius Balbus in the reign of Augustus[1]. Of the first of them we only learn that the name of its commander was Septimius Flaccus, and that the explorers arrived at the country of the Aethiopians after a march of three months towards the south. The account of the other expedition is somewhat more explicit, for it tells us that its leader, Julius Maternus, associated himself with the king of the Garamantes in an invasion of Aethiopia, and in his company, after four months marching southward, arrived at a district abounding in rhinoceroses, called Agisymba[2]. These scanty details do not enable us to determine the exact position to be assigned to that region, but it appears clear that they crossed the Sahara, and reached some part of the Soudan. A more perplexing question presents itself when we endeavour to decide what rivers are intended by the Gir and Nigir, which Ptolemy introduces into his tables of western Africa. We have seen that the former of these two names is a general term signifying 'stream' in the native languages of this part[3], and the same thing is true of the latter also[4]. It could consequently be applied to many rivers, and this circumstance requires to be taken into consideration in any attempt to identify the Nigir with the famous river of Timbuctoo, as well as the fact that at the present day the native name of the river which we call the Niger is Joliba in the upper part of its course, and Quorra in the lower. It is difficult, indeed, to identify the two rivers—which Ptolemy describes as large in size, and as flowing into lakes in the interior of the country—with any known African rivers; but from what he says of them it seems more likely that they represent streams north than south of the Sahara[5].

Rivers Gir and Nigir.

From Ptolemy we turn to one of his contemporaries, Pausanias, who was in all respects a great contrast to him, and was indeed an antiquarian rather than a geographer;

Pausanias.

---

[1] *v. supra*, p. 223.   [2] Ptol. 1. 8. 5.   [3] *v. supra*, p. 291.
[4] Kiepert, *Lehrbuch d. a. Geographie*, p. 224.
[5] Ptol. 4. 6. 13, 14; cp. Bunbury, *op. cit.*, vol. 2. pp. 618—28.

yet his book, which he calls an *Itinerary of Greece*, demands more than a passing notice, inasmuch as it stands alone in antiquity as a topographical description of a country. It is true that his topography is mainly confined to cities and sacred places, and the principal objects on the routes which connected them with one another; and that features of the country, such as mountains and rivers, obtain recognition only so far as they have legends or memories of historical occurrences attached to them : but in a country like Greece, which was thickly sown with towns, the data which are thus provided are of inestimable value for purposes of map-making.

The period at which Pausanias wrote was eminently suitable for the work which he undertook, for at no time in all probability had the monuments of Greece been so numerous and in such good preservation as they were in the middle of the second century of our era. Here and there, indeed, he speaks of temples as being in a ruinous condition, but the decay which this implies was probably not greater than that which appears in the deserted monasteries in our own country at the present day; and this was counterbalanced by the work of restoration, which had been carried out on a large scale through the munificence of the emperor Hadrian in the early part of that century. In Pausanias himself we may trace a resemblance, faint indeed in colour and inferior in all its features, to Herodotus. In the religious, or rather superstitious awe with which he regards questions and objects connected with the worship of the gods, he even surpasses his great predecessor. In like manner as Herodotus moralises on the nemesis which attends on overweening prosperity, Pausanias draws attention to the transitoriness of human greatness as illustrated by the decadence of a large number of the great cities of the world—a topic which he introduces in connection with the desolate condition of Megalopolis in Arcadia in his time, in contrast with the proud hopes with which it was originally founded by Epaminondas[1]. The mysteries and the oracles inspire him with unbounded reverence. He is gifted also with something of the same quaint power of observation

His Resemblance to Herodotus.

[1] Pausan. 8. 33.

as the historian, and by this he is similarly led into digressions, which frequently contain information on points which lie beyond the range of his immediate subject. His accuracy has generally been acknowledged by those who have followed in his footsteps. When ancient sites are cleared by the spade of the excavator from the soil which has accumulated in the course of ages, the buildings whose foundations are thus revealed are found to correspond with remarkable closeness to Pausanias' descriptions. In wandering about amongst them with his work as your handbook, "you feel that you are following an invisible guide—a ghost among ghosts[1]."

Though Pausanias, as has been said above, had no interest in geography for its own sake, yet owing to his love of curious objects, especially when they were in any way connected with mythological associations, he was led to dwell on numerous phenomena, which illustrate at least the physical branch of that subject. This was the case in a marked manner with springs of water, which are in all countries a fertile source of legends. Thus in one passage he notices the different colours which these display in various places. One of them, he says, in the neighbourhood of Joppa in Palestine had a blood-red hue; another, in the district of Atarneus opposite Lesbos, flowed with black water; while a third, in the neighbourhood of Rome on the further side of the Anio, was white. The last-named source was no doubt the Aquae Albulae near Tibur, which from its milk-white sulphureous water is known as La Solfatara at the present day; and its low temperature, on which Pausanias remarks, is still a characteristic feature, notwithstanding that vapours arise from its surface. Above all, he draws attention to the 'grey-green' water of Thermopylae (γλαυκότατον ὕδωρ)—an epithet, the truth of which may be verified at the present day, since the water of these sources, which is very clear, has that colour owing to the sediment with which the bed of the channels in which it runs is incrusted[2]. Elsewhere he draws attention to the warm springs

His Illustrations of Physical Geography.

Fountains.

Their Different Colours.

---

[1] Dean Stanley, in Sir T. Wyse's *Impressions of Greece*, p. 316.
[2] Pausan. 4. 35. 9, 10.

which are found in Greece, such as the so-called Bath of Helen
near Cenchreae on the Isthmus of Corinth[1], and
that on the peninsula of Methana in Argolis. Of
the latter of these he says,—"The inhabitants
relate that it was when Antigonus son of Demetrius was King of
Macedon that the water first appeared; but it was not in the
first instance water that gushed forth, but a mass of fire burst
out of the earth, and after this ceased to burn the water rushed
out, which even down to my time continues to flow, hot and
excessively salt[2]." Another source in the west of Arcadia he
speaks of as having jets of flame in its neighbourhood[3]. Still
more interesting is his mention of the fountain of
Deine, which appeared in the sea on the Argolic
coast near Thyrea, and which may still be seen
about a thousand feet from the shore, rising in the midst of the
salt water with a column of such volume as to force itself above
the sea-level, and throw off concentric eddies all round[4]. The
water which supplied this fountain he believed to be derived
from the drainage of the Argon Pedion near Mantineia, which
passed beneath the intervening range of Mount Artemisium by
an underground channel; and at the present day it is thought to
proceed from that neighbourhood, though rather from the plain
of Tegea than from that of Mantineia.

Warm
Springs.

Fountain of
Deine.

To notice a few other natural features to which Pausanias
draws attention—he describes the grotto at Taenarum, and remarks that there were no signs of
subterraneous descent in it, such as the legends of the poets
implied[5]: as to another point, however, his account is less
accurate than that of Strabo, for he identifies the temple of
Poseidon there with the grotto, whereas the earlier writer, as
Leake has shewn, was right in regarding them as separate
places, though near to one another[6]. Of the
Corycian cave, in the upland region of Mount Parnassus above Delphi, he speaks with much greater

Caverns.

The
Corycian Cave.

[1] Pausan. 2. 2. 3.   [2] 2. 34. 1.   [3] 8. 29. 1.
[4] 8. 7. 1, 2; cp. Leake, *Travels in the Morea*, vol. 2. p. 480; E. Curtius,
Peloponnesos, vol. 2, p. 373.   [5] Pausan. 3. 25. 4, 5.
[6] Strabo, 8. 5. 1; Leake, *Travels in the Morea*, vol. I. pp. 296—300.

enthusiasm, for he regards it as the most remarkable cavern he had ever seen, on account of its size and height, of the amount of light which penetrates into it, rendering unnecessary the use of torches, and of the stalagmites which are formed on the floor by the dripping from the roof—all which details correspond to its present appearance. From describing this spot he proceeds, with his usual fondness for digression, to notice three other caves with which he was acquainted in the west of Asia Minor— one called Steunos in Phrygia, which was consecrated to Cybele, another by the town of Themisonium in the neighbourhood of Laodiceia, in which the inhabitants took refuge at the time of the invasion of the country by the Gauls, and a third near Magnesia ad Maeandrum, which was famous for a wonder-working statue of Apollo of great antiquity[1]. Pausanias also displays great interest in trees. Thus he notices the immense height reached by the cypresses at   Trees. Psophis in Arcadia[2], and the girth of the plane trees near Pharae in Achaia, within the hollow trunks of which banquets used to be held[3]; and he also mentions those which he believed to be the most ancient trees existing in the Greek sanctuaries; the four most conspicuous in that respect being the agnus castus which grew in the temple of Hera at Samos, the sacred oak at Dodona, and the olive trees in the Athenian Acropolis and at Delos[4]. The same taste leads him occasionally to remark on the vegetation of certain districts, as, for instance, where he describes the vast extent of oak-forest which lay between Mantineia and Tegea, and was called Pelagus, apparently from the aspect of the sea-like expanse of waving trees[5]. He mentions also that cotton, an extremely rare product in ancient times, was grown in Elis in his day. He   Cotton. calls it 'byssus,' but clearly distinguishes it from both flax and hemp, and adds that it was not found elsewhere in Greece[6].

But, notwithstanding that Pausanias has contributed in these and other ways to the enlargement of our geographical

---

[1] Pausan. 10. 32. 2—7.   [2] 8. 24. 7.   [3] 7. 22. 1.
[4] 8. 23. 5.   [5] 8. 11. 1.
[6] 5. 5. 2; cp. 6. 26. 6, and E. Curtius, *Peloponnesos*, vol. 1, p. 438; vol. 2, p. 10.

knowledge, the objects which chiefly attracted his attention

Pausanias' Researches in Greece.
were the cities with their public buildings, and the temples and other holy places which were found at short intervals from one another throughout the whole country. With the view of investigating these he travelled far and wide in Greece, collecting information everywhere on the spot, and carefully noting down his own observations. As

His Descriptions of Olympia and Delphi.
might be expected, he devoted himself with especial enthusiasm to the examination of the great centres of antiquarian and mythological interest, such as Olympia and Delphi; and the excavation of these two sites in our own day, which in the one case has been already accomplished, and in the other is now in progress, has afforded ample opportunities of testing the accuracy of his enquiries. With regard to this point it is not too much to say that the descriptions which he drew up for the information of his contemporaries have proved a satisfactory guide to modern explorers. At Olympia, to which place alone Pausanias devotes forty chapters of his work, the correspondences are hardly less than marvellous. To exemplify this by a single instance—at the north-eastern angle of the Altis, or sacred enclosure, the foundations of the Treasuries, which he describes, are still remaining, and in front of them the bases of the Zanes, or statues of Zeus, the expense of erecting which was defrayed by the fines levied upon athletes who had transgressed the laws of the Olympic contests; and, in addition to this, between the extremity of the line which these formed and the Hall of Echo, exactly where he places it, a vaulted passage of some length has been found, which was the private entrance to the Stadium. And not only has his account of the position of the various buildings and of their architectural and ornamental details been verified, but the dedications on the bases of some of the statues are found to be almost in the same words which Pausanias has used in speaking of them. In like manner, at Delphi the Treasuries of the Athenians, the Sicyonians, and the Siphnians, which have been discovered at the sides of the Sacred Way that ascended in zigzags the steep slope by which the temple was approached from below, are all mentioned by our author.

A careful study of Pausanias' *Itinerary* enables us to trace
with some confidence the routes which he followed   Routes
in the course of his various tours through Greece.   which he
                                                       followed.
For the Peloponnese these were three in number—
one in the east and south of that region, from Megara by Corinth,
Argos, the Argolic Acte, Sparta, the Taenarian peninsula and
Messene, to the frontier of Messenia and Arcadia; a second from
the frontier of Arcadia and Elis by Olympia, Achaia, and Sicyon
to Corinth; and finally a circular tour through Arcadia. In
northern Greece he seems to have made four journeys, but here
the question of the routes which he took is more complicated[1].
In his description of districts he generally, though not universally,
observed the principle of beginning with the central city, and
then describing the roads that radiate from it. This is especially
noticeable in the case of Mantineia and Megalopolis, from the
former of which towns four, from the latter five, divergent routes
are traced[2]. In numerous instances also it is possible to assign
the reason why the traveller preferred one of two routes in
passing from one place to another, by pointing out the objects
of special interest which attracted him in this or that direction.
For instance, in journeying from Sicyon to Phlius he does not
appear to have followed the direct road, for he does not describe
it, whereas he does carefully describe the more circuitous one by
way of Titane; and his reason for preferring this is easily dis-
coverable in the interest which he shews in the rites observed in
the temple of Asclepius in the last-named town[3]. It was from the
journals which Pausanias kept on these tours that
his work was ultimately compiled. The notes   Contents of
                                                 his Book.
which were thus accumulated were then amplified,
and were combined with historical and mythological notices,
which were largely drawn from the treatises of earlier writers.
The *Itinerary of Greece* is divided into ten books, the first of
which is devoted to Attica and Megaris, and the seven following
to the various provinces of the Peloponnese, two of them being

---

[1] See Heberdey, *Die Reisen des Pausanias in Griechenland*, p. 112.

[2] *Ibid.* pp. 40, 81—3, 89—90.

[3] *Ibid.*, p. 41.

assigned to Elis on account of the importance of Olympia, while the ninth and tenth treat of Boeotia and Phocis.

An interesting controversy has prevailed of late years with regard to the trustworthiness of Pausanias as an authority. The traditional view of him as a pains-taking archaeologist, conscientious in his investi-gations, and somewhat witless in his simplicity, was so firmly established, that it was startling to find that the contrary opinion could be maintained, and that the very traits which had produced an impression in his favour could be adduced as testimony against him. At the same time it could not be denied that there were certain features, both in his character as an author, and in his mode of dealing with his subject, which might reasonably excite suspicion. For *naïveté* and religious scrupulousness are certainly unusual traits in a writer of the second century after Christ ; and when we find that he uses such expressions as 'they say,' and even 'I heard,' when quoting statements which are clearly borrowed from earlier writers, we are led to enquire whether his veracity is unimpeachable. On the strength of these and similar points it is maintained that the peculiar personality which is everywhere present to the student of Pausanias' work is merely a mask assumed for purposes of deception, and that its peculiar features are devices of art, intended to throw dust in the reader's eyes. His statements, also, that he had seen certain places and objects with his own eyes, and his mention of local *cicerones* who had furnished him with information on the spot, are to be regarded as mere pretences. Great stress is also laid on the extent of his indebtedness to other works—an obligation which within certain limits is admitted on all hands, though it should be added that this is found much more in the historical and mytho-logical, than in the geographical and descriptive sections of his book. In accordance with this view Pausanias is to be regarded, not as a traveller or an independent investigator, but as a mere compiler, who utilised local handbooks for his purposes, and in default of these borrowed his notices of places from writers, some of whom lived several centuries before his time, so that he even described cities, which at the time when he wrote were for the

The Question of his Veracity.

The View Adverse to Pausanias.

most part ruined or deserted, as if they were still flourishing. As he informs us that his place of residence was somewhere in Lydia[1], he is supposed hardly to have left that country; or, if he travelled in Greece at all, it was only over a small portion of it and in a superficial manner, so that he was able by that means to insert in his book recollections of his tours, with the object of giving it a modern colouring.

A little concession has turned the edge of some of the most formidable of these objections. The suspicious character of the ambiguous terms which Pausanias uses in quoting from other treatises is admitted, but they are shown to have been commonly employed by other ancient writers whose veracity is unquestioned; and he is proved to have introduced them *bona fide* and not with the view of disguising the origin of the statements, by the examination of a number of passages, where these expressions are used undisguisedly with reference to earlier compilations. It is also allowed that the name which he sometimes applies to *cicerones* (ἐξηγηταί) is on other occasions, and perhaps more frequently, intended to signify local handbooks, or, as we say, 'guides.' Nor is it doubted that he studied both these and all the other available books which related to the places which he visited, nor that he made extracts from these when it suited his purposes—an admission which explains the existence of numerous coincidences between his statements and those of other writers, but in no way justifies the charge of wholesale plagiarism. The question whether his descriptions of cities are anachronistic, and therefore could not have been derived from personal observation, in many cases cannot be determined from want of data, but in some instances these places are proved by the testimony of coins to have been still in existence in his age. With regard to the whole question it is well to bear in mind the improbabilities that are involved in this attempt to discredit Pausanias. In the first place it is no easy task for a writer to assume the mask so completely, as to leave the impression (which he does) that there is nothing counterfeit either in his enquiries or his religion. And, secondly, it is not likely that Pausanias would have exposed

Explanations of his Statements.

Difficulties involved in the Supposition.

Pausan. 5. 13. 7.

himself to the ridicule of his contemporaries by taking his materials wholesale from writers who were familiar at that period, or
by describing a well-known city like Athens as it existed some
centuries before—and nothing less than this is implied. Moreover, it is the reverse of an easy task to make descriptions
obtained at second hand from other writers pass muster as if they
were derived from personal observation. The mere difficulty of
determining the relative position of buildings and other objects
within a certain area without ocular inspection is so great, that it
seems impossible that a writer should have grouped them so accurately in his narrative as to have furnished again and again the
clue to their identification by modern explorers; and this is what
Pausanias has done. Good service has also been rendered in his
defence by an enumeration of the passages in the *Itinerary* which
imply autopsy on his part. By this it is shewn that there are
fifty-five instances, in which the words used, if they are not un-
qualified falsehoods, are direct statements of personal observation;
and the same thing is indirectly implied in a hundred and eleven
others, in many of which it is further confirmed by other expressions which occur in the same context. In some cases we even
find that Pausanias corrects the statements of an earlier authority

Recent Testi-
monies in his
Favour.
from his own inspection. Certain it is, that the confidence of modern archaeologists in the trustworthiness of this writer has not been lessened by these
discussions. Thus Miss Harrison, in the Preface to her "Mythology and Monuments of Ancient Athens" (p. vii.), says with
special reference to this subject, 'I feel bound to record my con-
viction that the narrative of Pausanias is no "Reise Romantik,"
but the careful, conscientious, and in some parts amusing and
quite original narrative of a *bona fide* traveller.' Prof. Gardner, in
his "New Chapters of Greek History" (p. 80), remarks, 'No part
of Pausanias' work bears more satisfactory evidence of autopsy than
does the book which treats of Mycenae.' And Mr G. C. Richards,
one of the British excavators of Megalopolis, assures us that the
result of the discoveries at that place is 'to establish the substantial
accuracy of that author in one more instance.'[1]

[1] *Excavations at Megalopolis*, p. 105: Supplementary Paper, No. 1, of the
Hellenic Society. The leading works that have been written on the subject

XVI.]   STEPHANUS BYZANTINUS.   363

The most serviceable treatise on geography which was produced after the time of Pausanias was the *Ethnica*
of Stephanus of Byzantium. This author, about   **Stephanus**
                                            Byzantinus.
whose period very little is known, is believed by his
editor, Westermann, who is the chief authority on the subject, to
have lived at Constantinople during the beginning and middle of
the sixth century, in the reign of Justinian I.[1] His
work was a geographical lexicon, containing the   **His *Ethnica*.**
names of countries and places that were known in antiquity, arranged in alphabetical order, to which a variety of information
relating to their topography, history, mythology and etymology
was appended. Unfortunately, the greater part of it survives only
in an epitome, which was made at a somewhat later period by a
grammarian called Hermolaus; and even this, if we may judge
by the extremely meagre character of the articles in certain parts
of the treatise, would seem to have been still further abbreviated
by subsequent copyists[2]. Its principal usefulness at the present
day arises from its supplementing the knowledge which we obtain
from other sources, for the number of places which are named in
it is very great—under the head of Alexandria alone eighteen
cities of that name are introduced, under Heracleia twenty-three,
and under Apollonia twenty-five—and the less important towns
and tribes are not neglected. Two fragments of the original work
of Stephanus, relating to Spain and Sicily, are preserved in the
De Administrando Imperio and the *De Thematibus* of the Emperor
Constantine Porphyrogenitus; the later articles under the letter Δ
also exist in a separate manuscript; and the conclusion of the
treatise, from X to Ω, to judge from the greater fulness of treatment which is found in that part, seems to be in the condition
in which the author left it. From these portions we learn how
much we have lost in not possessing the complete work, for
in them we find that the compiler's statements are usually verified
by quotations from ancient authors, amongst whom the name of

---

of Pausanias' trustworthiness are—for the attack, Kalkmann, *Pausanias der
Perieget*, Berlin, 1886; for the defence, Gurlitt, *Ueber Pausanias*, Graz, 1890;
Heberdey, *Die Reisen des Pausanias in Griechenland*, Vienna, 1894.

[1] Stephani *Ethnica*, ed. Westermann, p. vi.

[2] *Ibid.* p. xxiv.

Strabo is of frequent occurrence. The primary object of the writer was, no doubt, grammatical, for he makes a point in every case of giving the gentile names derived from those of the towns and countries, and often descants on these at disproportionate length; but he also records mythological traditions and historical events with which we should otherwise be unacquainted. Occasionally, too, his etymological remarks are not without value for the study of geography, owing to the light which they throw on the significance of place names. Thus under the heads of Agnûs, the Attic deme, and Schoenûs, a place in Arcadia, we find him noticing how frequently this termination was used in the nomenclature of places in Greece, to signify the abundance of certain trees and plants in their neighbourhood. Besides Agnûs, which is derived from the agnus castus, he mentions five other demes of Attica which have this peculiarity—Acherdûs from the wild pear-tree, Phegûs from the esculent oak, Myrrhinûs from the myrtle, Rhamnûs from the thorn, and Marathûs from the fennel. In like manner, in addition to Schoenûs, which is called from the rush, he names Pityûs, which is derived from the pine, Daphnûs from the bay, Ericûs from the heather, Scillûs from the squill, and Selinûs from parsley. The method of comparison which these observations imply seems like an anticipation of modern forms of enquiry.

Character of its Contents.

Two writers of this later period remain to be noticed, Solinus and Orosius, though their importance is due, not to any additions which they made to geographical knowledge, but to the influence which they exercised during the middle ages. Their works, rather than those of the famous authors of antiquity, were the source of the classical geography of the men of letters and the map-makers of that period. The earlier of these, C. Julius Solinus, who probably lived in the third century of our era, composed a book entitled *Collectanea Rerum Memorabilium*, which was intended to be a survey of the different countries of the world, with notices of the most interesting objects in them and of the peculiarities of their inhabitants. How great its influence was, is shewn by the use which was made of it by writers like Augustine

Solinus.

His Memorabilia.

and Priscian, and especially by Isidore of Seville, the fame of
whose profound learning, existing as it did in the midst of the
darkness of the seventh century, caused his *Origines* to be widely
read by those who came after him[1]. To these we may add, as a
specimen of those authors who availed themselves of Solinus'
writings at a much later date, the literary adviser   Mediaeval
of Dante's youth, Brunetto Latini, whose encyclo-   Estimate of
paedic work, *Il Tesoro*, however we may estimate it   him.
at the present day, was highly valued by his contemporaries.
Not only does Brunetto derive many of his facts of natural history
from Solinus, but his geography also is largely drawn from him.
Thus, to take one or two instances, the account which we find in
the *Tesoro* of the practice of 'dumb commerce' in China, the
mention of Canopus as a conspicuous star in the island of Taprobane, the story of the Tigris passing through the Lake of Van, and
the description of the burning mountain in south Africa, which
was originally derived from Hanno's narrative already mentioned,
are all directly borrowed from the *Memorabilia*[2].

After thus noticing the high position as an authority which
this writer once occupied, it is curious to observe
the low estate to which he has fallen in our own   Modern
day. Mommsen, in his excellent edition of Solinus,   Estimate.
in order to shew the sources from which his information is derived,
has noted throughout in the margin the name of the author from
whom each several statement is borrowed: and by this means
what already was generally believed has been proved in detail,
namely that the whole work is a mere compilation. By far the
greater part of it—including all the passages which we have noticed
as being reproduced by Brunetto Latini—is taken from Pliny; a
certain amount also from Mela, and from sources which we cannot
now identify. The editor severely adds:—'the statements which
Solinus introduced on his own account are altogether valueless,
and we may be thankful that they are so few[3].' It may be

[1] Compare the tables in Mommsen's ed. of Solinus, pp. 255 foll.
[2] Dumb commerce, Brun. Lat. *Tesoro*, ed. Gaiter, vol. 2, p. 22, Sol.
Memorabilia, 50. 4; Canopus, B. L. p. 26, Sol. 53. 7; Tigris, B. L. p. 18,
Sol. 37. 5 foll.; burning mountain, B. L. p. 50, Sol. 30. 14.
[3] Pref. p. xi.

mentioned, however, in his favour, that he is the only ancient writer who notices the Isle of Thanet (*Tanatus Insula*). This he describes as receiving the breezes of the Gallic strait (Straits of Dover), and as being separated from the mainland of Britain only by a narrow inlet : it rejoices in corn-land and a fruitful soil, and moreover dispenses its benefits beyond its own borders, for not only does it harbour no snakes itself, but the earth that is exported from it kills the snakes in any country to which it is taken[1].

Paulus Orosius, who was a native of Tarragona in Spain, and lived in the early part of the fifth century, was the author of a work entitled *Historiae adversus Paga-nos*. This, as he tells us in his Preface, was under-

Orosius.

His *Historiae*.

taken at the suggestion of St. Augustine, in order to answer the complaint of the heathen of that age, that the calamities which had then fallen on the empire were due to the neglect of the ancient divinities arising from the spread of Christianity, by shewing that similar disasters had befallen mankind from the earliest period. In reality it is an epitome of the annals of the world down to the writer's own time, and in this character it became the chief mediaeval authority for the facts and dates of ancient history. It is frequently quoted by Bede, and was translated into Anglo-Saxon by Alfred the Great. In Dante's prose works Orosius is several times referred to by name, and in other places he can be recognised as his authority, though unacknowledged. By way of an introduction to this historical sketch, an

Its Geographical Section.

outline of universal geography is prefixed to it, which is principally taken up with describing the boundaries of countries. It has numerous errors, and the relative positions of the various lands are strangely distorted; but, notwithstanding this, its popularity at a later period was not less than that attained by the historical portion of the work. The influence of this geographical section is frequently traceable in the *Divina Commedia*, and in the *De Monarchia* Dante refers to it in support of the statement that Mount Atlas and the Fortunatae Insulae are the western limits of Africa[2].

[1] *Memorabilia*, 22. 8.
[2] Dante, *De Monarch.* 2. 3 ; Oros. *Hist.*, 1. 2. 11.

The impression which a study of these later writers on
geography leaves most strongly imprinted on our
minds, is that of the transitoriness of the influence
of Ptolemy's geographical work in antiquity—or
rather, perhaps, of the slight extent to which it at
any time affected the ordinary Roman mind.　The same thing
may be said of the greater part of the knowledge of distant
countries that was acquired after the Augustan age.　Most of
the old errors now reappear, and the concep-
tion of the map of the world is much rather that
of Strabo than that of Ptolemy.　The habitable
globe is once more confined to the northern hemisphere.　The
southward extension of Africa is ignored, and the Nile is supposed
to cross that continent from west to east in a line parallel to the
Southern Ocean.　Egypt is regarded as forming part of Asia, and
Africa commences on the western side of that country.　The
Ganges flows into the Eastern Ocean, and the Caspian, the true
character of which as an inland piece of water Ptolemy had re-
asserted after centuries of misconception, is once more treated as
an inlet from the sea.　These and numerous other errors were
perpetuated by subsequent writers, and, with the addition of other
fictitious features derived from ecclesiastical sources, became
embedded in mediaeval cartography.　It should be remembered,
as a partial explanation of this, that Ptolemy's *Geography* was not
translated into Latin until the year 1405 A.D., and consequently,
in proportion as the knowledge of the Greek language died out in
the West, the chances of its contents being known in that part of
the world steadily diminished.　The Arabian geographers, indeed, became acquainted with it, and through them certain of its
principles were imparted to European scholars; but the effect
thus produced was very limited in its range.　With the revival of
letters, however, a new era dawned for Ptolemy's reputation, and
a nearer acquaintance with his work, which was then rendered
accessible to readers, not only established his authority, but
caused even an exaggerated importance to be attributed to his
statements.

In the course of the survey of Ancient Geography which we

Marginal notes:

Transient
Character of
Ptolemy's
Influence.

Earlier Errors
revived.

have now concluded, we have traced the development of the science from its earliest beginnings, when it was confined to a small portion of the east of the Mediterranean, until the time when it embraced the whole of the habitable world that was known to the ancients.

Retrospect and Summary.

We have seen that the Phoenicians were the first civilised people who acquired information on this subject, but that the selfishness of their commercial policy prevented them from imparting to others the knowledge which they possessed themselves; in consequence of which the accumulation of facts bearing on geography, and the practice of recording them in such a way as to render them useful to contemporaries and instructive to future generations, was reserved for the Greeks—a people who, both by the versatility of their intellect and the communicativeness of their temperament, were especially qualified to undertake such a task. The first intimations of an acquaintance on the

Continuous Advance of Knowledge of General Geography,

part of that race with distant lands and peoples have been traced in the incidental mention in the Homeric poems of strange sights which were characteristic of other latitudes, and of objects of commerce which must have been derived from far countries. After this, when the great outburst of colonising enterprise took place which prevailed during the eighth and seventh centuries before Christ, the shores of the Aegean, the Propontis and the Euxine towards the east, those of Sicily, Italy, and to some extent of Gaul and Spain, to the west, and even Egypt and the neighbouring parts of Libya, were revealed to them. Then followed the wars with Persia; and the interest which these excited in that great kingdom and in the races of which it was composed stimulated enquiry into the continent of Asia. The information which was obtained from the two sources just named was embodied in the work of Herodotus, and was verified and enlarged by the personal investigations of that writer. Subsequently to this the knowledge of special districts was increased by the expedition of Hanno the Carthaginian along the west coast of Africa, and by the retreat of the Ten Thousand under Xenophon from Mesopotamia to the Black Sea over the highlands of Armenia. But the period that witnessed the most marked advance in geographical knowledge was the latter half of the fourth century before our era. It was at that time that Alexander carried his victorious arms as far eastward as Bactria and India, and explored the shores of the Indian Ocean; while in the opposite direction Pytheas was investigating the western coasts of Europe and the wonders of the northern sea. The task of enlarging the field of knowledge now passed into the hands of the Romans, and we have seen how the campaigns of Lucullus and Pompey in Armenia and Iberia, the progressive subjugation of Spain, Gaul, and Britain, and finally the expeditions that were undertaken against Germany and other countries to the northward of the Alps, revealed to view large areas, about which before that time only vague rumours had prevailed. The facts that were thus brought to light were diligently harvested by learned men amongst the Greeks. The Augustan age formed the culminating point of these discoveries, and it was during that period that the sum of the information which had thus been acquired was once for all brought together, and diligently sifted and arranged, in the comprehensive work of Strabo.

We have also traced side by side with the growth of this part of the subject the gradual development of scientific enquiry about the earth and its component elements. In the domain of physical *and of Scientific Geography.* geography it has been seen how the early observation of earthquake movements and volcanic phenomena by the Greeks led up to the speculations of Aristotle on the causes which produced them, and afterwards to the examination and comparison of them by travellers like Posidonius; and how the tides of the ocean were made known to the dwellers about the Mediterranean, and the causes of their recurrence were explained, by Pytheas and other voyagers. In mathematical geography the process of development has been even more apparent. There we have noticed the early introduction of the gnomon as an instrument of measurement, and the primitive attempts at map-making and the division of the world into continents. At the same time the Homeric conception of the earth as a circular plane, which was still maintained by the Ionian school of philosophers, and was not wholly exploded in Herodotus' time, gave way before the belief in its sphericity, the arguments for which were formally stated by Aristotle. Further advances were made at a later period by means of the measurement of the circumference of the earth, and the computation of the size of the habitable world, by Eratosthenes; and the commencement of a system of parallels and meridians was made by that man of science and Hipparchus. It was reserved for Ptolemy after the lapse of several centuries to complete this, and at the same time the new and scientific system of projection which he invented laid the foundation on which a great part of modern cartography is based.

ADDITIONAL NOTES. By M. CARY

Pp. 3, 4. The Mediterranean Sea

The standard geographical treatise on the Mediterranean is A. Philippson, *Das Mittelmeergebiet*. But there is no better way of studying the conditions of ancient travel in the Mediterranean than to read the descriptive passages in V. Bérard's books on the Odyssey, especially in *Les Phéniciens et l'Odyssée* (2nd edition); *Calypso et la mer de l'Atlantide*; *Nausicaa et le retour d'Ulysse*. The first chapter in J. Holland Rose, *The Mediterranean in the Ancient World*, will also be found useful.

P. 4, ll. 14-17. Exclusiveness of the ancient Egyptians

The Egyptians made voyages of exploration both in the Mediterranean and in the Red Seas. Their intercourse with Phoenicia, where they went to fetch the cedar-wood of Lebanon, dated back at least to 3000 B.C. From their Red Sea ports they visited the land of 'Punt' (northern Somaliland) in quest of frankincense. These Red Sea cruises, which also commenced c. 3000 B.C., culminated in a great expedition during the reign of Queen Hatshepsut (c. 1500 B.C.), extending to Socotra and the southern coast of Arabia. Towards the end of the second millennium, however, the Egyptians allowed their overseas trade to fall into the hands of foreign peoples (Phoenicians and, subsequently, Greeks), and they never attempted to acquire any consistent idea of the neighbouring continents. The lands to the north of Egypt (Asia Minor and the Aegean area) were known to them vaguely as 'the Isles of the Very Green.' On Egyptian seafaring, see J. H. Breasted, *History of Egypt*, especially pp. 274-8.

Pp. 4-6. Phoenicians and Minoans

The part played by the Phoenicians in opening up and colonising the Mediterranean region is now considered to have been less extensive than was formerly believed. The derivations of place-names in Greece and other Mediterranean lands from Semitic roots, which used to be accepted as proof of Phoenician settlement, have now for the most part been discredited. But the chief reason

for reducing the rôle of the Phoenicians has lain in the archaeological exploration of the Mediterranean countries, which has
brought to light much new evidence on their prehistoric condition.
In particular, the discoveries made in the Greek lands, and foremost among these the excavations of Sir Arthur Evans on the
Cretan site of Cnossus, have revolutionised our ideas of early
seafaring in the Mediterranean.

A Greek legend, to which little attention has been paid until
recent years, preserved the memory of a king Minos of Cnossus,
who exercised the earliest of all lordships over the Greek seas. It
has now been disclosed that Cnossus was the centre of a powerful
prehistoric monarchy and the seat of the earliest high civilisation
in Europe. This pre-Hellenic or 'Minoan' civilisation was based on
a maritime commerce which extended to Egypt in one direction,
to Sicily and possibly to Spain in another. The voyages of the
early Cretans were made on sea-going ships with a keel and a high
bow, which were better all-weather craft than the mere river-boats
of the Egyptians. Intercourse between Crete and Egypt was opened
at least as early as 3000 B.C., and the visits of Cretan mariners to
the western Mediterranean probably began not later than 2500 B.C.
On the other hand the earliest evidence of Phoenician intercourse
with foreign lands—an Egyptian tomb-painting near Thebes—dates
back no further than c. 1450 B.C. It is clear, therefore, that the
Minoans were the real pioneers of Mediterranean navigation, and
that the Phoenicians merely extended and completed their work
in a later age.

In the course of the second millennium Greece received a new
population of Indo-European immigrants. About 1400 B.C. a body
of invaders, who may be identified with the 'Achaeans' of Homer,
established itself at Mycenae in Argolis and set up a rival capital
to Cnossus; soon after this date the Achaeans went on to invade
Crete and to destroy Cnossus. Despite the fall of Cnossus,
the ascendancy of the Aegean peoples in the Mediterranean was
maintained almost to the end of the second millennium, indeed
it was confirmed by the settlement of Achaean or Minoan populations in Cyprus, and on the coasts of southern Asia Minor and
Syria. But towards the end of the second millennium the prehistoric civilisation of Greece underwent a general decline, and

with the irruption of another group of Aryan invaders, the Dorians (c. 1100 B.C.), it came to an end. By the beginning of the first millennium the Greeks (as the inhabitants of Greece may henceforth be called) had abandoned the maritime enterprise of the Minoans and had left the Mediterranean to be re-discovered by the Phoenicians. Details of Minoan seafaring will be found in Sir Arthur Evans, *The Palace of Minos at Knossos*, vol. 1, § 14; vol. 2, §§ 35, 39, 42; in G. Glotz, *The Aegean Civilisation*, bk. 2, chs. 4 and 5; and in A. R. Burn, *Minoans, Philistines and Greeks.* Bérard, *Les Phéniciens et l'Odyssée*, vol. 2, ch. 5, still maintains the priority of the Phoenicians and denies a Cretan lordship over the seas; but in this opinion he now stands almost alone.

At the end of the second millennium the Phoenicians entered upon the heritage of the Minoans (from whom they had probably received an admixture of population). Their penetration of the Aegean area was less complete than the delusive derivations of Greek place-names from Semitic roots, and the now generally discredited equation, Heracles = Melkarth, suggested to scholars of an earlier generation. Yet their presence in Greek waters at the beginnings of Greek history is repeatedly attested by Homer and Herodotus, and it is confirmed by the diffusion among the Greeks of an alphabet of Phoenician origin, which they adopted not later than 800 B.C.

In the western Mediterranean the Phoenicians reached the Straits of Gibraltar at an early stage. In the opinion of the Greeks the Tyrian colony of Gades had been planted soon after the Trojan War, i.e. in the twelfth century B.C. (Strabo, 1. 3. 2, p. 48). Phoenician remains in Spain give no support to this tradition, for none of them are anterior to the eighth century. Yet the passage from the Book of Kings, referred to on p. 7 of the text, is good evidence that the way to the Straits was familiar to the Phoenicians by 1000 B.C. This way was probably discovered in the first instance by coasting along the shore of Africa, where the Tyrian colony of Utica was believed to have been founded in 1101 (Pliny, *Nat. Hist.*, 16, § 216). A second base for the exploration of the West was established in Sicily, where the Phoenicians made settlements on all three coasts, previous to the coming of the Greeks (Thucydides, 6. 2). On the other hand the Phoenicians did not follow out the route along the European coast; they founded no colonies in Italy or France, and left scarcely any remains in these countries. It is also doubtful whether they colonised Sardinia or the Balearic Isles before the advent of the Greeks into the western Mediterranean.

P. 7, l. 7. Tarshish or Tartessus

The name 'Tartessus' was given by the Greeks to a district of southern Spain, to its chief town, and to a river (the Guadalquivir), at the mouth of which that city was situated. The Tartessians claimed that they had an ancient civilisation and a law-book dating back to 6000 B.C. (Strabo, 3. 1. 6, p. 139, where the MSS read νόμοι ἑξακισχιλίων ἐτῶν, not ἐπῶν, as in Meineke's text); and it is probable that their principal city had been an entrepot for Atlantic trade since at least 2000 B.C. But the first indisputable evidence of commerce between Tartessus and the eastern Mediterranean is the passage in the Book of Kings, mentioned in the text. Several other references to 'Tarshish' in the Old Testament (notably those in Ezekiel 27) show that the Phoenicians of Tyre maintained their connexion with this city until the sixth century.

The exact site of the city has not yet been ascertained. In any case, it lay farther out from the Straits than Gades (with which later writers of antiquity confused it), and it was a native town, not a Phoenician colony.

From the fact that Tartessus is not mentioned again in Greek literature after Hecataeus it may be inferred that by 500 B.C. it had sunk into insignificance or, more likely, had been destroyed by the Carthaginians, who had by then gained control of the Straits and were setting up a monopoly of the trade of southern Spain with Mediterranean lands. On the prehistoric trade of southern Spain see V. G. Childe, *The Dawn of European Civilisation*, ch. 9, and A. Schulten, *Tartessos* (a somewhat imaginative yet highly instructive book).

P. 8, l. 35. High peaks attract storms

This statement is not strictly accurate. Nevertheless the coastal ranges accentuate the dangers of navigation in the Greek seas, by reason of the καταιγίδες or sudden squalls which blow down from the mountains with great force on days of clear weather.

P. 10, l. 15. Dangerous currents near headlands

Mediterranean currents in general are of no great speed or range, except at times when a persistent gale increases their force.

P. 11, l. 8. The Mediterranean a tideless sea

The Atlantic tides, being intercepted by the Straits of Gibraltar, have little influence on the Mediterranean basin, whose water-level has a seasonal variation seldom exceeding one or two feet. Nevertheless the tide is of perceptible strength in narrowing channels between converging shores. The strange alternations and the great force of the current in the Euripus, which rises at times to a velocity of 6–7 knots, is due to a tide travelling up the two arms of the Euboic channel at unequal speeds. The difference in the level of the water in either channel, consequent upon this tidal motion, creates a stream through the Chalcis Straits which reverses its direction at irregular intervals.

In the Straits of Messina a tidal race flows alternately to north and south through the centre of the channel, and counter-currents set in along either shore. Between these opposite streams whirlpools form here and there.

P. 11, l. 23. Heracles a fire-god

It is hardly correct to describe Heracles as a fire-god. His association with thermal springs was a natural development from the widespread worship which he received as a god of healing.

P. 13, l. 6. Geographical works in Latin

Besides the works of Mela and Pliny, we still possess the geographical poem of Avienus, mentioned on p. 36 and elsewhere. But as a contributor to geographical science Avienus was even more negligible than Mela or Pliny.

Pp. 19, 20. The Argonauts

The Argonaut legend in all probability commemorated an actual raid by adventurers from Greek lands into the Black Sea, ending in a haul of gold from Colchis. In that country drift-gold was collected on fleeces hung out in the mountain streams (Strabo, 11. 2. 19, p. 499). Since Jason was assigned to the second generation before the Trojan War, his cruise may be dated c. 1250 B.C. But the legend must not be taken as proof of the systematic opening up of the Black Sea in prehistoric times. Archaeological evidence of such early intercourse between the Aegean and the Black Sea is almost wholly lacking; and Homer's knowledge of the way into the Black Sea extended only a little distance into the Sea of Marmora. The detailed knowledge of the coast of Asia Minor which is revealed in the later forms of the Argonaut legend (as in Apollonius Rhodius) was the result of Greek exploration in the eighth and following centuries. On the growth of the Argonaut legend, see Miss J. R. Bacon, *The Voyage of the Argonauts*; on its historical basis, see Burn, *op. cit.*, ch. 9.

Pp. 20, 21. The River Oceanus

This outer stream was believed to have water-connexions with the inner seas. According to Hesiod, *Catalogue of Women*, fr. 45, the Argonauts returned home from the Black Sea by the river Phasis and the Ocean stream, which carried them to Libya, from which point they shouldered the good ship Argo to the Mediterranean Sea.

P. 24. Ithaca

The discrepancies noted in the text between Homeric Ithaca and modern Thiaki have since given rise to the view that the home of Odysseus should be sought in the adjacent island of Leucas. This theory has been advocated with great ingenuity and persistence by W. Dörpfeld (most recently in *Alt-Ithaka*, a book of two volumes), and it has been endorsed by W. Leaf, *Homer and History*, ch. 5. But it has not found general acceptance. For a recent re-statement of the claims of Thiaki, see Sir Rennell Rodd, *Homer's Ithaca*.

Pp. 24, 25. The Homeric Catalogue

The view that the Homeric *Catalogue of Ships* was of later date than the *Iliad* has recently been further developed by Leaf (*op. cit.*, passim, and especially pp. 80–86). But strong arguments for regarding it as an integral and original part of the *Iliad* have been advanced by T. W. Allen, *The Homeric Catalogue of Ships*, especially ch. 11.

Pp. 26, l. 5; 27, l. 1. The Aethiopians

It is possible that Homer had some vague inkling of the Sudanese, who are the swarthiest of all negroes. But instead of locating the Aethiopians definitely in the far south, he vaguely relegated them (in the *Iliad*) to the borders of Ocean, i.e. to those regions beyond the known world where imaginative authors of all ages have placed their idealised societies of 'noble savages.' In the *Odyssey* Homer partitioned the Ethiopians into a far western and a far eastern section. This new location of their abodes was not the product of fresh information about the habitats of the dark-skinned tribes, but an inference from Homer's belief that the earth was a flat disc, and that the sun at dawn and dusk grazed its rim, so that the adjacent peoples were scorched to blackness.

Pp. 29, 30. The Pygmies

Hecataeus added the detail that in order to drive off the cranes the Pygmies dressed up in rams' fleeces and horns, and agitated rattles. (Jacoby, *Die Fragmente der griechischen Historiker*, vol. I, fr. 328.)

Pp. 31–33. Amber

The earliest amber to reach the Mediterranean was brought by the sea-route from Heligoland. About 1600 B.C. Baltic amber began to come down to the Adriatic and passed on to Peloponnesus by way of Pylos. A land route by which Jutish amber reached Italy was also established, but this went by way of the German rivers and the valley of the Inn rather than through Gaul. There is no evidence that amber ever travelled with tin across Gaul. On the early amber trade see V. G. Childe, *op. cit.*, pp. 136, 137; J. M. de Navarro, *Geographical Journal*, 1925, pp. 481–507.

P. 32, l. 14. The Hyperboreans

The Hyperboreans were usually imagined by Greek writers from the time of Hesiod as an idealised society under the special protection of Apollo—a northern counterpart to the 'blameless Aethiopians' of Homer. Their homes were placed anywhere in the north beyond the borders of the known world. But Herodotus' Hyperboreans were clearly a real people with a definable abode. According to an ingenious theory of C. T. Seltman, *Classical*

Quarterly, 1928, pp. 155–9, they were Greek emigrants who had ventured themselves far into the Danube lands and had thus lost touch with the mother-country, yet still contrived to remit a yearly offering to Apollo. According to Herodotus the starting-point of their journey was 'Scythia,' which may here be taken to mean the Rumanian corn-lands.

The gifts of the Hyperboreans were almost certainly not amber, but ears of wheat, the firstfruits of their harvest. In Callimachus' *Hymn to Delos* (ll. 283, 284) the offerings are described as καλάμη τε καὶ ἱερὰ δράγματα...ἀσταχύων.

P. 34. The amber river Eridanus

Jutish amber travelled to Italy by way of the Rhine and the Inn, but not, so far as is known, along the Rhône. The identification of the Eridanus with the Padus first occurs in Pherecydes, a writer of the early fifth century. (Jacoby, *Fragm. griech. Hist.*, vol. I, fr. 74.)

Pp. 35, 36. The early tin trade

In prehistoric days supplies of tin perhaps reached the Mediterranean lands from Bohemia, but throughout historical times the main source of tin was in the Atlantic coastlands. The earliest Atlantic consignments probably came from Brittany, but the trade of the Carthaginians in tin was with Cornwall. The Spanish tin mines do not appear to have been worked before the Roman conquest. (Cary, *Journal of Hellenic Studies*, 1924, pp. 166, 167.)

Pp. 37–39. The Cassiterides

The doubts of Herodotus, 3. 115, as to the existence of Tin Islands in the Atlantic have been confirmed by modern prospectors, who have ascertained that no important deposits of tin have ever been exploited on any Atlantic islands. The term 'Cassiterides' may originally have been a floating expression. But the land to which Strabo referred under that name was undoubtedly Cornwall, which the early Mediterranean traders, by an error common among explorers of all ages, mistook for a cluster of islands. See T. Rice Holmes, *Ancient Britain and the Invasions of Julius Caesar*, pp. 483–498; F. J. Haverfield, in Pauly-Wissowa-Kroll, *Realencyclopädie der classischen Altertumswissenschaft*, s.v. Kassiterides.

P. 38, l. 26. P. Crassus

The context in which Strabo relates the voyage of Crassus to the Cassiterides makes it almost certain that his starting-point was Spain. Crassus should therefore be identified with the governor of Further Spain in 96–93 B.C., rather than with the well-known lieutenant of Caesar in Gaul. If the explorer of the Cassiterides was Caesar's lieutenant, he kept his secret well, for Caesar was under the delusion that the source of British tin was in the interior of the island (*Bellum Gallicum*, 5. 12. 5).

Ch. 3. Greek colonisation

For a recent survey of the Greek colonial expansion, in which full account is taken of its geographical factors, see J. L. Myres, in *Cambridge Ancient History*, vol. 3. ch. 25.

P. 46, l. 13. Phoenicians at Lampsacus

It is now generally believed that the name of Lampsacus was of Asianic, not of Semitic origin. There is no good evidence of Phoenician navigation in the Black Sea or its approaches.

P. 46, l. 25. Black Sea fisheries

The Greeks were also attracted to the estuaries of the Danube and the Dnieper by reason of their great wealth of fish. The abundance of fish at Byzantium (where a back-eddy from the Bosporus current swirled the fish towards the shore) was specially noted by Tacitus, *Annals*, 12. 63. 2; and the importance of the fishing industry at Cyzicus was attested by its coin-type, the tunny. On Greek colonisation in the Black Sea, see M. Rostovtzeff, *Iranians and Greeks in South Russia*, pp. 61–64; E. H. Minns, *Scythians and Greeks*, ch. 2.

P. 47. Sinope

According to an alternative tradition Sinope was founded in 630 B.C. That a Greek colony should have been established at so distant a point of the Black Sea in the early years of the eighth century is on the face of it most unlikely. Yet remains of the so-called 'sub-Mycenaean' and 'orientalising' pottery in its hinterland tend to confirm the earlier foundation-date. It may however be assumed that the original colony was merely a small trading station (like many other Milesian foundations), and that Sinope did not come into existence as a town until c. 630 B.C.

On the importance of Sinope as a collecting centre for the local coasting trade, and for the high-grade iron of the hinterland, see the instructive article by W. Leaf in *Journ. Hell. Stud.*, 1916, pp. 1–15.

P. 50, l. 25. Cumae

The claim of Cumae to date back to the eleventh century B.C. was clearly untenable. But the remains of the earliest Greek settlement date back to 750 B.C., if not earlier.

Pp. 54, 55. Massilia

On the foundation of Massilia, see M. Clerc, *Massalia*, vol. 1, bks. 1, ch. 4; 2, ch. 1. The earliest Greek remains on the site go back at least half a century beyond the traditional foundation-date. It is shown by Clerc that there is no good evidence of a previous Phoenician settlement on the site.

P. 55, l. 17. Greek colonies in Spain

On the Greek settlements in Spain, see Schulten, *op. cit.*, ch. 4, and R. Carpenter, *The Greeks in Spain*. The first Greek voyagers to Spain presumably set out from Cumae to Sardinia and the Baleares, where a number of place-names with the typical Ionic ending of -οῦσσα betokens a chain of Greek naval stations. Their first landing-point in Spain was probably the Puenta de Ifach, a high promontory near Cape Nao, where the settlement of Hemeroscopeium should be located. Greek outposts were also established at Dianium (mod. Denia), and perhaps at Lucentum (Alicante); but these were probably Massilian foundations of the sixth or fifth century.

A short-lived Greek colony was also planted (probably by Phocaeans c. 600 B.C.) at Maenace, to the east of the Phoenician station of Malaca (Strabo, 3. 4. 1, p. 156).

Pp. 55, 56. Cyrene

The story of the foundation of Cyrene is told in considerable detail by Herodotus, 4. 150–159. The colonists made two unsuccessful settlements at unsuitable points of the Libyan coast before they found the favoured site of Cyrene.

P. 57, n. 1

According to some scholars it was also under the second Psammitichus (593–588 B.C.) that the colony at Naucratis was founded. But the traditional date has been confirmed by finds of Naucratite pottery which are certainly anterior to 600 B.C. See P. N. Ure, *The Origin of Tyranny*, pp. 103–116.

P. 58, l. 3. Colaeus

Colaeus was making for Egypt, when a persistent easterly gale bore him off to the Straits of Gibraltar (Herodotus, 4. 152). A similar adventure befell the Portuguese mariner Pedro Cabral in 1500 A.D. In an attempt to repeat Vasco da Gama's voyage to India Cabral was blown by the trade-winds from West Africa to Brazil, and thus became one of the discoverers of South America.

From the name Ὀφιοῦσσα, which was given to C. Roca near Lisbon, it may be inferred that occasional Greek seafarers proceeded beyond Tartessus, presumably in quest of the Atlantic tin lands. From an ambiguous passage in Pliny (7. 197), *plumbum* (*sc. album*, i.e. tin) *ex Cassiteride insula primum adportavit Midacritus*, it may perhaps be concluded that a Greek skipper named Midacritus went as far as Cornwall. But Pliny possibly meant to say no more than that Midacritus brought home a cargo of Cornish tin from the entrepôt of Tartessus.

Pp. 60, 61. Xanthus of Lydia

Xanthus also observed fossilised shells at various points in the interior of Asia Minor, and he correctly deduced therefrom that these inland regions had once been under the sea (Strabo, 1. 3. 4, p. 49). With this acute remark Xanthus laid the foundations of geology. But this science was never studied by the Greeks in the same systematic manner as geography.

P. 63, l. 2. The supposed rise of the Nile out of the Ocean

In accordance with this theory, Hecataeus used the Nile to bring the Argonauts home from the Ocean into the Mediterranean (fr. 18 a, Jacoby).

P. 63, l. 31. The Nile inundations

These are not due in any great measure to the White Nile, whose flood water is largely dissipated in the swamps above

Khartum. The main volume of water is brought down from Abyssinia by the Blue Nile and the Atbara.

P. 64, l. 15. Map-making

Much information on ancient maps will be found in Berger's *Geschichte der wissenschaftlichen Erdkunde der Griechen*, and in the article by Kubitschek, in Pauly-Wissowa-Kroll, s.v. Karten. On the maps of Herodotus, see Myres, *Geographical Journal*, 1896, pp. 605 ff.

P. 66, l. 17. The influence of Delphi on colonisation

In a few instances (as in the case of Cyrene) the oracle of Delphi actually suggested a site for settlement. But its main function was to give a moral sanction to the settlers to hold their new land against the previous occupants or against later Greek comers. See A. S. Pease, *Classical Philology*, 1917, pp. 1–20.

P. 69. Europe and Asia

The derivation of the names of Europe and Asia from Semitic words has now been generally abandoned. The name of Europe is plainly of Greek origin, and the division of the earth's surface into separate continents was essentially a Greek idea. Its nucleus lay in the contrast between the opposite shores of the Aegean Sea, which is already implicit in the *Iliad*. In Hesiod (*Theogony*, ll. 357, 359) the two coasts and their hinterlands (symbolically represented as daughters of Oceanus) carry the names of Europe and Asia. As a geographical expression, 'Europe' originally stood for Central Greece, as opposed to the Aegean islands and the Peloponnesus (*Homeric Hymn to Apollo*, l. 251); subsequently it comprised the whole Greek mainland and the lands of the north Aegean. As the colonial movement increased the range of geographical knowledge, Europe came to include all the land this side of the Dardanelles, and the northern coast of the Black Sea. 'Asia' originally designated the immediate hinterland of Ionia (*Iliad*, 2. 461). It was progressively extended to all Asia Minor, and eventually to all the land east and south of Europe. But by the time of Hecataeus Libya had been detached from Asia and made into a third continent. This new division was no doubt the result of Greek travel in Egypt, which revealed the importance of the Suez isthmus as a boundary between the land-masses.

P. 70. Hecataeus

The geographical fragments of Hecataeus are collected in Jacoby, *Die Fragmente der griechischen Historiker*, vol. 1. For an analysis of Hecataeus' work, see the same author in Pauly-Wissowa-Kroll, s.v. Hekataios.

P. 73, l. 12. Hecataeus on Spain

Hecataeus had a fairly continuous knowledge of the coasts of southern and eastern Spain. His range of information in regard to the west of Europe was appreciably wider than that of Herodotus. The comparative ignorance of Herodotus illustrates the success of the Carthaginian counter-attack upon the Greeks in the western Mediterranean.

P. 73, l. 28. The Araxes

Hecataeus imagined that the Araxes was a tributary of the Tanais or Don (fr. 195, Jacoby). This error shows that he had anticipated Herodotus in confusing the Araxes with the Jaxartes (see p. 82 of the text).

Ch. 5. Herodotus

A summary of Herodotus' contributions to geography will be found in How and Wells, *A Commentary on Herodotus*, Appendix 8. Of previous works on this subject, How and Wells single out the chapter in this text as the clearest and most accurate.

P. 84, l. 15. Herodotus and the Alps

The first reference to the Alps in Greek literature may be discerned in the source of Avienus, a Massiliote writer of the sixth century (see the editorial note on p. 109, l. 29). This author traced the course of the Rhône from 'a gleaming cavern near the Sun Mountain, and through a large lake' (pp. 641 ff.). Herodotus' ignorance of the Alps was matched by that of Aeschylus and Euripides, who derived, not the Danube, but the Rhône, from Iberia (Pliny, 37. 31).

P. 84, l. 16. Alpis and Carpis

In these mysterious rivers we may recognise the Save and the Drave, which Herodotus would naturally imagine as flowing in a northerly direction, because of his belief that the Ister flowed in a continuous easterly direction in its upper and middle courses.

If Herodotus's ideas about the upper Danube were wild, his information concerning its lower course and its tributaries in the Balkan peninsula was fairly accurate. He owed this knowledge to Greek travellers from the colonies near the Danube estuary, who had explored the lower reaches of the river and several tributaries on either bank. See V. Pârvan, *Dacia*, ch. 3.

P. 85, l. 22. Rivers of South Russia

The Dnieper was known to the Greeks as far as the rapids near Kieff; but at no time did ancient Mediterranean travellers penetrate far into the interior of Europe by way of the Russian rivers.

Herodotus imagined the rivers of south-western Russia as having their source in four large lakes. Two of his contemporaries, Damastes (fr. 1, Jacoby) and Hellanicus (fr. 187, Jacoby), postulated a range of mountains, the Ῥίπαια Ὄρη, as a watershed between the Black Sea and the northern Ocean. The belief in the Rhipaean mountains persisted throughout ancient times and was not finally abandoned until the eighteenth century. See Kiessling, in Pauly-Wissowa-Kroll, s.v. Ῥίπαια Ὄρη.

Pp. 87, 88. The Argippaei and others

Herodotus' information about the tribes of the Asiatic steppe was ultimately derived from a seventh-century traveller named Aristeas, who presumably ascended the valley of the Don and struck across the Volga or the northern end of the Caspian Sea towards the Oxus valley, where the Issedones are to be located. The reputation which Aristeas acquired as a wonder-worker, and the fanciful account which he gave of fabulous men and beasts beyond the Issedones, are not sufficient reason for discrediting his travels. It was no doubt due to him that the Greeks of the fifth century correctly thought of the Caspian as an inland lake; but it is strange that Herodotus makes no distinct mention of the Volga.

The Issedones had also come to the notice of Hecataeus (fr. 193).

P. 90, l. 12. The Royal Road

It is almost incredible that the 'Royal Road' or main Persian line of communications through Asia Minor followed the circuitous curve described by Herodotus. The route which he traces was in reality the older trunk road of the Hittite kingdom, whose capital, Boghaz-Kevi, lay in the bend of the middle Halys. In all probability the regular Persian posting road was identical with the Graeco-Roman road described further down p. 90 in the text. Herodotus may have been misled by the fact that in 481–480 B.C. Xerxes' Grand Army made use of the more northerly route. See W. M. Calder, *Classical Review*, 1925, pp. 7–11.

P. 95. Dumb commerce

The scene of these silent negotiations was probably in Senegambia. The same manner of conducting business was observed on the West African coast by medieval travellers, and even by explorers of the early nineteenth century.

P. 96, 1. 26. The Troglodyte Aethiopians

Herodotus also knew of two other Aethiopian peoples. (1) The Sudanese negroes, of whom he had no doubt seen specimens during his stay in Egypt (3. 17–23). In eulogising these as a long-lived and finely built race he may have been influenced by Homer (editor's note to pp. 26–27); but his description of them was not far wide of the mark. Herodotus believed that African Aethiopia stretched to the south-western border of Ocean (3. 114). This was probably an inference from the story of the Nasamones (pp. 96, 97 of the text), who had met with a negro population in the region of the Niger. (2) The dark-skinned but lank-haired pre-Aryan races of Sind and Beluchistan (7. 70). Occasional Greek travellers under the aegis of the Persian king Darius might have had sight of these.

Pp. 96, 97. The expedition of the Nasamones

The track of the Nasamones probably lay southward to the oasis of Aujila, thence south-west across the oasis of Murzuk and Asben (to the west of L. Chad). The city by the Niger may have been Timbuctu, from which the Niger is believed to have receded in the last two thousand years.

Pp. 99–101. The circumnavigation of Africa

Herodotus' story has been carefully analysed by W. Müller, *Die Umsegelung Afrikas durch phönikische Schiffer*, and E. H. Warmington, in Cary and Warmington, *The Ancient Explorers*, ch. 5.

Müller shows that it would have been quite possible for the Phoenicians to raise one crop of wheat in the temperate zone of South Africa, and another in Morocco. Warmington points out that vessels sailing round Africa with the clock would mostly be favoured by the coastal currents. The fact that the cruise of the Phoenicians was not repeated does not prove that it did not take place. Little came of the voyages of Nearchus and of Pytheas, whose historical character is assured. On the other hand it is rightly pointed out in the text that the detail about the appearance of the sun in the northern sky does not definitely confirm the veracity of Herodotus' informants. It is wisest to preserve Herodotus' non-committal attitude in regard to his own narrative.

P. 101. Scylax of Caryanda

The historical character of Scylax's cruise is confirmed by an inscription of King Darius at Suez, in which he declares that he had dug a canal from the Nile to the Red Sea, and had given orders for ships to proceed by this waterway to Persia. (G. B. Gray, in *Camb. Anc. Hist.*, vol. 4, p. 200.)

P. 103. The voyage of Sataspes

If Sataspes reached the Guinea coast, he outdistanced all other ancient navigators in West African waters. But previous to meeting the Guinea current he might have been held up in the equatorial doldrums, in which the north-easterly trade winds die out on the latitude of C. Verde.

Pp. 104-109. The expedition of Hanno

The explorer Hanno need not be identified with the son of Hamilcar, for his was a not uncommon name at Carthage. The only certain fact about him is that he was a contemporary of Himilco (p. 109, n. 2). In that case his voyage took place about 500 B.C. (editor's note to pp. 109, 110). The translation of his report into Greek may have been due to the historian Polybius, who followed in Hanno's wake (p. 209).

The fragmentary condition in which the Greek text has come down to us has given rise to much discussion among modern scholars as to the length of Hanno's cruise and the situation of his stopping-points. It has been supposed that the 'burning mountain' which Hanno saw was a volcano in Camerun. But in all probability Hanno did not sail beyond Sherboro' Sound, the limit assigned to his cruise in the text. The island of Cerne has been sought at many different points, but its identification with Herne, as in the text, is on the whole the most satisfactory. Hanno's 'gorillae' were probably chimpanzees. They were certainly not gorillas as we now know them, for these brutes are of superhuman size and strength, and attack men without hesitation.

Later explorers did not overpass Hanno's farthest south until c. 1450 A.D.

Pp. 109, 110. The expedition of Himilco

The voyage of Himilco may be dated soon after the reduction or destruction of Tartessus, which took place c. 500 B.C. (editor's note to p. 7, l. 7). We need not doubt that Himilco reached the British tin lands; but it was left to later Carthaginian captains to discover the open-sea route from Spain to Cornwall.

The identification of Himilco's 'sea of weeds' with the Sargasso Sea (on which I threw doubts in *The Ancient Explorers*, p. 32) is probably correct. From the confused account of Avienus (ll. 380 ff.) it does at least seem clear that Himilco stood out or (more likely) was blown out a long way into the open Atlantic. But there is no good evidence that the Carthaginians henceforth frequented the Azores. Phoenician coins are reputed to have been unearthed on the Azores in the eighteenth century, but this find is not well authenticated.

P. 109, l. 29. Avienus

Though Himilco was unquestionably the ultimate source of Avienus for his account of the discovery of Britain, his main informant was probably a Massiliote captain who had visited Tartessus towards the end of the sixth century, and had acquired a general knowledge of the Spanish coast as far as C. Roca or even to Corunna. See the authoritative edition of Avienus by A. Schulten and P. Bosch-Gimpera.

P. 110, n. 4. Albion and Hierne

Albion was a pre-Celtic name for Britain. Sacra Insula = Ἱερὴ Νῆσος, which is an amplification of Hierne.

Pp. 112–118. The retreat of the Ten Thousand

This is a subject on which the author was peculiarly well qualified to write, by reason of his extensive travels in Armenia. But in the absence of precise indications in Xenophon, the line of the Greek march from the head waters of the Tigris to the mountains above Trapezus cannot be traced with certainty.

Pp. 118–120. The 'Periplus' of Scylax

From internal evidence this work can confidently be dated at c. 350 B.C. There is no need to assume that its author was masquerading under the borrowed name of Scylax of Caryanda (p. 101). In all probability he really bore the name of Scylax, which was not particularly rare. His information was largely derived from the historian Ephorus, who summed up the geographical knowledge of the Greeks previous to the campaigns of Alexander the Great. The reconstruction of Ephorus' geography is a task that still awaits modern scholars.

Pp. 120, 121. The bifurcation of the Ister

Fictitious river-forkings provided the later Greek writers with a convenient key to numerous geographical puzzles. Apollonius Rhodius (on the authority of Ephorus, or of the third-century historian Timaeus) sent the returning Argonauts up the Ister as far as Scylax's forking-point; thence by an arm of the Padus into the Rhône; thence to a Rhône-fork which they would have followed into the western Ocean, but for a divine intervention; and so back into the Mediterranean. (*Argonautica*, bk. 4.) On Aristotle's manipulation of river-forks, see the following note.

Pp. 135, 136. Mistakes concerning the Jaxartes

Aristotle's belief that the 'Araxes' flowed into the Tanais was derived from Hecataeus (editor's note to p. 73, l. 28). His splitting of the Tanais enabled him to reconcile the theory of Hecataeus with the rival opinion of Herodotus that the Araxes fell into the Caspian Sea (p. 82).

P. 136, l. 19. Patrocles on the Caspian Sea

Whether Patrocles really believed that the Caspian Sea communicated with India by way of the northern Ocean is not certain. During an exploratory cruise in the Caspian, which he made by order of King Seleucus, he apparently sailed some distance up the arm that once connected it with the Aral Sea, and discovered a trade-route from India to the Caspian by way of the river Oxus (Strabo, 11. 7. 3, p. 509). Probably it was along this route, rather than by way of the Ocean, that he traced the water-connexion between the Caspian and India. His waterway is described by Strabo, 2. 1. 18, p. 74; 11. 11. 6, p. 518, as a περίπλους, and by Pliny (6. 58) as a 'circumvectio.' These terms would apply no less to an inner circle along the Oxus valley than to the outer rim of Ocean.

Nevertheless the belief that the Caspian opened on to the Ocean had a long lease of life. It was implicit in Hesiod's description of the return of the Argonauts (ed. note to pp. 20, 21). It was seemingly shared by Alexander (as reported in Arrian, *Anabasis*, 5. 26. 1). Mela asserted, on the authority of Cornelius Nepos, that shipwrecked Hindus had been cast up on the shore of Germany (3. 45). The same author's remark, that the Caspian broke into Asia like a river (3. 38), suggests that a nascent knowledge of the Volga was being misused to confirm the theory of a connexion with Ocean. More accurate information about the Volga (p. 351) enabled Ptolemy to conclude that the Caspian was a lake. See W. Tarn, *Journ. Hell. Stud.*, 1901, pp. 10–28.

P. 137, l. 27. The fortress of Aornos

This stronghold appears to have been definitely located by Sir Aurel Stein in the Swat valley, where the converging ridges of Pir-Sar and Una-Sar constitute a natural redoubt with a broad and habitable plateau at the summit. See Sir Aurel Stein, *On Alexander's Track to the Indus*, and the commentary thereon by W. Tarn in *Classical Review*, 1929, pp. 180, 181.

P. 138, l. 21. Alexander's turning point

Alexander's object in advancing beyond the Indus basin was to reach the eastern Ocean. According to the generally accepted view (recently endorsed by U. Wilcken, *Alexander the Great*, pp. 85, 86), the king had heard of the Ganges and intended to follow it to the Bay of Bengal. According to another theory (put forward by Tarn in *Journ. Hell. Stud.*, 1923, pp. 93–101, and *Camb. Anc. Hist.*, vol. 6, p. 402), he shared Aristotle's view that the Ocean did not lie far beyond the Punjab.

Pp. 141–143. The voyage of Nearchus

Nearchus habitually over-estimated the distances traversed by him: in some cases he almost doubled them. For a similar error, compare Pytheas' false estimate of the circuit of Britain (editor's note to p. 157, l. 1). Previous to the invention of the log, seafarers were always prone to exaggerate their daily sailings. Fortunately for the success of his journey, Columbus miscalculated his rate of progress, and was thus encouraged to hold on.

P. 146, l. 19. The Red Sea canal

The originator of this waterway was a Pharaoh of the Twelfth Dynasty (soon after 2000 B.C.). It was repaired in turn by Necho, by Darius, by Ptolemy Philadelphus, by Augustus and by Trajan. But it was never long before the sand-drift again choked it; consequently it was of little commercial value.

P. 147, l. 4. Ptolemaic colonies in Somaliland

In addition to the colonies named in the text, the Ptolemies established a number of stations on the Somali coast, on either side of C. Guardafui, as bases for elephant-hunts. From these depots the hunting parties penetrated far enough into the hinterland to obtain accurate information about the source of the Blue Nile and the cause of the Nile floods.

Pp. 147, 148. Megasthenes

The surviving portions of Megasthenes' report on India have been carefully studied by Miss B. C. Timmer, *Megasthenes en de indische Maatschappij.* Her conclusions are that he misinterpreted the Hindu religion and caste system, but gave an accurate account of Chandragupta's court and administration. Excavations at his capital (mod. Patna) have confirmed Megasthenes' description of it.

Pp. 152–164. The voyage of Pytheas

The literature on Pytheas, already voluminous when the first edition of this book appeared, has since grown much larger. The most useful works on the subject are: K. Müllenhoff, *Deutsche*

Altertumskunde, vol. 1; G. Hergt, *Pytheas*; T. Rice Holmes, *Ancient Britain and the Invasions of Julius Caesar*, pp. 217–227. An edition of the fragments of Pytheas' treatise Περὶ Ὠκεάνου is being prepared by a French scholar, G. Broche. The account of Pytheas' cruise in this book requires very little correction or amplification.

The date of Pytheas' journey cannot be fixed with accuracy, but it must have fallen between 330 and 300 B.C.

P. 155, n. 4. Travel by the N. coast of Spain

The observation of Pytheas, quoted in this note, must have appeared to Strabo not only false but absurd, for he imagined the Spanish and French coasts as running continuously from west to east. Yet it was strictly true. The high waves of the Bay of Biscay made the open-sea passage dangerous for the small boats of ancient seafarers. On the other hand the passage along the Spanish coast was facilitated by an easterly current.

P. 156, l. 22. Ictis

The identification of Ictis with St Michael's Mount, made in this text, is confirmed by Rice Holmes, *op. cit.*, pp. 499–514. There is no MS authority for the alternative reading Vectis (i.e. the Isle of Wight).

P. 157, l. 1. Pytheas' measurement of Britain

Pytheas estimated the circumference of Britain at 42,500 stades (c. 4700 miles), or more than double the true figure (Diodorus, 5. 21. 4). But such exaggerations of naval distances were by no means uncommon among ancient navigators. (See editor's note to pp. 141–143.)

P. 158. Pytheas' visit to the German coast

The view taken in the text, that Pytheas did not enter the Baltic, is almost certainly correct. The amber island of 'Abalus' which he visited (Pliny, 37. 35) is to be identified with Heligoland.

P. 159, l. 5, and n. 1. Tides in Pentland Firth

Ordinary tides in Pentland Firth rise to a mere ten or twelve feet. But when a spring tide runs against an Atlantic gale the sea is forced up to a peak of more than fifty feet, and the spray is tossed up a full hundred feet higher.

P. 159, l. 8. Thule

The identification of Thule with Mainland in the Shetlands rests on the authority of Ptolemy. But the Shetlands could not possibly be described as lying at six days' sail from Britain. In all probability Thule was Norway. It extended beyond the Arctic circle, yet mead was made in it from honey, i.e. part of it lay south of lat. 61°, beyond which bees do not adventure themselves. Norway is the only country within easy reach of Britain that fulfils these conditions. On this point see especially Hergt, pp. 52–69; Rice Holmes, pp. 225, 226; F. Nansen, *In Northern Mists*, pp. 56–62; R. Hennig, *Von rätselhaften Ländern*, pp. 95–139.

P. 163, l. 1. The Pulmo marinus

The ingenious explanation of this mysterious substance which is offered in the text is difficult to reconcile with Pytheas' statement, that land and sea were immersed and held fast in it. According to Hergt, whom we may again follow here, Pytheas' words referred to the pervasive clammy moisture of a sea-fog in high latitudes.

P. 164, l. 8. The 'Guttones'

This tribe has been identified with the Goths. If that were correct, Pytheas must have sailed the length of the Baltic, for the original abode of the Goths was near the Vistula. But the best MSS of Pliny (37. 35) read 'Guiones,' in whom we may recognise the 'Inguaeones,' a people of north-western Germany. (D. Detlefsen, *Die Entdeckung des germanischen Nordens im Altertum*, pp. 6–9.)

P. 164, l. 14. Scythia

This term was used by Greek writers until and even after the voyage of Pytheas to denote all the northern land beyond 'Celtice' or Gaul. The first Greek writer to describe the Germans as a distinct race would appear to have been Posidonius.

Pp. 168 ff. The measurement of the earth

On this subject see, in addition to the standard work of Berger previously quoted, K. Miller, *Die Erdmessung im Altertum*. For the remains of the geographical works of Eratosthenes and Hipparchus, see Berger, *Die geographischen Fragmente des Eratosthenes*, and *Die geographischen Fragmente des Hipparchos*.

P. 172, l. 1.   Eratosthenes' great circle

There are considerable discrepancies in modern calculations of
Eratosthenes' earth-perimeter, which has been estimated at anything between 20,000 to 25,000 geographical miles (in round
figures). These differences arise partly from a doubt whether
Eratosthenes' own figure was 250,000 or 252,000 stades; but the
chief cause of uncertainty is the length of the stadium in terms of
which he was reckoning. The calculation in the text rests on the
assumption that he used the Attic-Roman stadium, $=\frac{1}{8}$ of a Roman
mile. This view has the apparent support of a passage in Pliny,
12. 53, whose meaning, however, is not beyond dispute.

P. 190, l. 18.   The return of Eudoxus

The eventual fate of Eudoxus is uncertain. After one false start
he set out again, but all that Posidonius (who was Strabo's informant on this subject) could say about the end of the venture
was that 'they ought to know at Gades and in Spain.' It was
asserted by Mela, 3. 9. 90, and by Pliny, 2. 169, on the authority
of Cornelius Nepos, that Eudoxus accomplished his object. But if
he had really circumnavigated Africa, the effect of his discoveries
in an age when geographic curiosity had been fully awakened must
have been considerable; and Posidonius, who upheld the theory
of a waterway round Africa (Strabo, 2. 3. 5, p. 100), could not
have professed ignorance of them. On the other hand it is unlikely
that Eudoxus returned to Gades a second time and reported the
definite failure of his expedition. In that case Nepos (who could
easily have made enquiries of Pompey's and Caesar's friend
Cornelius Balbus, a native of Gades), would hardly have stated
as a positive fact that Eudoxus had been successful. The most
probable conclusion is that (like the Vivaldi brothers who attempted
to repeat his voyage in 1291 A.D.) he perished on the journey.

P. 191, l. 23.   Soundings in the Mediterranean

Sardinia is situated between two marine precipices in which the
sea floor sinks to about 2000 fathoms. In the Ionian Sea measurements of nearly 2500 fathoms have been taken in modern times.

Pp. 192, 193.   Observations on the tides

An astronomer of the second century, Seleucus of Babylon,
went on to assume a causal relation between the tides and the

moon's phases, thus foreshadowing the modern discovery that gravitation is a universal force. (Tarn, *Hellenistic Civilisation*, 2nd edition, p. 270.)

P. 194. Aristotle's wind-points

In Aristotle's scheme the wind-points were arranged at uniform intervals of three to each right angle. It has been ingeniously explained by D'Arcy Thompson (*Classical Review*, 1918, pp. 49–56), that this division was suggested by the apparent solstitial and equinoctial positions of the rising and setting sun in Mediterranean latitudes, which lie apart at distances of approximately thirty degrees.

Pp. 196, 197. Erosion by rivers

In recognising the erosive power of rivers Polybius was in advance of Herodotus, who believed that the Vale of Tempe (along which the river Peneus gradually ground a bed for itself through a limestone cliff) had been caused by an earthquake (7. 129).

P. 197, l. 13, and n. 3. Posidonius' visit to Britain

The late author who is quoted here as evidence for a journey by Posidonius to Britain was almost certainly in error. Since Posidonius' travels in western Europe were anterior to Caesar's invasion of Britain, a visit to the Thames estuary on his part would have been a notable voyage of discovery. Yet Strabo, who quotes profusely from Posidonius, gives no hint of such a visit.

P. 209, l. 12. Polybius' journeys in Libya

On Polybius' exploration of the West African coast, see p. 106 of the text. This voyage was made after the destruction of Carthage in 146 B.C., at the instance of its captor, Scipio Aemilianus. It had no enduring consequences.

P. 209, l. 19. Polybius' passage over the Alps

Polybius was probably the first Greek to obtain a tolerably correct idea of the general trend of the Alps, and of their magnitude. Apollonius Rhodius (following Ephorus or Timaeus) imagined that the Argonauts could row through the Alpine chain from Italy to Gaul (4. 625–629). He had heard of 'stormy lakes' hard by the 'Hercynian Rock' (i.e. the Alps), but he had no clear knowledge of their relation to the river-system of Europe.

The Alpine pass which Polybius traversed in the wake of Hannibal has not yet been identified. It was probably the Mt Genèvre route, or one of the tracks across the ridge of Mt Cenis.

P. 219, l. 11. The site of Tigranocerta

The indications of Strabo and Tacitus, who locate Tigranocerta to the south of the Tigris, cannot be brought into accord with the narrative of Plutarch, who states that Lucullus, advancing from Melitene, crossed both the Euphrates and the Tigris before he set siege to the city. Since Plutarch's account was almost certainly derived from Sallust, it deserves preference. See Rice Holmes, *The Roman Republic*, vol. 3, pp. 409–425, or H. A. Ormerod, *Camb. Anc. Hist.*, vol. 9, pp. 366, 367.

P. 225. Madeira

The Madeira islands were first discovered by Carthaginian seamen c. 500 B.C. (Diodorus, 5. 19, 20). But they do not appear to have received regular visits from any ancient seafaring people.

P. 226. The Canaries

It may be taken for granted that this group of islands was known to the Carthaginians, for some of them are ordinarily visible from the mainland of West Africa. But even after Juba's voyage of discovery they had no permanent population in ancient times.

The name of 'Fortunate Isles,' by which later writers of antiquity described the Canaries and the Madeira group indiscriminately, was not conferred upon them from any general knowledge of their amenities, but because they were identified with the legendary 'Isles of the Blest,' which had been located in the far west since the time of Hesiod (*Works and Days*, ll. 169–172) and Pindar (*Olympia*, 2. 68 ff.).

P. 229. Caesar's conquest of Gaul

The extent to which Caesar's campaigns in Gaul extended the geographical knowledge of that country at Rome may be gauged by a remark of Cicero (*De Provinciis Consularibus*, § 22), that every day brought news to him of names previously unknown.

P. 231, l. 3. Portus Itius

The rival claims of Boulogne and of Wissant to represent the ancient Portus Itius remain unsettled. On the other hand it is now generally agreed that in both his British campaigns (55 and 54 B.C.) Caesar landed on the east coast of Kent. See the elaborate discussion by Rice Holmes on *Ancient Britain*, pp. 518–665, and the controversy between him and F. J. Haverfield in *Classical Review*, 1913 and 1914.

P. 231, l. 23. Caesar's report on Britain

Caesar had a substantially correct idea of the size of Britain, whose coasts he estimated to be 500, 700 and 800 Roman miles in length (c. 450, 640 and 700 English miles). But he gave the island a tilt, so that one side of the British triangle faced north, and another 'westward towards Spain.' By means of a water-clock he confirmed the report (which Pytheas had no doubt been the first to spread), that the summer nights of Britain were shorter than those of Mediterranean lands. (*Bellum Gallicum*, 5. 13.)

P. 233, l. 17. The Roman naval campaign of A.D. 5

In this year Tiberius' fleet sailed as far as the 'Cimbric Promontory,' i.e. C. Skager at the northern extremity of Jutland. But the Roman navy never went on to explore the Baltic.

P. 234. The Roman campaigns in the Danube lands

One notable result of the Roman advance into the Danube basin was to make known the entire course of that river, whose upper regions had always baffled the curiosity of the Greek geographers. The preliminary raid of Octavian into Pannonia in 35 B.C. had the effect of proving that the 'Danuvius' of southern Germany and the 'Ister' of the Balkan lands were one and the same stream. (F. de Pachtère, *Mélanges d'archéologie et d'histoire*, 1908, pp. 78–89.) In 15 B.C. Tiberius visited the source of the Danube (Strabo, 7. 1. 5, p. 292), thus completing its discovery.

Tiberius' subsequent operations in South Germany cleared up another mystery. Greek geographers had heard vaguely of a 'Hercynian Forest' which stretched across the European continent to the border of the Atlantic (Diodorus, 5, 21. 1, following Ephorus or Timaeus). Caesar, who had questioned German captives about this forest, was led to believe that sixty days' travelling would not bring you out at the other end (*Bell. Gall.*, 6. 25). After Tiberius' invasion of Franconia and Bohemia in 6 A.D. the Hercynian Forest was defined as the belt of woodland that extends from the Main to the Saale and the Elbe.

Ch. 12. The *Geography* of Strabo

A translation of Strabo, by H. L. Jones, is available in the Loeb Classical Library (8 vols., 1913–27). A good bibliography of recent works on Strabo will be found in vol. 1 of this series.

His *Geography* may also be studied in Tozer's *Selections from Strabo*, an annotated edition of its most important passages.

P. 239, 1. 33. Cicero's sons

The Quintus Cicero who studied at Athens was a nephew of the orator.

P. 243. Date of Strabo's *Geography*

The view expressed in the text, that the greater part of Strabo's work was composed in the reign of Augustus, is now generally accepted.

P. 252, 1. 22. Strabo on the British Isles

Strabo had the opportunity of supplementing Caesar's description of Britain from the reports of travellers who were beginning to frequent the Kentish coast and London since the days of Augustus. But his account contained little that Caesar had not already said. He amplified Caesar's bare mention of Ireland by describing the savage customs of its inhabitants, but these he confessedly reported from hearsay only. In conformity with his erroneous idea that the western coast of Europe had a general trend from west to east, he placed Ireland to the north of Britain. (Strabo, 4. 5. 1–4, pp. 199–201.)

P. 258. Strabo on Asia Minor

Strabo's descriptions of one important corner of Asia Minor, the Troad, has been minutely analysed by W. Leaf (*Strabo on the Troad*, Bk. 13, Cap. 1). It is here shown that the geographer, who had no personal acquaintance with this region, was unable to obtain a clear conspectus of it from his informants, and made several bad blunders on points of detail.

P. 260, l. 10. The expedition of Aelius Gallus

In 25 B.C. Augustus made an ill-advised attempt to break the commercial monopoly of the Himyarite Arabians in the southern Red Sea by directing an overland expedition against one of their towns, Mariaba. His general Aelius Gallus set siege to this town after a laborious march of six months' duration from the Gulf of Akaba across the central Arabian desert, but he failed to reduce it. This was the only serious attempt to open up Arabia in ancient times. The hardships suffered by Gallus' force discouraged the Caesars from further efforts to penetrate Arabia.

P. 262. Pomponius Mela

The latest editor of Mela, C. Frick, assigns his work to the reign of Caligula. He points out that Mela does not appear to know the annexation of Mauretania in the early reign of Claudius, nor its division into two separate provinces.

For fresh information about Britain Mela referred the reader to its forthcoming invasion by a Roman emperor (presumably Caligula). He repeated Strabo's disparaging remarks about the people of Ireland, but paid a compliment to its luscious meadows. He imagined that Ireland was nearly as large as Britain (3. 6. 49, 53).

P. 274. The *Periplus Maris Erythraei*

The opinion now prevalent is that the Περίπλους τῆς Ἐρυθρᾶς Θαλάσσης was composed in the reign of Nero, though some scholars ascribe it to the time of Domitian. A translation of the Greek text, and a copious commentary, with many references to the later commerce of the regions described, have been provided by W. H. Schoff, *The Periplus of the Erythraean Sea*.

P. 275, l. 15. Zanzibar

The farthest south of Greek exploration in East African waters was C. Delgado, which was discovered by one Dioscorus (probably c. 100 A.D.). The opposite island of Madagascar was known to Greek travellers by hearsay only. (Ptolemy, 1. 9. 3.)

P. 279. Hippalus and the direct route to India

Nothing is known of Hippalus, except that he discovered the law of the monsoons, and that the wind which henceforth bore

Greek ships to India was named after him (*Periplus*, ch. 57; Pliny, 6. 100, 104). Some scholars assign him to the first century B.C.; but the absence of references to him in Strabo indicates that he made his great discovery, at the earliest, in the reign of Augustus. In all probability the exploration of the direct route began in the opening years of the Christian era, and was the result of a Roman expedition to Aden, c. 1 B.C., which wrested that station from the control of the Sabaean Arabians. (*Periplus*, ch. 26; Pliny, 2. 168.)

Hippalus probably took off from C. Fartak on the South Arabian coast and found the Indian mainland near Barygaza (mod. Broach). Subsequent Greek skippers followed a more southerly course; soon after 50 A.D. the boldest of them (profiting perhaps by the involuntary voyage of exploration of Annius Plocamus' agent, p. 272) made for Muziris (Cranganore) and Nelkynda (Kottayam) in southern India. On these voyages of discovery see M. P. Charlesworth, *Classical Quarterly*, 1928, pp. 92–100; E. H. Warmington, in *Ancient Explorers*, pp. 73–80.

Pp. 280, 281. Eastern Asia

The island of Ceylon was not frequently visited by Greek traders, and geographers were left to make rather wild guesses as to its size (p. 345). On the other hand Greek merchants found their way to the inland capitals of the chief Indian rajahs.

From the time of Nero occasional seafarers crept up the east coast of India as far as the Ganges. Early in the second century one of the most remarkable of ancient pioneers, who was appropriately named Alexander, made a short cut across the Bay of Bengal and continued his journey along the coast of Siam to a Chinese port named Kattigara, which is usually identified with Hanoi in the Bay of Tongking, though some would place it on the site of Hang-Chow, at the mouth of the Yang-tse-Kiang (so Hennig, *Klio*, 1929–30, pp. 256 ff.). Alexander and his successors probably cut across the Malayan isthmus by land, for ancient geographers seemingly had no clear information about Singapore and the Sumatra Straits. On the other hand some of Alexander's followers worked northward from Malaya to Burma, and in 166 A.D. a company of Greek adventurers, who styled themselves 'envoys' of the emperor M. Aurelius Antoninus, presented their credentials at the court of the emperor Huan-ti in Lo-yang.

Pp. 287, 288. Agricola

On the details of the Roman advance into northern Britain, see the edition of Tacitus' *Agricola* by J. G. C. Anderson. In 208–211 the emperor Septimius Severus undertook several laborious campaigns in Scotland, during which he probably advanced beyond the limits of Agricola's expedition. A Roman camp (as yet unexplored) near Aberdeen perhaps marks his farthest north. But his son Caracalla abandoned all the territory north of Hadrian's Wall.

It was Agricola's intention to open up Ireland at the head of an invading force. This enterprise was vetoed by the emperor Domitian, and it was left to stray Roman or Gallic traders to make occasional visits to Ireland, more especially to its eastern coast.

P. 289. Germany and Scandinavia

In the reign of Nero a Roman agent of the emperor's Minister of Sports made a journey from the middle Danube to the Baltic amber coast by way of Moravia, Silesia and Posnania (Pliny, 37. 45). He brought back a sufficient load of amber to stud the safety nets at the Roman beast-hunts, and he initiated a new trans-continental trade-route to Sweden, the importance of which is attested by copious finds of Roman coins on the Swedish islands. But ancient travellers seemingly did not discover that the land of the 'Suiones,' which they approached from the Vistula, and 'Scandinavia,' which they entered from Jutland, were one and the same.

P. 294, n. 1. The Roman frontier system

For Hadrian's Wall, see J. C. Bruce, *A Handbook to the Roman Wall* (9th ed.); for the Wall of Antoninus, see Sir George Macdonald, *The Roman Wall in Scotland* (2nd ed.). For the Roman frontiers in Germany, see H. F. Pelham, *Essays*, pp. 178 ff.; B. W. Henderson, *Five Roman Emperors*, chs. 6 and 7. Details of the other Roman frontier lines will be found in V. Chapot, *The Roman World*, passim.

P. 294, n. 2. Hadrian's 'allocutio'

The text of Hadrian's speech is also given in Dessau, *Inscriptiones Latinae Selectae*, no. 2847.

P. 299. The Roman roads

Comprehensive descriptions and diagrams of the main roads in the Roman empire will be found in the article 'Via' by M. Besnier, in Daremberg-Saglio, *Dictionnaire des antiquités grecques et romaines*. For Roman roads in Britain, see the map of Roman Britain by O. G. S. Crawford, based on the Ordnance Survey.

P. 306. Roman Itineraries

For a fuller account of these, see Kubitschek, in Pauly-Wissowa-Kroll, s.v. Itineraria.

As a pendant to the Roman road-books, mention may be made of the Greek sailing directions, of which three are preserved in whole or part: (1) The *Periplus of the Erythraean Sea*, excerpted on pp. 273–281. (2) The *Periplus of the Euxine Sea*, composed by a governor of Cappadocia, Flavius Arrianus, at the instance of Hadrian. (3) The Σταδιασμὸς τῆς Μεγάλης Θαλάττης, a competent survey of the Mediterranean coasts. This manual was probably based on the standard work Περὶ Λιμένων by Timosthenes, an admiral of Ptolemy Philadelphus.

Ch. 15. Ancient lore of mountains

On this subject Mr Tozer was peculiarly qualified to speak, for he was an accomplished Alpinist and had made the ascent of many peaks in the Mediterranean lands and the Near East.

P. 323, l. 13. Erroneous beliefs about views from high points

In Orosius, a Spanish writer of the fifth century, the puzzling statement is made, that a tall lighthouse was reared at Brigantia (Corunna), 'ad speculam Britanniae' (i. 2. 71). If this is to be taken literally, it would seem to embody a persistent belief, that Spain was not only on the way to Britain, but within sight of it.

P. 325. A military mountain climb

From the pen of Arrian (*Anabasis*, 4. 18, 19) we possess a description of an escalade by Alexander's troops in Sogdiana. With the help of iron tent-pegs, which they fixed into the frozen snow on the mountain side, and of linen ropes, with which they hauled each other up like modern Alpinists, Alexander's cragsmen clambered to the summit of an impregnable fortress. They lost thirty men in the ascent, but had the satisfaction of obtaining the surrender of the dumbfounded garrison, and of bringing in to Alexander a captive princess, Roxane, whom the king took to wife.

Pp. 328–335. Ancient signals

For a fuller treatment of this subject, see W. Riepl, *Das Nachrichtenwesen des Altertums*, pp. 25 ff., 43 ff., 91 ff.

Pp. 335, 336. Measurement of mountains

The philosopher Thales (c. 600 B.C.) was said to have ascertained the height of an Egyptian pyramid by measuring (1) the shadow of the pyramid, from the half-way point on its base, (2) his own shadow, (3) his own height. A simple application of the rule-of-three gave him the height of the pyramid.

Ch. 16. Ptolemy

A text of Ptolemy's *Geography*, with a Latin translation, notes and maps, has been provided by C. Müller (1883–1901). For a recent discussion of Ptolemy's methods see O. Cuntz, *Die Geographie des Ptolemaios*.

After the decline of classical antiquity the *Geography* of Ptolemy continued to be studied in the Islamic countries. The appearance of a Latin translation in 1410 gave a great impetus to geographical studies in Europe, and to renewed exploration of the world.

Pp. 341, 342. Ptolemy's error about the length of the habitable world

In estimating the length of Eurasia at not less than 180°, Ptolemy unwittingly gave support to Seneca's wild surmise that a voyage from Spain to India would take 'very few days' (*Quaestiones Naturales*, prologue, § 13). The fifteenth-century quest for an all-water route to the Indies, which resulted in the discovery of America, was stimulated by Ptolemy's false calculations.

P. 346, l. 17. The Indian Ocean a lake.

The starting-point of Ptolemy's error may be sought in a confusion between the western and eastern Aethiopians (ed. notes to pp. 26, 27 and 96), which suggested that the basins of the Upper Nile and of the Indus could not lie far apart, and that a river 'Ethiops' (i.e. the Indus) was confluent with the Nile (Aeschylus, *Supplices*, ll. 284–6, *Prometheus Vinctus*, ll. 807–812). Alexander, who observed crocodiles in the tributaries of the Indus and Egyptian plants on their banks, accepted these as proofs that Indus and Nile were indeed one (Strabo, 15. 1. 25, p. 696). His march to the Indus estuary, it is true, finally disproved a connexion between that river and the Nile; yet the belief that the unknown East and unknown Africa might be contiguous lingered on. The reason which induced Ptolemy to revive this notion was no doubt the one implied in the text, that he heard vague reports about the interminable southward trend of the Malay peninsula, perhaps also of large land-masses in the Malay archipelago, and constructed out of these materials a land-bridge between the Far East and Africa.

This false conclusion on Ptolemy's part helped to produce the illusion, which persisted among modern geographers until the voyages of Captain Cook, of a Terra Australis extending continuously in the temperate latitudes of the southern hemisphere.

P. 352. The land route to China

Greek exploration of Central Asia stopped short of the Pamir plateau. In concert with the kings of Parthia, Augustus organised a trans-continental route as far as Merv and Kandahar, and a description of this road by one Isidorus of Charax has come down to us under the name of *Parthian Stations*. (Translation and commentary by W. Schoff.) But no regular trade was established at this stage between the Mediterranean lands and the Far East.

Towards the end of the first century A.D. the Chinese rulers of the Han dynasty occupied the Tarim plateau and organised communications as far as Kashgar and Tashkurgan. In 97 A.D. a

Chinese envoy visited a city of the Roman empire (presumably Antioch), and wrote a favourable report on the conditions of government and of trade in the western empire. (Extracts from this document are given in Schoff, *The Periplus of the Erythraean Sea*, pp. 275 ff.) Early in the second century a Greek trader named Maes Titianus visited Kashgar and Tashkurgan; others proceeded as far as Lop-Nor and Miran at the eastern edge of the Tarim plateau, where Sir Aurel Stein has found frescoes and many smaller art-objects of Graeco-Roman style. These travellers brought back a general idea of the mountain system of Central Asia, but China remained a closed book to them. Hence ancient geographers did not discover that the 'Seres' at the end of the trans-continental route and the 'Thinae' on the sea track beyond Malaya were one and the same people. On Chinese exploration, see F. Hirth, *China and the Roman Orient*.

P. 352. The Nile and the Mountains of the Moon

Ptolemy's source of information about the East African lakes and the sources of the Nile was probably a traveller named Diogenes, who had followed the coast to the neighbourhood of Zanzibar and perhaps penetrated from this point as far as the lakes themselves (Ptolemy, 1. 9. 3). The erroneous idea of a mountain range extending some five hundred miles across Africa was perhaps begotten by a vague knowledge of the great glacier ridge of Mt Ruwenzori beyond the lakes. The Ruwenzori range, however, is separated from the Kenya and Kilimanjaro systems by a deep rift valley.

SELECT BIBLIOGRAPHY

(1) *General treatises.*

The books on ancient geography by BUNBURY and BERGER, cited in the Preface, remain standard works for the more advanced student. Berger's book has attained a second edition. (Veit, Leipzig, 1903.)

(2) *Passages from ancient writers on geography.*

H. F. TOZER, *Selections from Strabo.* (Clarendon Press, 1893.)

E. II. WARMINGTON, *Greek Geography.* (Dent, 1934.) A comprehensive anthology of geographical passages, in translation, with a general introduction on Greek geography. This is a very useful companion volume to the present book.

(3) *Ancient geographical discovery.*

M. CARY and E. H. WARMINGTON, *The Ancient Explorers.* (Methuen, 1929.)

(4) *Dictionary articles.*

The articles by SIR EDWARD BUNBURY in SMITH'S *Dictionary of Ancient Geography* are still worth consulting. More detailed monographs will be found in PAULY-WISSOWA-KROLL, *Real-encyclopädie der classischen Altertumswissenschaft.* Those in the more recent numbers of this series (since 1919) are particularly full and well informed.

(5) *Special subjects.*

Books and articles on special topics of ancient geography have been cited in the editorial notes at the appropriate places.

INDEX.

Acampsis, river, 114
Acesines, river, 138
Acrocorinth, the, measurement of the height of, 337
Actae of Herodotus, 83; compared with the 'sphragides' of Eratosthenes, 181
Aden, 276
Adramyttium, the same name as Hadrumetum, 5
Adulis, port of Auxuma, 274
Aegean Sea, Phoenician settlements in the, 5
Aeneas Tacticus, on signalling stations, 332; his method of signalling, 334
Aeschylus, on the boundary between Europe and Asia, 68; on the meaning of the name Rhegium, 197; his description of the fire-beacons, 328
Aethale (Elba), 73
Aethiopia, expedition of Petronius into, 224; gold-mines of, 186; Auxuma the capital of, 274; expeditions of Septimius Flaccus and Julius Maternus into, 353
Aethiopians, meaning of the name, 26; mentioned in the Iliad, 26; more definitely in the Odyssey, 27; in Herodotus, 93, 96; in Agatharchides, 204
Aetna, the poem of, 321
Africa, described by Herodotus, 94—7; its northern coast, 94; its interior, 95—7; believed to have been circumnavigated, 99; its southward projection unknown to Eratosthenes, 182; and to Strabo, 250; noticed in the 'Periplus Maris Erythraei', 275; and by Ptolemy, 345; Africa described by Dionysius Periegetes, 283; later errors about, 367

Agatharchides, his work on the Erythraean Sea, 185; on the inundation of the Nile, 63; on the Aethiopian gold-mines, 186—8; on the fauna of Aethiopia, 201; on the Ichthyophagi, 203; on the Aethiopian tribes, 204
Agathodaemon, 345
Agathyrsi, 86
Agisymba, 353
Agricola, his campaigns in Britain, 287; his chain of forts, 288; his expedition to the Orcades, 288
Agrigentum, 54; described by Polybius, 212
Agrippa, his wall-map, 236; the original source of the Itineraries, 306; his roads in Gaul, 236
Alans, first mentioned by Dionysius Periegetes, 284
Albani, customs of the, 222
Albion, 110, 346
Albis (see Elbe)
Alexander the Great, effects of his conquests, 122; his political and social aims, 123; his Eastern expedition, 125 foll.; its importance for geography, 123, 124; his death at Babylon, 141
Alexandria, its importance to geography, 14; its Museum and Library, 145, 166; its central position, 145; Strabo's careful description of, 260
Alexandria ad Caucasum, 133, 137
Alexandria Eschate, 135
Allahabad, 150
Alpheius, river, its disappearance, 10
Alpis, 84
Alps, passes over the, 210; Roman roads over, 301, 304; Strabo's description of their features, 315; estimates of their height, 335

Altai Chain, first mentioned by Pto-
lemy, 351
Amanus, Mt, 126, 257; crossed by
the main Roman road, 305
Amasis, his encouragement of the
Greeks, 57
Amber trade, in Homer, 31; route
through Pannonia, 32; route
through Gaul, 32; in the hands of
the Phoenicians in the Mediterra-
nean, 33; at the mouths of the Po,
33; in the German Sea, 164
Ammonium, 128
Amu Daria, river, 134
'Anabasis,' of Xenophon, 113; of
Arrian, 124
Anaxagoras, on the inundation of the
Nile, 63; on earthquakes, 198
Anaximander, his views on the shape
of the earth, 60; introduced the
gnomon into Greece, 64; the first
map-maker, 64; on earthquakes,
197
Anthropology, 203; Strabo's interest
in, 246
Antichthones, 262
Antimenidas, 58
Antonine Itinerary, the, 306
Antoninus, his wall in Britain, 288
Aornos, 137
Apes, mode of catching in India, 201
Aquae Albulae, 355
Arabia, carefully described by Era-
tosthenes, 183
Arabia Eudaemon, 276
Arabian Geographers, acquainted with
Ptolemy's 'Geography,' 367
Arabian Gulf (Red Sea), 81
Arachosia, 133, 140
Aral, Sea of, unknown to the ancients,
82, 134
Ararat, Mt, 114, 130
Araxes, river, 73, 114, 116; con-
fusion of Herodotus about, 82; its
junction with the Cyrus, 221
Arbela, battle of, 129
Arcadia, disappearance of rivers in,
196
Archimedes, on the convexity of the
sea, 168
Archytas, 169
Arctic circle, different meanings of
the term, 179, 180
Arctic regions, described by Pytheas,
162
Arctic Sea, supposed to be navigable,
285

Arelate, 300
Argaeus, Mt, ascents of, 247, 321;
Strabo's description of, 321
Argippaei, a Kalmuck tribe, 87
Argonautic legend, 19; its historical
significance, 20
Ariana, description of, 130
Aristagoras, his map, 65; his share
in the Ionian revolt, 70; on the distance from Ionia to Susa, 90
Aristobulus, 124
Aristotle, his illustrations frequently
derived from Greece, 11, 185; his
notice of dwarfish tribes in Africa,
29; on the inundation of the Nile,
63; instructor of Alexander the
Great, 125; his mistake about the
Jaxartes, 135; his importance to
scientific geography, 145, 166; on
the zones, 179; on rivers, 196; on
earthquakes and volcanic action,
198; on historical geography, 205
Armenia, geographical features of,
113, 114; Xenophon's march across,
116—18; campaigns of Lucullus in,
218
Armorica, 110; visited by Pytheas,
155; Strabo's error about, 155
Aromata, prom., 274
Arrian, his history of Alexander's
campaigns, 124; description of the
Oasis of Ammon, 128; account of
the voyage of Nearchus, 141; his
Periplus, 294
Arsanias, river, 219, 270
Arsene, lake, 268
Artacoana, 133
Artemidorus, 190
Asia, boundaries of, 68, 69; meaning
of the name of, 69; scanty notices
of the geography of in Herodotus,
89; Strabo's account of, 256; no-
tices of Eastern Asia, 280
Asia Minor, products of, 46; mis-
taken views about the width of, 79,
89, 323; carefully described by
Strabo, 258
Aspects of nature revealed by Alex-
ander's expedition, 124
Astaboras, river, 146, 204
Astacus, 50
Astarte, represented by the Greek
Aphrodite, 5; worship of at Eryx,
6; plants the pomegranate in Cy-
prus, 39
Atabyrium, in Rhodes, temple of
Zeus on its summit, 318; the same

name as Tabor, 3; found also in Sicily, 212; measurement of its height, 336

Atak, 137

Athos, Mt, an altar on its summit, 318

'Atlantic Islands,' the, 225

Atlantic Ocean, first mentioned by Herodotus, 80; visited by Himilco, 111

Atlas, supporting the heavens, 21; chain of, 95; crossed by Suetonius Paullinus, 291

Augila, Oasis of, 96

Augusta Vindelicorum (Augsburg), 304

Augustan age, the culminating point of the study of geography, 15, 238

Automoli, 93, 147

Auxuma, 274

Avienus, on the Oestrymnides, 36, 110; his 'Ora Maritima,' 109; his Latin Translation of the 'Periegesis' of Dionysius, 286

Azov, Sea of, breeding-place of the tunny, 46; (see Maeotis)

Bab el-Mandeb, Straits of, 274

Babylon, described by Herodotus, 77; occupied by Alexander, 129; death of Alexander at, 141

Babylonia, system of canals in, 259

Bactra, 134

Bactria, invaded by Alexander, 134

Balbus, his expedition against the Garamantes, 223

Baltic Sea, 289

Bambotum, river, 106

Banyan tree, described by Onesicritus, 139

Baraces, inlet, 277

Barca, 56

Barygaza (Baroche), 277, 281

Becare, 280

Belerion, prom., 156

Beluchistan, 140

Bent, Mr, on the Hadramaut, 203; on the Locust-eaters in Abyssinia, 204; on the cave-dwellers of Dhofar, 276

Berenice, commercial station at, 146; Roman road to, 306

Berger, Dr H., on the Periplus of Scylax, 119; on Pytheas' parallels of latitude, 161

Bessus, satrap of Bactria, 131; capture of by Alexander, 135

Bingheul-dagh, 114

Bissagos, Bay, 106

Bitlis, 116, 269

Bolan Pass, 140

Bore of the Indus, 139; of the Nerbudda, 277

Boundaries of the three continents, 67, 68, 82, 282

Bradley, Mr H., on Ptolemy's Geography of the British Isles, 348; his explanation of Ptolemy's error about the position of Scotland, 347

Brahmans, tenets of noticed by Herodotus, 92; their life described by Megasthenes, 152

Brenner Pass, 304

Britain, its tin trade, 36; visited and described by Pytheas, 156; invaded by Caesar, 230; its sunless climate, 245; conquests of Claudius, Suetonius Paullinus, Agricola, and Antoninus Pius, 287, 288; Tacitus' description of, 288; Roman roads in, 302—4; Ptolemy's map of, 346 —51

Brittany, visited by Pytheas, 156; its trade with Britain, 36, 156

Brunetto Latini, his copious use of Solinus, 365

Bucephala, 138

Budini, 86

Bunbury, Sir E. H., on the wanderings of Ulysses, 29; on the circumnavigation of Africa, 101

Buvinda, river, 351

Byzantium, 50

Cabaeon, prom., 156

Cabeiri, worship of in Samothrace, 5; meaning of the name, 5

Cabul, 130, 133

Caesar, his conquest of Gaul, 228; his ethnographical and geographical notices, 229; his description of the country of the Veneti, 230; his expeditions into Britain, 230; into Germany, 232

'Camarae' vessels on the Euxine, 223

Camarina, 53

Cambay, Gulf of, 277

Camulodunum, 287

Canal from the Nile to the Red Sea, 146

Canaries, islands, 226, 342

Candahar, 133

Cantin, Cape, 105

Cantion, prom., 156, 348
Cappadocia, absence of trees in, 258
Cardinal points, determined in Greece by the winds, 41
Carmania, 140
Carpathians, the, first mentioned by Ptolemy, 351
Carpis, 84
Carthage, its admirable position, 6; compared to that of Sinope, 47
Carthage, New, described by Polybius, 213; silver mines of, 210
Casius, Mt, ascended by Hadrian, 314
Caspatyrus, 74, 101
Caspian Gates, 131
Caspian Sea, mentioned by Hecataeus, 73; regarded by Herodotus as an inland sea, 81; also by Aristotle, 136; supposed by Alexander to be the Palus Maeotis, 132; regarded as an inlet from the ocean, 136, 282; the error corrected by Ptolemy, 345; revived at a later period, 367
Cassiterides, islands, opinions as to their situation, 37, 38; voyage of Publius Crassus to, 38; their existence disbelieved by Herodotus, 80
Caste System in India, 151
'Catalogue of Ships' in Homer, geographical value of, 24
Cataracts of the Nile, described by Herodotus, 92
Caucasus, called by Aeschylus the highest of mountains, 68; described by Theophanes, 220; tribes of, 222; crampons used, and tobogganing practised in, 315
Cave-dwellers, in Arabia, 276
Caverns, described by Pausanias, 356
Celts, 79, 84, 191, 253; in North Italy, 120
Cerne, island, 104, 105, 119, 283
Ceylon (see Taprobane)
Chalcedon, 50
Chalcidice, 49
Chalcis, its colonies in Thrace, 49; in Italy, 50
Chandragupta, 148
Chersonese, Tauric, 85; accurately described by Strabo, 255
Chersonesus, town of, 50
Chester, 287
China, 281
Chitral, traversed by Alexander, 137
Choaspes, river, 90

Chryse, 281, 285, 346
Cicero, on mountain scenery, 317
Cilician Gates, pass of the, crossed by Alexander, 126
Cimbrian Promontory, 290
Cimmerian Bosporus, 82, 85
Cimmerians, the, in Homer, 30; their inroad into Asia Minor, 84
Cinnamon Country, the, 147, 173
Cinyps, river, 94
Circumnavigation of Africa, 99
Climata, of Hipparchus, 175; of Ptolemy, 343
Climate, Strabo's remarks on, 245
Climax, pass of, 126, 246
Clota, 350
Codanus Sinus, 289
Colchester, the first Roman colony in Britain, 287
Coliacum, prom., 273
Colonies, the Greek, causes of the establishment of, 43; qualifications for the site of, 44, 51; early development of, 44; geography promoted by, 45; Delphic oracle influential in founding, 66
Commagene, 91, 257
Comorin, Cape, 273, 280
Continents, division of the world into, 67, 181; their boundaries, 67, 68; their names, 69; opinion of Herodotus, 81, 82; the three compared by Strabo, 252
Cophen, river, 137
Coptos, commercial station on the Nile, 146; Roman road to, 305
Coral, between India and Ceylon, 273
Corbilo, 37
Corinth, its connexion with the purple trade, 5
Corinth, Isthmus of, its importance to Greece, 214
Corycian Cave, described by Pausanias, 356
Cosmas Indicopleustes, 160
Cosmical beliefs of Herodotus, their primitive character, 78
Cotton in India, noticed by Herodotus, 92; in Greece, 357
Cottonara, 280
Crampons, used in the Caucasus, 315, 316
Crassus, Publius, his voyage to the Cassiterides, 38
Craterus, his return march from the Indus, 139, 140

Croton, 51

Culture early developed in the Greek colonies, 44

Cumae, 50

Curtius, his history of Alexander's campaigns, 124; description of the country to the south of the Caspian, 132; of Bactria, 134

Curzon, Hon. G. N., on the Oxus, 134; on the Zerafshan, 135

Cutch, Gulf and Runn of, 277

Cyllene, Mt, measurements of the height of, 336, 337

Cypress, the, in Greece, 40; derived from Afghanistan, 40

Cyrenaica, in Homer, 26

Cyrene, its site and commerce, 56

Cyrus, river, date of its junction with the Araxes, 221

Cyzicus, its situation, 47; its famous arsenal, 48

Dachinabades, meaning of the name, 278

Dacia, reduced to a Roman province by Trajan, 290; abandoned by Aurelian, 291

Dante, on the common source of the Tigris and Euphrates, 271; his use of Orosius as a geographical authority, 366

Danube, the northern boundary of the Roman empire, 235

Daphnae, in Egypt, 56

Darius Codomannus, opposed to Alexander, 125, 126, 129; his death, 131

Darius Hystaspis, completed the Nile and Red Sea canal, 146

Dead Sea, the, described by Pliny, 266

Deccan, the, not known to the ancients before the Christian era, 149; noticed in the 'Periplus Maris Erythraei,' 278; etymology of the name, 278

Deine, fountain in the sea, 356

Delphi, regarded as the centre of the earth, 65; its importance in the Homeric age, 66; at a later period, 66; described by Pausanias, 358

Delta of Egypt, speculations on its formation, 61, 197

Demavend, Mt, 131

Denmark, known as the Cimbrian promontory, 290

Descriptive Geography, the subjects it treats of, 2

Desjardins, M., on the Peutinger Table, 310, 311

Dhofar, region of, 276

Dicaearchus, 170; his contributions to map-making, 180; his measurements of the height of mountains, 336

Dio Cassius, on Hadrian's frontier system, 295

Diodorus, on the Cassiterides, 37; on the island of Basilia, 164; on sunrise seen from Ida, 323

Dionysius Periegetes, his geographical poem, 281—7

Dioscorides, island of, 276

Dioscurias, 49, 222

Dongola, 224

Dorieus, 66

Drangiana, 133, 139

Drusus (the elder), his campaigns in Germany, 232; his navigation of the Northern Ocean, 232; his conquest of Rhaetia, 234

Dumb Commerce, mentioned by Herodotus, 94; by Pliny and Solinus, 365

Dwarfs, in Africa, 97; mentioned in the story of Sataspes, 103 (see Pygmies)

Early notices of distant countries among the Greeks, chiefly of Phoenician origin, 20

Early travellers, means of testing their reports, 17

Earth, measurement of the, 168 foll.; by Eratosthenes, 170; by Posidonius, 192

Earthquakes, in Greece, 11; in Lydia, 61; speculations on, 197—200; relieved by volcanoes, 199

Ecbatana, Alexander's depot at, 130

Egnatian Way, the, 236

Egypt, mentioned in Homer, 26; position of the Greeks in, 56, 57; described by Herodotus, 92; occupied by Alexander, 127; a home of learning under the Ptolemies, 145; Strabo's travels in, 241, 260

Eirinon, inlet, 277

Elbe, river, Augustus' limit of the empire, 289

Elburz, chain of, 131

Electrides, islands, 164

Elephant-hunting on the Astaboras, 146; in India, 152

Embassies from the West to Alexander, 141; from Taprobane to Rome, 273

Emodus, mountains, 149; meaning of the name, 149

Empedocles, story of his death on Etna, 320

Emporiae, 55

Eneti, tribe, known to Herodotus, 84

Ephorus, the forerunner of Polybius, 206; his advanced criticisms, 207

Epithets, local, accuracy of in Homer, 23

Erannaboas, river, 150

Eratosthenes, on the local epithets in Homer, 23; on the inundation of the Nile, 63; his twofold division of the world, 67; his measurement of the earth, 170—72; of the habitable world, 172—4; his parallels of latitude, 174, 175, 181; his meridians of longitude, 177, 178, 181; on the zones, 180; his map of the world, 180; his Sphragides, 181; his geographical treatise, 182

Eridanus, river, etymology of the name of, 34; disbelieved in by Herodotus, 80

Ermine Street, 303

Erythraean Sea, 80; Agatharchides' work on, 185

Erzeroum, 117

Essenes, the, described by Pliny, 266

Etna, ascended by Hadrian, 314; Seneca's notice of, 319; Strabo's description of the summit of, 319 —321

Etymander, river, 133

Eudoxus of Cnidos, his astronomical observations, 165

Eudoxus of Cyzicus, his voyages, 189

Euphrates, its course known to Herodotus, 90; its sources in Armenia, 114, 117; its stream crossed by Xenophon, 116; by Alexander, 128; described by Strabo, 257; its supposed common source with the Tigris, 271; Roman military frontier along, 298; crossings at Thapsacus and the Zeugma, 305

Euripus, currents of the, 11, 185, 192

Europe, boundaries of, 67—9; meaning of the name of, 69; where first mentioned, 69; Herodotus' knowledge of, 83, 84

Euxine, Greek colonies on the, 46; dangers and attractions of, 46

Evans, Mr A. J., 32

Exampaeus, in Scythia, 85

Expeditions, before the time of Alexander, 98 foll.; of Alexander, 122 foll.; of Pytheas, 152 foll.; of Polybius on the African coast, 209; of Agricola to the Orcades, 288; of Suetonius Paullinus to Central Africa, 291; of Nero to the Nile, 291; of Septimius Flaccus to Aethiopia, 353; of Julius Maternus to the Soudan, 353

Fartak, Cape, 276

Fauna, observation of, 201

Ferro, used as a prime meridian, 342

Flinders Petrie, Mr, discovery of Naucratis by, 57

Flora, observation of by Theophrastus and others, 200; by Strabo, 246

Fortunatae Insulae, 226; Ptolemy's prime meridian, 342

Fosse Way, 303

Fountains, described by Pausanias, 355

Freshfield, Mr D. W., on the crampons of the Caucasus, 316

Friesland, amber from the coast of, 163, 164

Frontier fortresses, Roman, 294; chiefly organised by Hadrian, 295

Gades, meaning of the name, 7; noticed by Herodotus, 84; its immense commerce, 253

Gaetulia, 95

Galicia, tin mines of, 35, 37

Gambia River, 106

Ganges, the, known to Megasthenes, 149; believed to flow into the Eastern Ocean, 250, 286; the error corrected, 281; and repeated, 367

Garamantes, the, 96, 353; expedition of Balbus against, 223

Gardner, Prof. P., 57; on Pausanias' veracity, 362

Gaugamela, 129

Gaul, early trade-route through, 32; the Roman province in, 228; Caesar's conquest of, 228 foll.; his description of, 229; Roman roads in, 236, 300, 302; completeness of the river-system in, 253

Gauls, the, described by Posidonius, 205

Gaza, captured by Alexander, 127
Gedrosia, 140
Gela, foundation of, 53
Geloni, 87
Geminus, 159
Geographical discoveries, their stimulating effect, 15, 16
Geographical eras and centres, 13—15
Geography, its central position among the sciences, 1 ; its subdivisions, 2 ; the study almost confined to the Greeks, 12 ; its limited character in antiquity, 16 ; advanced by the Greek colonies, 43 ; by Alexander's expedition, 123 ; by the Roman conquests, 216 ; its decline after Ptolemy, 367
Geology, Strabo's interest in, 245
'Germania' of Tacitus, its ethnographical interest, 289
Germany, invaded by Caesar, 232 ; campaigns of Drusus and Tiberius in, 232, 233 ; the country less known afterwards, 289
Ghuzni, 133
Gir and Nigir, rivers, 353
Glaesiae, islands, 164
Glaesum, etymology of the word, 164
Gnomon, invention of the, 64 ; an improved kind used by Eratosthenes, 170
Gold mines, Aethiopian, 186
Golden Chersonese, 281, 346
Gorillas, 108
Granicus, battle of the, 125
Greece, a suggestive country for the study of geography, 9, 184 ; its principal features, 10, 11 ; imperfectly described by Strabo, 256 ; Pausanias' description of, 354 foll.
Greek explorers, 12
Greeks, the, their qualifications for the study of geography, 8
Guardafui, Cape, 100, 147, 274
Gymnias, 117

Habitable world, measurement of by Eratosthenes, 172—4 ; by Ptolemy, 341
Hadramaut, district of, 142, 276 ; inhabitants of, 203
Hadrian, the chief organiser of Roman frontier defences, 294 foll. ; his ascents of mountains, 313, 314 ; his restoration of buildings in Greece, 354

Haemus, Mt, ascended by Philip V of Macedon, 322 ; Pliny's estimate of its height, 335
Halys, river, not mentioned in Homer, 22 ; the western limit of the Cappadocians, 90 ; crossed by the Royal Road, 90
Hanno, expedition of, 104 ; his 'Periplus,' 104
Harang, island, 107
Harmosia, 142
Harpasus, Xenophon's name for the Acampsis, 117
Harrison, Miss, on Pausanias' veracity, 362
Harud, river, 133
Heberdey, on Pausanias' routes in Greece, 359 ; on his veracity, 360—63
Hecataeus, on the formation of the Delta, 62 ; on the inundation of the Nile, 63 ; his division of the world into continents, 67, 68 ; the Father of Geography, 70 ; his political wisdom, 70 ; his sources of information, 71 ; his geographical work, 71 ; its general geography, 72 ; its contents, 73, 74
Hecatompylus, 132
Hellas, in Homer, 23
Hellespont, compared with the Straits of Gibraltar by Polybius, 214
Helmund, river, 133
Hemeroscopeium, 55
Heptastadion of Alexandria, 146
Heraclea, 50
Heracleides Ponticus, on the rotation of the earth, 166
Heracles, representing the Phoenician Melcarth, 5, 20 ; the fire-god, 11
Herat, 130, 133
Herodotus, his life, 76 ; extent of his travels, 77 ; his general view of geography, 78 ; his primitive cosmical beliefs, 78 ; his attempts at drawing a meridian, 79 ; his conception of the map of the world, 80 ; contents of his work, 83 ; date of its composition, 76 ; his remarks on frankincense and cinnamon in Arabia, 7 ; his disbelief in the Cassiterides, 38 ; on the Nile and the Delta of Egypt, 61—3 ; on Mardonius' line of fire-beacons, 330 ; on the shield displayed at Marathon, 331
Hesiod, his description of the Styx, 24

Hibernia, Caesar's notice of, 231; Ptolemy's account of, 351
Himalaya, its classical names, 149
Himera, 54
Himilco, his expedition, 36, 109
Hindostan, the peninsula of, known to the author of the 'Periplus Maris Erythraei,' 278; Ptolemy's error about, 345
Hindu Kush, 124, 133; crossed by Alexander, 134, 137
Hippalus, voyage of, 279
Hipparchus, his confidence in Pytheas, 155, 160; his Climata, 175; his method of determining longitudes, 178
Hippopotami, 106
Historians of Alexander's expedition, 124
Historical Geography, the subjects it treats of, 2; as found in Aristotle, 205; in Ephorus, 206; in Polybius, 208, 211; in Strabo, 246, 252
History of Geography, its importance, 1
Hogarth, Mr, 91
Homer, extravagant veneration of as a geographical authority, 256
Homeric conception of the earth, 20
Homeric Poems, geography of the, 21 foll.; rumours of distant countries in, 29; trade-routes implied in, 31; foreign trees mentioned in, 40; accuracy of local epithets in, 23
Honey, poisonous, affecting Xenophon's and Pompey's soldiers, 118
Horace, on the pine-trees of Pontus, 46; on the site of Tarentum, 52
Hot springs in Greece, 11; described by Pausanias, 355, 356
Humboldt, on the Sargasso Sea, 111; on the merits of Strabo's work, 249
Hydaspes, river, 138
Hyderabad, 138
Hydraotes, river, 138
Hypanis, river, 85
Hyperboreans, their offerings sent to Delos, 32
Hyphasis, river, 138, 150
Hyrcani, subdued by Alexander, 132

Iardanos, river in Crete, the same name as Jordan, 5
Iberia (in Asia), described by Theophanes, 220
Iberians, described by Posidonius, 204

Ichthyophagi, on the coast of Gedrosia, 142; on the coast of Arabia, 203
Icknield Street, 303
Ictis, island, 156
Ida, Mt, description of sunrise from, 323
Iliad, the inner geography of, 21—24; outer geography of, 25; its notices of the Aegean islands and Asia Minor, 22; of Greece, 23
Imaus, mts., 149; in Ptolemy the Altai chain, 352
India, known to Hecataeus, 73; Herodotus' account of, 92; ancient administration of, 150; caste-system in, 151; its southern projection known to the author of the 'Periplus Maris Erythraei,' 277—9; wrongly represented by Ptolemy, 345
Indian Ocean, visited by Alexander, 139; supposed by Ptolemy to be surrounded by land, 346; (see Erythraean Sea)
Indians, life of the, 151; widow-burning practised by, 152
Indus, river, crossed by Alexander near Atak, 137; descended by Alexander, 138; delta of, 138; bore of, 139; Dionysius Periegetes, description of, 286
Inlets from the Ocean, 81
Inundation of the Nile, various explanations of, 62, 63
Ionian School, the, 14; their geographical speculations, 59, 60; opinions as to the formation of the Delta, 61
Iran, description of, 130
Isidore of Seville, 271, 365
Issedones, mentioned by Hecataeus, 73; by Herodotus, 88
Issus, battle of, 126
Ister, river, not mentioned in Homer, 25; correspondence to the Nile, 78, 79; course of according to Herodotus, 79; supposed to divide into two branches, 120; (see Danube)
Isthmus between the Euxine and the Caspian, 68
Isthmus of Suez, 68
Istri, tribe of, mentioned by Scylax, 121
Ithaca, inaccurately described in the Odyssey, 24
Itineraries, Roman; two kinds of,

236, 306; the Antonine, 306; its probable date, 306; not a completely homogeneous document, 307; its contents, 308; the Maritime Itinerary, 308; the Jerusalem Itinerary, 309; the Peutinger Table, 310; its transcription and probable date of composition, 311
Ituna, estuary, 349
Ivernia, 346

Jaxartes, river, reached by Alexander, 135; mistakes concerning it, 135
Jerusalem Itinerary, 309; the Holy Places first described in, 309
Jihoun, river, 134
Job, the Book of, mining operations described in, 188
Jomanes, river, 150
Jordan, river, described by Pliny, 265
Juba, his treatise on Africa, 226
Julius Maternus, his expedition into the Soudan, 353

Kafiristan, traversed by Alexander, 137; visited by Sir G. S. Robertson, 137
Karachi, 142
Katakekaumene, volcanoes of the, 61
Khartoum, 147
Khyber Pass, traversed by Hephaestion and Perdiccas, 137
Kiepert, Prof. H., on the etymology of Eridanus, 34
Kilimanjaro and Kenia, Mounts, perhaps the Mountains of the Moon, 352
Kohik, river, 135
Korosko, 224

Lambaesis, a Roman frontier station, 294
Lampsacus, meaning of the name, 5; founded by the Phoenicians, 46
Lassen, his corroboration of Megasthenes, 149; on the character of the ancient Indians, 152
Latitude, of Massilia determined by Pytheas, 154; parallels in the neighbourhood of Britain determined by him, 160; the parallels of Eratosthenes, 174, 175; of Ptolemy, 343
Legions, Roman, permanently fixed in certain camps, 298
Libya, in Homer the Cyrenaica, 26; commerce of by way of Cyrene,

56; origin of the name of, 70; (see Africa)
Lilybaeum, meaning of the name, 6
Liguria, a source of amber, 31; its rugged coast, 55
Limes, the Rhaetian and German, 296
Lincoln, 287
Lipari Islands, eruption in the, 199, 210
Lixus, river, 105
Locri Epizephyrii, 52
Locust-eaters, tribes of, 204 note
Londinium, the commercial centre of Britain, 287
Longitude, meridians of, difficulty of determining, 177; Hipparchus' method of measuring, 178; system of Ptolemy, 342, 343
'Look-out place,' used as equivalent to 'mountain height,' 326—8
Lotophagi, in Homer, 28; Polybius' description of their country, 28; rightly placed by Herodotus, 94; mentioned by Scylax, 121
Lotus plant, described by Polybius, 28 note
Lucian, his humorous description of a mountain ascent, 324
Lucullus, campaigns of in Armenia and Mesopotamia, 218, 272
Lyceum, Mt., altar on its summit, 318
Lyell, Sir C., his high praise of Strabo, 251
Lynceus, story of, 328

Macan, Mr R. W., on the Ister as the boundary of Scythia, 85; on the zones of Africa, 95
Macaria, a corruption of the name Melcarth, 5
Macauley Island, 108
Maceta, prom., 142, 277
Madeira, 225
Maeander, river, accretion of soil at its mouth, 61
Maeotis, Palus, its size overestimated by Herodotus, 81; its area lessened since classical times, 81; ice of, 85; breeding-place of the tunny, 46; misplaced by Ptolemy, 345
Malay Peninsula, 281
Man, Isle of, 231
Manaar, Gulf of, 273
Mannert, on the date of the Antonine Itinerary, 307; of the Peutinger Table, 311

Map-making, its early difficulties, 64; commenced by Anaximander, 64; reformed by Eratosthenes, 180; by Marinus, 339; by Ptolemy, 343 foll.

Maps, of Aristagoras, 65; of Eratosthenes, 180; of Marinus, 339; of Ptolemy, 345

Maracanda, 135

Marathon, the shield displayed at, 331

Mardi, the, subdued by Alexander, 132

Marinus Tyrius, Ptolemy's debt to him, 338; his attempt to reform the map of the world, 339

Maritime Itinerary, the, 308

Marvellous narratives, not necessarily incredible, 17

Massagetae, 82

Massilia, an early entrepôt of tin and amber, 32; founded by the Phocaeans, 55; its colonies, 55; a starting-point for geographical discovery, 55; its rivalry with the Phoenicians, 154; its political constitution described by Strabo, 253

Mathematical Geography, the questions it treats of, 2; early speculations on, 59, 60; slow development of, 165; promoted by Aristotle, 166; and Eratosthenes, 166; Strabo's imperfect treatment of, 251; developed by Marinus, 338; and by Ptolemy, 340

Mausoleum of Augustus, minutely described by Strabo, 254

Mead, used in Britain, 18, 157

Measurement of the earth, 168 foll., 192, 341; of the habitable world, 172, 341

Media, described by Polybius, 211

Mediterranean Sea, the starting-point for the history of geography, 3; its superiority over the other seas, 3

Megara, its colonies on the Propontis, 50

Megara Hyblaea, 53

Megasthenes, envoy from Seleucus Nicator to Chandragupta, 148; his work on India, 148 foll.; on catching apes, 201

Mekran, province of, 140

Mela, his Chorographia, 262; his knowledge of Southern Spain, 262; of the Baltic and Scandinavia, 289

Melanchlaeni, mentioned by Hecataeus, 73; by Herodotus, 86

Melcarth, represented by the Greeks as Heracles, 5, 20; as Melicertes, 6

Melitene, 298

Memnon, vocal statue of, 283

Memnon, commander under Darius, 126

Memphis, occupied by Alexander, 127

Menelaus, his voyages, 26

Menuthias, 275

Meridian line, Herodotus' attempts at drawing a, 79; (see Longitude)

Meroë, 92, 292; its latitude determined by Philon, 175

Merriam, Mr A. C., on telegraphing among the ancients, 330

Messana, its position, 51

Messina, Straits of, guarded by Rhegium and Messana, 51; capture of sword-fish in, 203

Metapontum, 52

Methana, eruption of, described by Ovid, 198; warm spring at, 356

Methone, 49

Miletus, a geographical centre, 14, 59; its colonies on the Euxine, 46 foll.

Miliarium Aureum at Rome, 299

Military posts, chains of, 297

Mines; gold, 186; silver, 210; tin, 35

Mining operations, described by Agatharchides, 186; in the Book of Job, 188

Mithridatic war, its importance to geography, 217

Mommsen, on the Rhaetian and German Limes, 296, 297; his estimate of Solinus, 365

Monsoon, the south-west, cause of the rainy season in India, 150; called by Megasthenes the Etesian winds, 195; afterwards called Hippalus, 279

Mountain ascents, made by Hadrian, 313; of Etna, 319; of Argaeus, 321; of Haemus, 322; description of a climb, 325

Mountains, differently viewed by the ancients and the moderns, 317; religious feeling about them in antiquity, 317, 318; their summits not always distinguished from the chain, 314; used as places of worship by the Persians and the Greeks, 318; regarded as look-out places, 326—8; as signalling stations, 328 foll.; estimates of their heights, 335

Mountains of the Moon, 352
Müllenhoff, on the early trade-route through Gaul, 33; on Pytheas' visit to the Tanais, 158; his depreciation of Strabo, 249
Müller, Dr C., on the voyage of Hanno, 105; on the Periplus of Scylax, 119
Mungo Park, on burning grass in Africa, 107
Murad-Su (Eastern Euphrates), 116
Mush, plain of, 116, 271
Musiris, 279
Mussendum, Cape, 142, 277
"Mutterrecht," practised by the Issedones, 88
Myos Hormos, commercial station at, 146, 274; Roman road to, 305

Namnadius, river, 277
Napata, 224, 292
Narbo, a commercial centre in the time of Hecataeus, 73; seat of a Roman colony, 228
Nasamones, expedition of the, 96; victory of Domitian over, 282
Naucratis, 57
Naxos, in Sicily, 53
Neapolis, its favourable position, 51; a centre of Hellenic culture, 51, 254
Nearchus, voyage of, 140, 141—3
Necho, circumnavigation of Africa ordered by, 99; Nile and Red Sea Canal commenced by, 146
Nelcynda, 278, 279, 281
Nerbudda, bore of the, 277
Neuri, were-wolf superstition among the, 86
Niger, river, 97, 291; not the Nigir of Ptolemy, 353
Nile, the river Aegyptus of Homer, 26; interest awakened by its strange features, 61; absence of tributaries, 61; derived from the Ocean stream, 63; regarded as the boundary between Asia and Africa, 68, 82; its correspondence to the Ister, 78, 79; its two branches unnoticed by Herodotus, 93; increased knowledge of it through the Ptolemies, 147; expedition of Petronius on, 224; Nero's expedition to, 291; marshy region of, 292; its sources in two lakes, 352
Northern Europe, long days and nights of referred to in Homer, 30; first explored by Pytheas, 153
Northern races, vaguely known to Homer, 25
Northern Sea, disbelieved by Herodotus, 80; Pytheas' account of, 158; navigated by Drusus, 232

Oases, the, described by Herodotus, 96; the Oasis of Ammon visited by Alexander the Great, 128; compared by Strabo to the spots on a leopard's skin, 248
Oceanus, the river, parent of waters, 20; encircling the earth, 20; origin of this idea, 21; in the far south, 29; in the far north, 30; the Nile derived from it, 63
Ocelis, 280
Odyssey, the inner geography of, 22, 24; outer geography of, 26—29
Oenotrian tribes, akin to the Greeks, 52
Oestrymnides, islands, 36, 110, 156
Olbia, 48; Herodotus' residence at, 85
Olympia, described by Pausanias, 358
Olympus, Mt., measurement of the height of, 336
Onesicritus, companion of Alexander, 124; his description of the banyan tree, 139
Opone, 275
Orcades, islands, Agricola's expedition to, 288
Orcas, prom., 156, 350
Organa, island, 142
Ormuz, 142; mentioned in 'Paradise Lost,' 142
Orosius, his 'Historiae,' 366; its geographical section, 366; its popularity in the middle ages, 366
Osismii, 156
Ostimii, 156
Ovid, his description of the eruption of Methana, 198
Oxus, river, crossed by Alexander, 134; its modern and ancient courses, 134; trade route along, 134, 266

Pachynus, prom., dreaded by Greek sailors, 53
Paestum, 51
Palaesimundus, capital of Taprobane, 273
Palestine, described by Pliny, 265
Palibothra, on the Ganges, 148

Palm-trees, imported into Greece, 39; at Jericho, 259

Palmyra, described by Pliny, 266

Pamir, mountains of the, 134; source of the Oxus in, 134

Pannonia, trade route through, 32; conquered by the Romans, 234; Roman road through, 304

Panormus, 54

Panticapaeum, 49

Paraetonium, 128

Parallels (see Latitude)

Parmenides, his theory of zones, 60

Parmenio, 126

Parnassus, meaning of its 'twin peaks,' 324

Paropamisus range, 133; crossed by Alexander, 134, 137

Parthia, Alexander in, 131

Pasitigris, river, 143

Pataliputra, 148, 150

Patrocles, on the connexion between the Caspian and the Indian Ocean, 136; Strabo's authority for north-eastern Asia, 257

Pattala, depot of Alexander at, 138

Pausanias, 353 foll.; his 'Itinerary of Greece,' 354; his resemblance to Herodotus, 354; his accuracy, 355; his illustrations of physical geography, 355; his descriptions of fountains, 355; of caverns, 356; of trees, 357; his descriptions of Olympia and Delphi, 358; routes which he followed in Greece, 359; contents of his book, 359; question of his veracity, 360—62

Pearl fishery, in the Persian Gulf, 142

Pelham, Prof., on the Roman frontier system, 294

Pelion, Mt., ancient description of its vegetation, 201; measurement of the height of, 336

Pentland Firth, rise of the tide in, 159

'Periegesis' of Dionysius Periegetes, its date, 281; its general geography, 282; its contents, 283—6; remarks upon it, 286

'Periodos,' name of Hecataeus' geographical work, 71

'Periplus,' of Hanno, 104; of Scylax, 118; doubts as to its genuineness, 119, 120; 'Periplus of the Erythraean Sea,' 274—81; of Arrian, 294

Persepolis, occupied by Alexander, 130; his return to, 140

Persian Gulf, not known to Herodotus, 81; pearl fishery in, 142

Persian kingdom, Herodotus' account of, drawn from a statistical document, 88

Persis, mountains of, 130; its three regions described by Strabo, 259

Peucelaotis, 137

Peutinger Table, the, 310—12

Phaeacia, not to be identified with Corfu, 27

Phaëthon, story of the sisters of, 33

Phanagoria, 49, 68

Pharos, island, in Homer, 26; visited by Alexander, 128; protection afforded by it to the harbours of Alexandria, 146

Phasiani, tribe, 116

Phasis, town of, 49

Phasis, river, regarded as the boundary between Europe and Asia, 68, 82; Xenophon's name for the Araxes, 117

Philip V. of Macedon, his ascent of Haemus, 322; his beacon stations, 332

Philon, determined the latitude of Meroë, 175

Phocaeans, their bold navigation, 54; their foundation of Massilia, 55

Phoenicians, their early maritime importance, 4; their settlements in the Aegean, 5; in Africa and Sicily, 6, 54; at Gades, 7; their selfish policy, 7; trees imported by them into Greece, 40; supposed to have circumnavigated Africa, 99; their connexion with the tin and amber trades, 33, 36, 154

Physical Geography, the subjects it treats of, 2; early speculations on, 60 foll.; treatment of the subject in antiquity, 184 foll.; interest of Polybius in, 210; of Strabo, 245; Pausanias' illustrations of, 355

Pindar, on Delphi as the centre of the earth, 65; on the story of Lynceus, 328

Plane-tree, imported into Greece from Asia Minor, 40

Pliny, his life, 263; character of his 'Natural History,' 264; its statistical geography, 265; on the Romans as geographers, 13; on the trade-route through Pannonia, 32; his explanation of the story of the sisters of Phaëthon, 34; on the amber islands, 164; on the features of Palestine, 265, 266; on the Tigris and Euphrates, 267—72; on Taprobane, 272; on the direct route to India, 279

Plutonium, the, at Hierapolis, 11

Political Geography, the subjects it treats of, 2

Polyaenus, author of the 'Strategemata,' 334

Polybius, how affected by the circumstances of his age, 208; his travels in Western Europe, 209; voyage on the African coast, 209; his interest in physical geography, 210; descriptions of countries, 211; of cities, 212—14; general remarks on historical geography, 214; on signalling stations, 332; on the art of signalling, 334; on the heights of mountains, 335; his depreciation of Pytheas, 18, 153, 157; his description of the lotus plant, 28; on the erosive power of rivers, 196; on deposits of alluvium, 197; on the capture of the sword-fish, 202

Pomegranate, imported into Greece, 39

Pompey, campaigns of, in Iberia and Albania, 219

Portus Alexandri, 142

Portus Herculis Monoeci, 55; origin of the name, 55

Poseidon, representing earthquakes, 11

Posidonius, 190; his travels, 191; error about the circumference of the earth, 191; on the tides, 193; on tidal waves, 197; on earthquakes and volcanic eruptions, 199, 200; on Plato's island of Atlantis, 200; on the Iberians and Gauls, 204, 205

Prasum, prom., 342

Projection, Ptolemy's system of, 343

Propontis, meaning of the name, 47

Pteria, "over against Sinope," 80

Ptolemais Epitheras, 146

Ptolemies, the, their patronage of literature, 145; their exploration of the Nile valley, 147

Ptolemy (the Geographer), an Alexandrian, 15, 340; his obligation to Marinus, 338, 339; his great reputation, 340; his chief errors, 341, 342, 345; his prime meridian, 342; his system of projection, 343; his

Climata, 343; his geographical treatise, 344; his maps, 345; his account of Britain, 346—51; of Ireland, 351; his additions to geographical knowledge, 351—3; brief duration of his influence in antiquity, 367

Ptolemy Euergetes, stations established by, near the Straits of Bab el-Mandeb, 147

Ptolemy Philadelphus, restored the Nile and Red Sea canal, 146; established stations on the Red Sea, 146

Pulmo Marinus, Pytheas' mention of the, 162

Punjab, Alexander's campaign in the, 137; rivers of, 137, 138, 150

Purple-fisheries of the Phoenicians in the Aegean, 5

Pygmies, the, mentioned by Homer, 29; meaning of the name, 29; a dwarfish race in Africa, noticed by Herodotus, Aristotle, and modern travellers, 29, 30, 97, 103

Pylae Caspiae, 131

Pylae Persicae, 130

Pyrene, city of, 84

Pyrenees, error about their direction, 252

Pythagoreans, the, taught the spherical form of the earth, 60

Pytheas, 12; varying estimates of him, 153; his work, 153; his scientific attainments, 154; his parallels of latitude, 160; his northern expedition, 17, 152; evidence in favour of it, 157; his remarks on the use of mead in Britain, 18, 157; on the rise of the tide in the Pentland Firth, 18, 159; on Britain and its inhabitants, 156, 157; on the Northern Sea, 158—60; on the "Sleeping-place of the Sun," 159; his supposed visit to the Baltic, 158; on the arctic circle, 159; his description of the arctic regions, 162; his visit to the amber coast, 163

Quorra, river, 353

Rainy season in India, 150

Ras Hafoun, 275

Rawlinson, Canon, on the Jaxartes of Herodotus, 82; on the fire-beacons of Mardonius, 331

Red Sea, mistakes about its width, 102; stations established on by the Ptolemies, 146

Retreat of the Ten Thousand, 112 foll.

Rha, river (Volga), first mentioned by Ptolemy, 351

Rhapta, 352

Rhegium, 51; meaning of the name, 197

Rhinoceroses, in the Soudan, 353

Rhodaune, river, 34

Richards, Mr G. C., on Pausanias' veracity, 362

Rio do Ouro, 104

Rivers, disappearance of in Greece, 10; their character, as described by Aristotle and others, 195—7

Roads, the Roman, their importance to geography, 235; description of them, 299 foll.; (see Royal Road)

Roman Empire, its natural limits, 293; its frontier defences, 293 foll.

Roman geographers, few and inferior, 13, 261; Strabo's and Pliny's opinions of them, 13

Rome, first mentioned in the 'Periplus' of Scylax, 120; Strabo's description of, 254

Royal Road, in India, 150; in Persia, 90; its course through Asia Minor, 90; through Cilicia, Armenia, Matiene, and Cissia, 91

Sagres, Mt., 108

Sahara, the, 97, 291; crossed by Julius Maternus, 353

St. Michael's Mount, 156

Sallust, on the common source of the Euphrates and Tigris, 272; his description of a mountain climb, 325

Samarcand, 135

Samos, meaning of the name, 5

Samosata, 298

Sargasso Sea, 111, 112

Saspires, 83

Satala, 298

Sataspes, voyage of, probably authentic, 103

Satibarzanes, satrap of Aria, 133

Sauromatae, 86

Scandinavia, regarded as an island, 289

Sciapodes, 74

Scilly Islands, 37

Scotland, erroneous position of on Ptolemy's map, 347

Scylax of Caryanda, 74; his voyage, 80, 101; improbability of it, 101; the so-called 'Periplus' of, 118

Scylla and Charybdis, an embodiment of the dangers of the Straits of Messina, 28

Scythia, Herodotus' knowledge of, 84, 85; position of tribes in, 85

Seistan, Lake, 130, 133

Seleucus Nicator, his empire in the East, 148; cedes the Indus valley to Chandragupta, 148

Selinus, 54

Sembritae, 93, 147, 173

Seneca, on Nero's expedition to the Nile, 292; on Etna, 319

Senegal River, 106

Septimius Flaccus, his expedition into Aethiopia, 353

Sera, city of, in China, 342, 352

Serica, origin of the name, 281

Shape of the earth, primitive views concerning the, 59, 60; arguments in favour of its sphericity, 167, 168

Sherboro Sound, 108

Sicels, the, akin to the Greeks, 53

Sidon, meaning of the name, 4; mentioned in Homer, 25

Signalling, development of the art of, 333—5

Silk, brought from China, 281

Sinope, an early trading-station, 47; colonised by the Milesians, 47; described by Polybius, 212; its position compared to that of Carthage, 47

Sirdar Pass, 131

Sir Daria, river, 135

Siris, name of a portion of the Nile, 283

"Sleeping-place of the Sun," 159

Sobat, river, 292

Socotra, 270

Sogdiana, 135

Solinus, his 'Memorabilia,' 364; its influence in the middle ages, 365; modern estimate of, 365

Soloeis, prom., 94, 103, 105

Somaliland, 147

Soudan, the, expeditions to, mentioned by Ptolemy, 352, 353

Southern Horn, in Africa, 108

Southern Ocean, belief in the continuity of the, 80

Spain, Roman conquest of, 226 foll.; Strabo's description of, 252; chief Roman road in, 300

Spartel, Cape, 94, 103
Speculations, early, on Mathematical Geography, 59, 60; on Physical Geography, 60 foll.
Sphericity of the earth, arguments of Aristotle and others in favour of, 167, 168
Sphragides of Eratosthenes, 181
Stanley, Dean, on Pausanias' descriptions, 355
Stephanus of Byzantium, 71; his 'Ethnica,' 363; etymological remarks in, 364
Strabo, his life and places of residence, 239, 240; extent of his travels, 240—42; his philosophical and political opinions, 242; date and place of the composition of his 'Geography,' 243; its comprehensiveness, 245; its artistic character, 247; various estimates of it, 248, 249; its contents, 251 foll.; on the advantages of the Mediterranean, 3; on the Romans as geographers, 12; on the Cassiterides, 37; on the summit of Etna, 319 —21; on Mt. Argaeus, 321; on the height of the Alps, 335
Styx, waterfall of, described by Homer, 23; by Hesiod, 24
Suetonius Paullinus, his conquests in Britain, 287; his crossing the Atlas, 291
Suiones, 290
Susa, occupied by Alexander, 129
Sutlej, river, not reached by Alexander, 138
Suttee, custom of in India, 152
Sword-fish, capture of in the Straits of Messina, 202
Syagrus, prom., 276
Sybaris, 51
Syene, close under the tropic, 100, 172
Syracuse, 53
Syrtes, the, 121

Tacitus, his 'Germania,' 289; his 'Agricola,' 288, 351
Taenarum, ancient descriptions of the grotto at, 356
Tamarus, river, 349
Tanais, river, regarded as the boundary between Europe and Asia, 68; mistakes concerning, 135, 136, 158
Tanais, town of, 49
Taprobane, mentioned by Megasthenes, 149; Pliny's account of, 272;

life of the inhabitants of, 273; its size overestimated by Ptolemy, 345
Tarentum, foundation of, 44; its advantageous site and fisheries, 52
Tarsus, 126
Tartessus, origin of the name, 7; its position in Southern Spain, 7; visited by the Phocaeans, 54; by Colaeus of Samos, 58; mentioned by Hecataeus, 73
Tatta, 139
Tauric Chersonese, noticed by Herodotus, 85; carefully described by Strabo, 255
Tauromenium, 53
Taurus, mts., not mentioned by Herodotus, 89; regarded as intersecting the whole of Asia, 181; accurately described by Strabo, 257
Teleboas, river, 116; its nearness to the source of the Tigris, 116, 271
Telegraphy, Mountain, 331 foll.
'Temple of the Winds' at Athens, 195
Ten Thousand, retreat of the, 112 foll.; their first view of the sea, 117
Thales, his views on the shape of the earth, 60; on the inundation of the Nile, 62
Thanet, Isle of, noticed by Solinus, 366
Thapsacus, 128, 305
Thebes, Egyptian, mentioned in Homer, 26
Theon Ochema, Mt, 108
Theophanes of Mytilene, his description of the Caucasus, 220; of the Iberi and Albani, 221—3: Strabo's chief authority for those regions, 257
Theophrastus, his 'History of Plants,' 200
Thera, volcanic island of, 11; eruption of, 200
Thermopylae, water of, described by Pausanias, 355
Thinae, 281
Thinge (Tangier), 74
This (China), 281
Thospites, lake, 267
Thrace, Herodotus' knowledge of, 84
Thucydides, mention of mountain telegraphy in, 331
Thule, first mentioned by Pytheas, 159; the arctic circle placed there, 159, 173; noticed by Dionysius Periegetes, 285; seen by Agricola's expedition, 288

Tibboos, 96, 105
Tiberius, the emperor, his campaigns in Germany, 233; in Rhaetia, 234
Tides, discovery of their movement by the Greeks, 192; influence of the moon on them first reported to the Greeks by Pytheas, 155; that of the sun and moon conjointly noticed by Posidonius, 193
Tigranocerta, position of, 219
Tigris, river, its course known to Herodotus, 90; its sources in Armenia, 114, 116; crossed by Alexander, 129; its upper course described by Strabo and Pliny, 267 foll.; its supposed disappearance, 270; its supposed common source with the Euphrates, 271; account of by Dionysius Periegetes, 285
Timaeus, 210
Timavus, river, remarks of Polybius on, 210
Timosthenes, on the winds, 194
Tin, largely used in the Homeric times, 35; not brought from India, but from Spain and Britain, 35; by way of Gades, 36; through Gaul, 36; Pytheas' voyage connected with, 154, 156
Tmolus, Mt, a look-out place, 322
Tobogganing, in the Caucasus, 316; practised by the Cimbri, 316
Torone, 49
Tracts of Africa according to Herodotus, 95
Trade-routes, primitive, evidence of in Homer, 31, 35; from the Ural mountains to the Sea of Azov, 87; from Upper Asia to Sinope, 91; from India to Europe by the Oxus, 134, 266; through Pannonia, 32; through Gaul, 32, 154; the direct trade-route to India, 279; from China to India, 281; from the Euphrates to Northern China, 352
Trade-winds, 103
Trajan, his conquest of Dacia, 290; of Mesopotamia, 293; his bridge over the Danube, 291
Transference to towns of names of tribes in Gaul, 229
Trapezus, its commercial importance, 47; visited by Xenophon, 117; a Roman military station, 299
Travel, advantage of to the geographer, 210, 241

Travellers' tales, how far trustworthy, 17
Trees, imported from abroad into Greece, 39, 40; Pausanias' description of, 357
Trisanton, river, 348
Tritonis, Lake, 94, 121
Troglodyte Aethiopians, 96, 204
Tyre, meaning of the name, 4; sieges of, 127; captured by Alexander, 127

Ulysses, mythical character of his wanderings, 27
Umbrians, known to Herodotus, 84
Ural mountains, gold of the, 87
Ushant, 156
Utica, early foundation of by the Phoenicians, 6
Uxisama, island, visited by Pytheas, 156

Van, Lake of, 114, 116, 257, 268, 269
Varar, estuary, 350
Vegetation, of India, 139; of Greece, as described by Theophrastus, 200; by Pausanias, 357; Strabo's interest in, 246
Veneti, the, in Brittany, 36; Caesar's description of their country, 230
Verde, Cape, 106
Vervedrum, prom., 350
Via Aurelia, 299; Aemilia Scauri, 300; Julia, 300; Flaminia, 300; Aemilia, 301; Appia, 304; Egnatia, 305; Candavia, 305
Viadrus, river (Oder), first mentioned by Ptolemy, 289
Victoria and Albert Nyanza Lakes, perhaps referred to by Ptolemy, 352
Virgil, on the zones, 180; on mountain scenery, 317
Viroconium, 303
Vistula, 289
Volcanic phenomena, in Greece, 11, 185; in Asia Minor, 61; speculations on, 197—200; at Methana, 198; in the Lipari Islands, 199; at Thera, 200; extensively noticed by Strabo, 254
Volga, the, first mentioned by Ptolemy, 351
Voyages, of Sataspes, 103; of Hanno, 104; of Himilco, 109; of Nearchus, 141; of Pytheas, 152; of Eudoxus

of Cyzicus, 189; of Polybius, 209; of Hippalus, 279

Wady Draa, 105
Wall-map of Agrippa, 236
Walls of Hadrian and Antonine in Britain, 288
Wanderings of Ulysses, their mythical character, 27
Watling Street, 303
Were-wolf superstition among the Neuri, 86
Western Horn, in Africa, 106
Whales, encounter of Nearchus' vessels with, 143
Winds, the, as known to Homer, 41; character of in Greece, 41; divisions of, 193; schemes of Aristotle and Timosthenes, 194; periodical, 195
Wonders, pseudo-Aristotelian treatise on, 112
World, the habitable, division of into continents, 67—9; shape of, 181; compared by Strabo to the Greek chlamys, 251; measurement of the length and breadth of by Eratosthenes, 172, 173; by Ptolemy, 341—3

Wroxeter, 303

Xanthus, the historian, 60
Xenagoras, his measurement of the height of Olympus, 336
Xenophon, 98; his 'Anabasis,' 113; his retreat from Cunaxa to Armenia, 115; across Armenia, 116—118; mention of mountain telegraphy by, 332

Yorke, Mr V. W., on the fortresses of the Upper Euphrates Valley, 299

Zabatus (Zab), river, 90, 129
Zagrus, Mt., 130
Zanzibar, 275
Zaradrus, river, 138, 150
Zerafshan, river, 135
Zeugma, over the Euphrates, 305
Zeus Ammon, Alexander's visit to the temple of, 128
Zones, theory of, taught by Parmenides, 60, 179; Aristotle's view of, 179, 180; Virgil's description of, 180

Biblo and Tannen's
ARCHIVES OF CIVILIZATION

udge, E. A. Wallis   **THE MUMMY**
2nd edition — 420 pp. — 88 Illus. and Folding-plates

Childe, V. Gordon
THE BRONZE AGE
31 figures and large folding map

ower, Eileen
ENGLISH MEDIAEVAL NUNNERIES
738pp — 8 Illus. — Map

Evans, Sir Arthur
PALACE OF MINOS AT KNOSSOS
7 vols., 3,688 pages — 764 half-tones — 42 color-plates

zer, H. F.
A HISTORY OF ANCIENT GEOGRAPHY
2nd Edition — With Additional Notes by M. Cary, D. Litt.
411pp. — 10 Maps

Pendlebury, J. D. S.
THE ARCHAEOLOGY OF CRETE
50 plates; 53 text-illustrations and 24 maps

wicke, F. M.
WAYS OF MEDIAEVAL LIFE AND THOUGHT
256pp

Sayce, R. U.
PRIMITIVE ARTS AND CRAFTS
An Introduction to the Study of Material Culture.
58 Illustrations

ace, Alan J. B.   **MYCENAE**
255pp. — 110 Illus. — 6 Folding maps — Large 4to.

Seymour, Thomas Day
LIFE IN THE HOMERIC AGE
Maps and Illustrations

DATE DUE